CIVIL AIRCRAFT MARKINGS 1976

JOHN W. R. TAYLOR

TWENTY-SIXTH EDITION

LONDON

IAN ALLAN LTD

This edition published 1976

ISBN 0 7110 0658 X

Published by Ian Allan Ltd, Shepperton, Surrey, and printed in the United
Kingdom by Jarrold and Sons Ltd, Norwich

International Civil Aircraft Markings

A2–	Botswana
A40–	Oman
A7–	Qatar
AN–	Nicaragua
AP–	Pakistan
B–	Taiwan (Nationalist China)
C–	Canada
C2–	Nauru
CC–	Chile
CCCP–*	Soviet Union
CF–	Canada
CN–	Morocco
CP–	Bolivia
CR–	Portuguese Overseas Provinces
CS–	Portugal
CU–	Cuba
CX–	Uruguay
D–	German Federal Republic (West)
DM–	German Democratic Republic (East)
DQ–	Fiji
EC–	Spain
EI, EJ–	Republic of Ireland
EL–	Liberia
EP–	Iran
ET–	Ethiopia
F–	France, Colonies and Protectorates
G–	United Kingdom
HA–	Hungarian People's Republic
HB–	Switzerland and Liechtenstein
HC–	Ecuador
HH–	Haiti
HI–	Dominican Republic
HK–	Colombia
HL–	Republic of Korea
HP–	Panama
HR–	Honduras
HS–	Thailand
HZ–	Saudi Arabia
I–	Italy
JA–	Japan
JY–	Jordan
LN–	Norway
LQ–, LV–	Argentine Republic
LX–	Luxembourg
LZ–	Bulgaria
N–	United States of America
OB–	Peru
OD–	Lebanon
OE–	Austria
OH–	Finland
OK–	Czechoslovakia
OO–	Belgium
OY–	Denmark
P2–	Papua New Guinea
PH–	Netherlands
PJ–	Netherlands West Indies
PK–	Indonesia and West Irian
PP–, PT–	Brazil
PZ–	Surinam
RP–	Philippine Republic
S2–	Bangladesh
SE–	Sweden
SP	Poland
ST–	Sudan
SU–	Egypt
SX–	Greece
TC–	Turkey
TF–	Iceland
TG–	Guatemala
TI–	Costa Rica
TJ–	United Republic of Cameroon
TL–	Central African Republic
TN–	Republic of Congo (Brazzaville)
TR–	Gabon
TS–	Tunisia
TT–	Chad
TU–	Ivory Coast
TY–	Dahomey
TZ–	Mali
VH–	Australia
VP–B	Bahamas
VP–F	Falkland Islands
VP–H	British Honduras
VP–L	Antigua
VP–P	Islands of Western Pacific High Commission
VP–V	St. Vincent
VP–X	Gambia
VP–Y, VP–W	Rhodesia
VQ–G	Grenada
VQ–H	St. Helena
VQ–L	St. Lucia
VQ–S	Seychelle Islands
VR–B	Bermuda
VR–G	Gibraltar (not used: present Gibraltar Airways aircraft registered G–)
VR–H	Hong Kong
VR–N	British Cameroons
VR–O	Sabah (North Borneo)
VR–U	Brunei
VR–W	Sarawak
VT–	India
XA–, XB–, XC–	Mexico
XT–	Upper Volta
XU–	Khmer Republic
XV–	Vietnam
XW–	Laos
XY–, XZ–	Burma
YA–	Afghanistan
YI–	Iraq
YJ–	New Hebrides
YK–	Syria
YR–	Romania
YS–	El Salvador
YU–	Yugoslavia
YV–	Venezuela
ZA–	Albania
ZK–, ZL–, ZM–	New Zealand
ZP–	Paraguay
ZS–, ZT–, ZU–	South Africa
3A–	Monaco
3B–	Mauritius
3C–	Equatorial Guinea
3D–	Swaziland
3X–	Guinea
4R–	Ceylon (Sri Lanka)
4W–	Yemen Arab Republic
4X–	Israel
5A–	Libya
5B–	Cyprus
5H–	Tanzania
5N–	Nigeria
5R–	Malagasy Republic (Madagascar)
5T–	Mauritania
5U–	Niger
5V–	Togo
5W–	Western Samoa (Polynesia)

* Cyrillic letters for SSSR

5X–	Uganda		9H–	Malta
5Y–	Kenya		9J–	Zambia
6O–	Somalia		9K–	Kuwait
6V–, 6W–	Senegal		9L–	Sierra Leone
6Y–	Jamaica		9M–	Malaysia
7O–	Democratic Yemen		9N–	Nepal
7P–	Lesotho		9Q–	Zaïre
7QY–	Malawi		9R–	Mozambique
7T–	Algeria		9U–	Burundi
8P–	Barbados		9V–	Singapore
8R–	Guyana		9XR–	Ruanda
9G–	Ghana		9Y–	Trinidad and Tobago

AIRCRAFT WITH BOTH CIVIL AND MILITARY MARKINGS

A number of British aircraft which have at one time carried civil registrations are now preserved in either flying or non-flying condition in Service markings. In some examples, the markings are those originally applied to the particular aircraft; in others, the aircraft have been restored to represent a typical period in the life of the type in question, but the serial number now carried is not that of the original airframe. As many as possible of the aircraft in this category, including a number of the exhibits of the Shuttleworth Collection and the RAF Museum, have been included again in proper registration sequence in this volume. The serial number which is actually displayed on these aircraft is shown in parentheses after the aircraft name. A typical example is the Bristol Fighter which flies as D8096 but was at one time on the civil register as G-AEPH.

AIRCRAFT TYPE DESIGNATIONS

(e.g. A.S.65—Airspeed Type 65)

A.	Beagle, Auster		G.	Grumman
AA–	American Aviation,		G.A.L.	General Aircraft
	now Grumman American		G.C.	Globe
AB–	Agusta-Bell		HM.	Henri Mignet
A.S.	Airspeed		H.P.	Handley Page
A.W.	Armstrong Whitworth		H.R.	Robin
B.	Blackburn, Bristol,		H.S.	Hawker Siddeley
	Boeing, Beagle		J.	Auster
B.A.C.	British Aircraft Corporation		L.	Lockheed
B.A.H.	British Airways Helicopters		L.A.	Luton
BN	Britten-Norman		M.	Miles, Mooney
Bo	Bolkow		MBB	Messerschmitt-Bölkow-Blohm
Bu	Bucker		M.S.	Morane-Saulnier
C.	Cierva		P.	Hunting (formerly Percival), Piaggio
CH.	Chrislea		PA–	Piper
CLA.	Comper		PC.	Pilatus
CP.	Piel		S.	Short, Sikorsky
D.	Druine		SA., SE,	
DC–	Douglas Commercial		SO.	Sud-Aviation, Aérospatiale
D.H.	de Havilland		S.R.	Saunders-Roe, Stinson
D.H.A.	de Havilland Australia		T.	Tipsy
D.H.C.	de Havilland Canada		UH.	United Helicopters (Hiller)
DR.	Jodel (Robin-built)		V.	Vickers-Armstrongs, B.A.C.
E.P.	Edgar Percival		V.S.	Vickers-Supermarine
F.	Fairchild, Fokker		W.S.	Westland

Acknowledgements

My sincere thanks go to the many friends, both personal and in the airline and aircraft industries, who have helped to make this book comprehensive and up-to-date. In particular, Gordon Swanborough gave invaluable assistance with the British registrations, helped by notes from D. Lewis; and Paul Duffy provided the complete Irish Civil Register. Members of LAAS International again helped to ensure that the considerable changes in the overseas fleet lists were recorded.

J.W.R.T.

BRITISH CIVIL
AIRCRAFT REGISTRATIONS

IN ALPHABETICAL ORDER

Corrected to January 1, 1976

Registration	Type	Owner or Operator	Where and when seen
G–EACN	*BAT BK23 Bantam (K123)	Shuttleworth Trust	
G–EBHX	*D.H.53 Humming Bird	Shuttleworth Trust	
G–EBIA	*S.E.5A (F904)	Shuttleworth Trust	
G–EBIB	*S.E.5A (F939)	Science Museum	
G–EBIC	*S.E.5A (F937)	RAF Museum	
G–EBIR	*D.H.51 (VP-KAA)	Shuttleworth Trust	
G–EBJE	*Avro 504K (E449)	RAF Museum	
G–EBJG	*Parnall Pixie III	Midland Aircraft Preservation Society	
G–EBJO	*ANEC II	Shuttleworth Trust	
G–EBKY	*Sopwith Pup (N5180)	Shuttleworth Trust	
G–EBLV	D.H.60 Cirrus Moth	Hawker Siddeley Aviation Ltd.	
G–EBMB	*Hawker Cygnet I	Hawker Siddeley Aviation Ltd.	
G–EBWD	D.H.60X Hermes Moth	Shuttleworth Trust	
G–EBYY	*Cierva C.8L	Musée de l'Air, Paris	
G–EBZM	*Avro 594 Avian IIIA	Aeroplane Collection Ltd.	
G–AAAH	*D.H.60G Gipsy Moth	Science Museum	
G–AACN	*H.P.39 Gugnunc	Science Museum	
G–AAHW	Klemm L.25-1A	R. E. Nerou	
G–AAIN	*Parnall Elf II	Shuttleworth Trust	
G–AAPZ	*Desoutter I (mod.)	Shuttleworth Trust (Torquay)	
G–AAUP	Klemm L.25-1A	R. S. Russell	
G–AAWO	D. H. 60G Gipsy Moth	J. F. W. Reid	
G–AAYX	*Southern Martlet	Shuttleworth Trust	
G–AAZP	D.H.80A Puss Moth	T. I. Sutton & B. J. Champion	
G–ABAA	*Avro 504K (H2311)	RAF Museum	
G–ABAG	D.H.60G Moth	D.H.C. Hull	
G–ABEE	*Avro 594 Avian IVM (Sports)	Aeroplane Collection Ltd.	
G–ABLM	*Cierva C.24	Science Museum	
G–ABLS	D.H.80A Puss Moth	J. D. Menzies	
G–ABMR	Hart 2 (J9941)	Hawker Siddeley Aviation Ltd.	
G–ABNT	*Civilian Coupe	G. O. Rees	
G–ABNX	Redwing 2	J. Pothecary	
G–ABOI	Wheeler Slymph	A. H. Wheeler	
G–ABTC	CLA.7 Swift	P. Channon	
G–ABUS	CLA.7 Swift	K. Sedgwick	
G–ABUU	CLA.7 Swift	J. Pothecary	
G–ABVE	Arrow Active 2	N. H. Jones	
G–ABWP	*Spartan Arrow	R. E. Blain	
G–ABXL	*Granger Archaeopteryx	Shuttleworth Trust	
G–ABYA	D.H.60G Gipsy Moth	Dr. I. D. C. Hay & J. F. Moore	
G–ACCB	*D.H.83 Fox Moth	Midland Aircraft Preservation Society	
G–ACDC	D.H.82A Tiger Moth	N. H. Jones	
G–ACDJ	D.H.82A Tiger Moth	F. J. Terry	
G–ACEJ	D.H.83 Fox Moth	Historic Aircraft Museum	
G–ACGT	*Avro 594 Avian IIIA	K. Smith	
G–ACIT	D.H.84 Dragon	J. Beaty	
G–ACLL	D.H.85 Leopard Moth	J. V. Skirrow	
G–ACMA	D.H.85 Leopard Moth	J. P. Filhol Ltd.	
G–ACMN	D.H.85 Leopard Moth	J. J. Parkes	
G–ACSS	*D.H.88 Comet	Shuttleworth Trust	
G–ACTF	CLA.7 Swift	A. J. Chalkley	
G–ACUU	Cierva C.30A	G. S. Baker (Skyfame Museum)	
G–ACVA	*Kay Gyroplane	Kay Gyroplanes Ltd	

* Historic aircraft, mostly preserved in non-flying condition.

Registration	Type	Owner or Operator	Where and when seen
G–ACWP	*Cierva C.30A (AP507)	Science Museum	
G–ADAH	D.H.89A Dragon Rapide	Royal Scottish Museum (Aeroplane Collection Ltd.)	
G–ADGP	M.2L Hawk Speed Six	D. A. Hood	
G–ADGT	D.H.82A Tiger Moth	D. R. & Mrs. M. Wood	
G–ADGV	D.H.82A Tiger Moth (BB694)	Air Cdre. A. H. Wheeler	
G–ADIA	D.H.82A Tiger Moth	R. M. Kilvington	
G–ADJJ	D.H.82A Tiger Moth	J. M. Preston	
G–ADKC	D.H.87B Hornet Moth	E. J. Roe	
G–ADKK	*D.H.87B Hornet Moth	C. W. Annis	
G–ADKM	D.H.87B Hornet Moth	F. R. E. Hayter	
G–ADLY	D.H.87B Hornet Moth	A. Haig-Thomas	
G–ADMT	D.H.87B Hornet Moth	Strathallan Collection	
G–ADMW	*M.2H Hawk Major (DG590)	RAF Museum	
G–ADND	D.H.87B Hornet Moth	The Shuttleworth Collection	
G–ADNE	D.H.87B Hornet Moth	C. B. L. Harding	
G–ADNZ	D.H.82A Tiger Moth	R. W. & Mrs. S. Pullan	
G–ADOT	*D.H.87B Hornet Moth	C. C. Lovell	
G–ADPJ	B.A.C. Drone	G. Eastell	
G–ADPR	*P.3 Gull	Shuttleworth Trust	
G–ADPS	Swallow 2	P. R. Harris	
G–ADRY	*Pou-du-Ciel (Replica)	P. Roberts	
G–ADSK	D.H.87B Hornet Moth	J. E. Wilson	
G–ADUR	D.H.87B Hornet Moth	Webster Aviation Ltd.	
G–ADXS	*Pou-du-Ciel	Mrs. C. L. Storey (Historic Aircraft Museum)	
G–AEBB	*Pou-du-Ciel	Shuttleworth Trust	
G–AEBJ	Blackburn B-2	Hawker Siddeley Aviation Ltd.	
G–AEDB	Kronfeld Drone	R. E. Ogden	
G–AEEG	M.3A Falcon	P. A. Mann	
G–AEEH	*Pou-du-Ciel	RAF Colerne	
G–AEFT	Aeronca C-3	C. E. Humphreys & ptnrs.	
G–AEGV	*HM-14 Pou-du-Ciel	Midland Aircraft Preservation Society	
G–AEHM	*Pou-du-Ciel	Science Museum	
G–AEKR	*Flying Flea (Replica)	E. Claybourne & Co. Ltd.	
G–AEKV	Kronfeld Drone	Wg. Cdr. J. E. McDonald	
G–AELO	D.H.87B Hornet Moth	I. D. C. Hay	
G–AEML	D.H.89 Dragon Rapide	J. P. Filhol Ltd.	
G–AEOA	D.H.80A Puss Moth	A. Haig-Thomas	
G–AEOH	*H.M.-14 Pou-du-Ciel	Gordon Riley	
G–AEPH	*Bristol F.2B (D8096)	Shuttleworth Trust	
G–AESE	*D.H.87B Hornet Moth	H. J. Shaw	
G–AETA	*Caudron G.3 (3066)	RAF Museum	
G–AEUJ	M.IIA Whitney Straight	C. H. Parker	
G–AEVS	*Aeronca 100	Historic Aircraft Preservation Society	
G–AEVZ	*Swallow 2	Royal Scottish Museum (Aeroplane Collection Ltd.)	
G–AEWV	Aeronca 100	J. R. Chapman	
G–AEXD	Aeronca 100	D. C. Everall	
G–AEXF	*P.6 Mew Gull	M. C. Barraclough & T. M. Storey	
G–AEXZ	Piper Cub J-2	Mrs. M. & J. R. Dowson	
G–AEYY	*Martin Monoplane	Northern Aircraft Preservation Society	
G–AEZG	D.H.87B Hornet Moth	Mrs. M. K. Wilberforce	
G–AFBS	M.14A Hawk Trainer	Skyfame Museum	
G–AFCL	Swallow 2	A. M. Dowson	
G–AFFD	Percival Q-6	MAPS	
G–AFGD	B. A. Swallow 2	B. Arden & ptnrs.	
G–AFGE	*Swallow 2	Torbay Aircraft Museum	
G–AFGH	Chilton D.W.I	J. T. Hayes & J. West	
G–AFGI	*Chilton D.W.I.	Skyfame Museum	

* Historic aircraft, mostly preserved in non-flying condition.

Registration	Type	Owner or Operator	Where and when seen
G–AFGK	M.IIA Whitney Straight	W. I. Scott-Hill & C. A. Herring	
G–AFHA	*Mosscraft M.A.I.	C. V. Butler	
G–AFIN	*Chrislea Airguard	Aeroplane Collection Ltd.	
G–AFIU	*Luton Minor (Parker C.A.4)	S. P. Connatty & I. V. Jones (N.A.P.S.)	
G–AFJB	*Wicko G.M.I	K. Woolley	
G–AFJR	Tipsy Trainer I	R. M. Long	
G–AFLW	M.17 Monarch	J. E. Randall	
G–AFNG	D.H.94 Moth Minor	A. Haig-Thomas	
G–AFNI	D.H.94 Moth Minor	B. M. Welford	
G–AFOB	D.H.94 Moth Minor	R. E. Ogden	
G–AFOJ	D.H.94 Moth Minor	R. M. Long	
G–AFPN	D.H.94 Moth Minor	K. C. Moore	
G–AFRV	Tipsy Trainer I	Capt. R. C. F. Bailey	
G–AFSC	Tipsy Trainer I	G. P. Hermer & ptnrs.	
G–AFSV	Chilton D.W.IA	R. C. F. Bailey	
G–AFTA	Hawker Tomtit (K1786)	Shuttleworth Trust	
G–AFVN	Tipsy Trainer I	W. Callow, D. H. Harris & E. A. Lingarde	
G–AFWI	D.H.82A Tiger Moth (BB814)	Portsmouth Naval Gliding Club	
G–AFWT	Tipsy Trainer I	N. M. Williams	
G–AFYD	Luscombe 8E	C. C. & Mrs. M. S. Lovell	
G–AFZE	Heath Parasol	K. C. D. St. Cyrien	
G–AGBN	G.A.L.42 Cygnet 2	J. & T. Robinson (Croydon) Ltd.	
G–AGHB	Hawker Sea Fury XI (WH589)	O. A. Hayden-Baillie	
G–AGJG	D.H.89A Dragon Rapide	Aerial Enterprises Ltd.	
G–AGJV	Dakota 4	Air Freight Ltd.	
G–AGLK	Auster 5D	W. C. E. Tazewell	
G–AGNV	*Avro 865 York I (LV633)	Skyfame Museum	
G–AGOH	*J/I Autocrat	Leicester County Council	
G–AGOS	R.S.3 Desford I (VZ728)	Sir W. J. D. Roberts	
G–AGSH	D.H.89A Dragon Rapide 6	Pioneer Aviation Trust	
G–AGTM	D.H.89A Dragon Rapide	Army Parachute Association *Valkyrie*	
G–AGTO	J/I Autocrat	Four T Engineering Ltd.	
G–AGTP	J/I Autocrat	Essex & Suffolk Gliding Club	
G–AGTT	J/I Autocrat	G. A. Allen & ptnrs.	
G–AGVF	J/IN Alpha	M. B. Taylor	
G–AGVG	J/I Autocrat	J. M. Alexander	
G–AGVN	J/I Autocrat	P. J. Elitt	
G–AGWE	Avro 19 Srs. 2	Strathallan Collection	
G–AGXN	J/IN Alpha	P. A. Davey	
G–AGXT	*J/IN Alpha	Stockport Aircraft Preservation Society	
G–AGXU	J/IN Alpha	Mrs. J. Lewis	
G–AGXV	J/I Autocrat	B. Brooks	
G–AGYD	J/IN Alpha	A. Tucker	
G–AGYH	J/IN Alpha	K. P. Donnan	
G–AGYT	J/IN Alpha	Portsmouth Naval Gliding Club	
G–AGYU	D.H.82A Tiger Moth (DE208)	A. Haig-Thomas	
G–AGYZ	Dakota 4	Air Freight Ltd.	
G–AHAG	D.H.89A Dragon Rapide	M. E. R. Coghlan	
G–AHAL	J/IN Alpha	Skegness Air Taxi Services Ltd.	
G–AHAM	J/I Autocrat	F. M. Graham	
G–AHAP	J/I Autocrat	G. C. Tudor-Jones	
G–AHAU	J/I Autocrat	Wasp Flying Group	
G–AHAV	J/I Autocrat	R. H. G. Kingsmill	
G–AHAY	J/I Autocrat	R. A. Hayne & M. J. Cuttell	
G–AHBL	D.H.87B Hornet Moth	Dr. Ursula H. Hamilton	
G–AHBM	D.H.87B Hornet Moth	P. Franklin	
G–AHCK	J/IN Alpha	P. A. Woodman	

* Historic aircraft, mostly preserved in non-flying condition.

Registration	Type	Owner or Operator	Where and when seen
G–AHCL	J/IN Alpha	I. J. M. Patton & K. D. Ballinger	
G–AHCN	J/IN Alpha	F. J. Andre	
G–AHCR	Gould-Taylorcraft Plus D Special	E. H. Gould	
G–AHED	*D.H.89A Dragon Rapide (RL962)	RAF Museum	
G–AHGD	D.H.89A Dragon Rapide	M. R. L. Astor	
G–AHGW	Taylorcraft Plus D	R. A. Yates	
G–AHGZ	Taylorcraft Plus D	H. M. Scottorn	
G–AHHH	J/I Autocrat	L. J. Howarth & J. T. Elliott	
G–AHHK	J/I Autocrat	W. J. Ogle	
G–AHHN	J/I Autocrat	D. F. Campbell	
G–AHHP	J/IN Alpha	Norton Flying Group	
G–AHHT	J/IN Alpha	A. M. Sutton	
G–AHIC	Avro 19 Srs. 2	Strathallan Collection	
G–AHIZ	D.H.82A Tiger Moth	C.F.G. Flying Ltd.	
G–AHKX	Avro 19 Srs 2	Strathallan Collection	
G–AHKY	*Miles M.18 Series 2	Etienne M. R. Deniel & Patricia Y. A. E. Coates	
G–AHLI	Auster 3	G. A. Leathers	
G–AHLK	Auster 3	J. Pegman	
G–AHLT	D.H.82A Tiger Moth	R. C. F. Bailey	
G–AHMJ	*Cierva C.30A	Shuttleworth Trust	
G–AHMN	D.H.82A Tiger Moth	G. A. Moore Nisbett	
G–AHNG	Taylorcraft Plus D	D. J. Pratt	
G–AHSA	*Avro 621 Tutor (K3215)	Shuttleworth Trust	
G–AHSD	Taylorcraft Plus D	A. Tucker	
G–AHSO	J/IN Alpha	Skegness Air Taxi Services Ltd.	
G–AHSP	J/I Autocrat	C. S. Frost	
G–AHSS	J/IV Alpha	J. K. Hall	
G–AHST	J/IN Alpha	P. H. Lewis	
G–AHSW	J/I Autocrat	K. W. Brown	
G–AHTW	A.S.40 Oxford (V3388)	Skyfame Museum	
G–AHUI	*M.38 Messenger 2A	Stockport Aircraft Preservation Society	
G–AHUV	D.H.82A Tiger Moth	W. G. Gordon	
G–AHWJ	Taylorcraft Plus D	A. Tucker	
G–AHXE	Taylorcraft Plus D	D. J. Pratt	
G–AHZT	M.38 Messenger 2A	E. Pratt	
G–AIBE	*Fulmar II (N1854)	F.A.A. Museum	
G–AIBH	J/IN Alpha	Skegness Air Taxi Services Ltd.	
G–AIBM	J/I Autocrat	J. L. Goodley	
G–AIBW	J/IN Alpha	J. L. Way	
G–AIBX	J/I Autocrat	Wasp Flying Group	
G–AIDE	M.17 Monarch	C. D. Cyster	
G–AIDK	M.38 Messenger 2A	C. C. Lovell	
G–AIDL	D.H.89A Dragon Rapide 6	The Midland Metal Spinning Co. Ltd.	
G–AIDN	V.S.502 Spitfire Tr. 8	J. S. & T. A. Davies	
G–AIEK	M.38 Messenger 2A (RG333)	Southend Historic Aircraft Museum	
G–AIFZ	J/IN Alpha	RAF College Flying Club Ltd.	
G–AIGF	J/IN Alpha	A. R. C. Mathie	
G–AIGM	J/IN Alpha	S. T. Raby	
G–AIGR	J/IN Alpha	Burton & Derby Flying Club	
G–AIGT	J/IN Alpha	C. Stewart	
G–AIGU	J/IN Alpha	T. Pate	
G–AIIH	Piper J-3C-65 Cub	J. W. Benson	
G–AIIZ	D.H.82A Tiger Moth	L.T. (Central Road Services) Sports Association Flying Club	
G–AIJM	Auster J/4	M. E. R. Coghlam	
G–AIJR	Auster J/4	B. Moss	
G–AIJS	Auster J/4	A. R. Weston	
G–AIJT	Auster J/4	Merlin Flying Club Ltd.	
G–AILL	M.38 Messenger 2A	H. Best-Devereux	
G–AIPR	Auster J/4	Shackleton Aviation Ltd.	
G–AIPW	J/I Autocrat	E. M. P. Cadman	
G–AIRC	J/I Autocrat	A. G. Martlew	

* Historic aircraft, mostly preserved in non-flying condition.

Registration	Type	Owner or Operator	Where and when seen
G–AIRI	D.H.82A Tiger Moth	J. M. Preston	
G–AIRK	D.H.82A Tiger Moth	C. R. Boreham, R. C. Treverson & R. W. Marshall	
G–AISA	Tipsy B Srs. I	A. Liddiard & H. Knight	
G–AISB	Tipsy B Srs. I	Cranfield Flying Group	
G–AISC	Tipsy B Srs. I	Wagtail Flying Group	
G–AIST	V.S. Spitfire I (AR213)	The Hon. P. Lindsay	
G–AISU	V.S. Spitfire 5B (AB910)	Royal Air Force	
G–AIUA	M.14A Hawk Trainer 3	S. Gotts & M. R. Gorman	
G–AIUL	D.H.89A Dragon Rapide 6	A. F. Ward	
G–AIVW	D.H.82A Tiger Moth Seaplane	N. H. Jones	
G–AIWA	P.28B Proctor I	M. C. Barraclough & T. M. Storey	
G–AIXA	Taylorcraft Plus D	P. J. Anderson	
G–AIXD	D.H.82A Tiger Moth	D. L. Lloyd	
G–AIXN	Sokol M. Ic	R. T. Phillips	
G–AIYR	D.H.89A Dragon Rapide	V. H. Bellamy	
G–AIYS	*D.H.85 Leopard Moth	J. H. Stevens	
G–AIZG	*V.S. Walrus I (L2301)	Historic Aircraft Preservation Society/Royal Navy	
G–AIZU	J/I Autocrat	E. A. Matty	
G–AIZY	J/I Autocrat	Lonmet (Aviation) Ltd.	
G–AIZZ	J/I Autocrat	E. A. Wright	
G–AJAB	J/IN Alpha	R. A. Mould	
G–AJAC	J/IN Alpha	R. C. Hibberd	
G–AJAE	J/IN Alpha	M. G. Stops	
G–AJAJ	J/IN Alpha	C. J. Alner	
G–AJAM	J/2 Arrow	R. C. Ashford, H. A. R. Stevens & J. V. Longley	
G–AJAS	J/IN Alpha	Lincoln Aero Club Ltd.	
G–AJBJ	*D.H.89A Dragon Rapide	Midland Aircraft Preservation Society	
G–AJCP	D.31 Turbulent	N. H. Kempt	
G–AJDR	*M.14A Hawk Trainer 3 (P6382)	Shuttleworth Trust	
G–AJDW	J/I Autocrat	A. L. Tuttle	
G–AJDY	J/I Autocrat	General Aviation Services	
G–AJEB	J/IN Alpha	Miss G. Bargery	
G–AJEE	J/I Autocrat	S. J. George	
G–AJEH	J/IN Alpha	Astral Surveys Ltd.	
G–AJEM	J/I Autocrat	N. A. Hind	
G–AJGJ	Auster 5	J. J. McLaughlin	
G–AJGT	D.H.104 Dove 7XC	Alderney Air Charter	
G–AJHO	D.H.89A Dragon Rapide	Army Parachute Association	
G–AJHS	D.H.82A Tiger Moth	R.A.E. Aero Club Ltd.	
G–AJHU	D.H.82A Tiger Moth	F. P. Le Coyte	
G–AJID	J/I Autocrat	L. W. Usherwood	
G–AJIH	J/I Autocrat	D. M. Campbell & ptnrs.	
G–AJIM	J/I Autocrat	G. R. R. St. Aubrey Davies	
G–AJIS	J/IN Alpha	A. G. Roads & ptnrs.	
G–AJIU	J/I Autocrat	H. R. Hewitt	
G–AJIW	J/IN Alpha	B. M. Baker (Hatfield) Ltd.	
G–AJIY	J/I Autocrat	Berry Ottaway & Associates	
G–AJJP	*Jet Gyrodyne (XD759/XJ348)	—	
G–AJOA	D.H.82A Tiger Moth	N. H. Jones	
G–AJOC	M.38 Messenger 2A	S. B. Jolly & J. Don	
G–AJOE	M.38 Messenger 2A (RH378)	T. T. Elliott	
G–AJOZ	*F.24W Argus 2	Aeroplane Collection Ltd.	
G–AJPI	F.27W-41a Argus	Shackleton Aviation Ltd.	
G–AJPZ	J/I Autocrat	D. J. Elliott	
G–AJRB	J/I Autocrat	Ground & Air Surveys Ltd.	
G–AJRC	J/I Autocrat	Severn Valley Aviation Group	
G–AJRE	J/I Autocrat	Lincoln Aero Club Ltd.	
G–AJRH	J/IN Alpha	J. P. Webster	

* Historic aircraft, mostly preserved in non-flying condition.

Registration	Type	Owner or Operator	Where and when seen
G–AJRK	J/I Autocrat	D. W. Miller	
G–AJTG	M.65 Gemini 3B	P. L. Ashworth	
G–AJTH	M.65 Gemini 1A	K. A. Learmonth	
G–AJUD	J/I Autocrat (KI9823)	R. J. Keyte	
G–AJUE	J/I Autocrat	A. J. E. Tiley & ptnrs.	
G–AJUL	J/IN Alpha	D. C. Hipwell	
G–AJUO	J/IN Alpha	A. M. L. McLean, G. W. Brown & M. R. Gibbons	
G–AJVH	Swordfish (LS326)	F.A.A. Museum	
G–AJWB	M.38 Messenger 2A	W. F. & M. R. Higgins	
G–AJXC	Auster 5	J. E. Graves	
G–AJXV	Auster 4	J. R. Ramshaw	
G–AJYO	J/5B Autocar	A. H. Chaplin & ptnrs.	
G–AKAA	Piper J-3C-65 Cub	J. W. Benson	
G–AKAT	*M.14A Magister (T9738)	Lincs Aviation Museum	
G–AKBO	M.38 Messenger 2A	J. H. H. Turner	
G–AKDN	D.H.C. 1a-1 Chipmunk 10	J. Tullett	
G–AKEL	M.65 Gemini 1A	J. M. Bisco	
G–AKER	*M.65 Gemini 1A	Lincolnshire Aircraft Preservation Society	
G–AKEZ	M.38 Messenger 2A	Torbay Aircraft Museum	
G–AKGD	M.65 Gemini 1A	D. G. Addicott	
G–AKGE	M.65 Gemini 3C	T. T. Parr	
G–AKGV	D.H.89A Dragon Rapide	S. J. Filhol	
G–AKHP	M.65 Gemini 1A	C. Spencer-Thomas	
G–AKHW	M.65 Gemini 1A	P. J. Messevry	
G–AKHZ	*M.65 Gemini	Stockport Aircraft Preservation Society	
G–AKIF	D.H.89A Dragon Rapide	Airborne Taxi Services	
G–AKIN	M.38 Messenger 2A	Spiller & Sons	
G–AKJU	J/IN Alpha	Arrow Air Services (Engineering) Ltd.	
G–AKKB	M.65 Gemini 1A	Miles Aviation & Transport (R. & D.) Ltd.	
G–AKKH	M.65 Gemini 1A	Shobdon Aviation Ltd.	
G–AKKR	*M.14A Magister (T9707)	RAF Museum	
G–AKNB	Dakota 3	Intra Airways	
G–AKOE	D.H.89A Dragon Rapide 4	J. E. Pierce	
G–AKOW	Auster 5	A. M. L. McLean	
G–AKPI	Auster 5 (NJ703)	B. H. Hargrave	
G–AKRS	D.H.89A Dragon Rapide	Tofton Aviation	
G–AKSS	D.H.104 Dove 1B	Fairey Surveys Ltd.	
G–AKUW	C.H.3 Super Ace	C. V. Butler	
G–AKVF	C.H.3 Super Ace	P. V. B. Longthorp	
G–AKVZ	M.38 Messenger 4B	P. H. Lours	
G–AKWS	Auster 5	R. L. H. Alexander & A. H. Macbeth	
G–AKXS	D.H.82A Tiger Moth	P. A. Colman	
G–AKZN	*P.30 Proctor 2E (Z7197)	RAF Museum	
G–ALAH	*M.38 Messenger 4A (RH377)	Aeroplane Collection Ltd.	
G–ALAX	*D.H.89A Dragon Rapide	Durney Aeronautical Collection	
G–ALBD	D.H.82A Tiger Moth	F. W. Fay	
G–ALBJ	Auster 5	R. H. Elkington	
G–ALBK	Auster 5	V. G. Manton	
G–ALBN	*Bristol 173 (XF785)	RAF Museum	
G–ALCK	*Proctor (LZ766)	Skyfame Museum	
G–ALCS	M.65 Gemini 3C	R. E. Winn	
G–ALCU	D.H.104 Dove 2B	S. J. Filhol	
G–ALFA	Auster 5	Apollo Air Group	
G–ALFT	D.H.104 Dove 6	Civil Aviation Authority	
G–ALGT	V.S.379 Spitfire 14 (RM619)	Rolls-Royce (1971) Ltd.	
G–ALJF	P.34A Proctor 3	J. F. Moore	
G–ALNA	D.H.82A Tiger Moth	Wessex Flying Group	
G–ALND	D.H.82A Tiger Moth	Bustard Flying Club Ltd.	
G–ALSP	*Bristol 171 (WV783)	RAF Museum	

* Historic aircraft, mostly preserved in non-flying condition.

Registration	Type	Owner or Operator	Where and when seen
G–ALSS	*Bristol 171 (WA576)	—	
G–ALTW	D.H.82A Tiger Moth	C. J. Musk	
G–ALUC	D.H.82A Tiger Moth	D. R. & Mollie Wood	
G–ALWB	D.H.C.I. Chipmunk 22A	Transmeridian Flying Group	
G–ALWC	Dakota 4	Fairey Surveys Ltd.	
G–ALWF	*V.701 Viscount	Cambrian Airways Ltd.	
G–ALWH	P.50 Prince 2A	The Decca Navigator Co. Ltd.	
G–ALWW	D.H.82A Tiger Moth	Drive Lease Ltd.	
G–ALXZ	Auster 5-150	T. Bessart & R. Witheridge	
G–ALYD	Auster 4	J. D. Lodder	
G–ALYG	Auster 5D	N. Lockwood	
G–ALZG	M.65 Gemini 3C	R. E. Winn	
G–AMAU	Hurricane 2C (PZ865)	Hawker Siddeley Aviation Ltd.	
G–AMAW	Luton L.A.4 Minor	J. R. Coates	
G–AMCA	Dakota 4	Fairey Surveys Ltd.	
G–AMDA	Avro 652A Anson I (N4877)	Skyfame Museum	
G–AMDN	Hiller UH-12A	Bristow Helicopters Ltd.	
G–AMFV	Dakota 3	Shackleton Aviation	
G–AMHJ	Dakota 6	Intra Airways Ltd.	
G–AMIU	D.H.82A Tiger Moth	R. & Mrs. J. L. Jones	
G–AMKS	D.H.104 Dove 1B	Fairey Surveys Ltd.	
G–AMKU	J/IB Aiglet	Southdown Flying Group	
G–AMLZ	P.50 Prince 6E	T. M. Clutterbuck	
G–AMME	M.65 Gemini 3A	P. Jackson	
G–AMMS	J/5N Aiglet Tr.	G. White & Sons	
G–AMOG	V.701 Viscount	British Airways *Scottish Princess*	
G–AMON	V.701 Viscount	British Airways	
G–AMPO	Dakota 4	McDonald Aviation Ltd.	
G–AMPW	J/5B Autocar	J. V. Inglis	
G–AMPY	Dakota 4	Intra Airways	
G–AMPZ	Dakota 6	Intra Airways	
G–AMRA	Dakota 6	—	
G–AMRF	J/5F Aiglet Trainer	J. Knight	
G–AMRK	G.37 Gladiator (L8032)	Shuttleworth Trust	
G–AMSM	Dakota 4	Air Freight Ltd.	
G–AMSU	*Dakota 3 (G–AMPP)	Dan-Air Services	
G–AMSV	Dakota 6	Skyways Cargo	
G–AMTA	J/5F Aiglet Trainer	Strabor (Aircraft) Ltd.	
G–AMTE	J/5F Aiglet Trainer	I. R. G. Thomas	
G–AMTM	J/I Autocrat	G. Jeffrey & ptnrs.	
G–AMUC	D.H.C.I Chipmunk 21	Flight-Line Ltd.	
G–AMUF	D.H.C.I Chipmunk 21	P. S. Bubbear	
G–AMUH	D.H.C.I Chipmunk 21	D. H. Whalley	
G–AMVP	Tipsy Junior	A. R. Wershot	
G–AMWW	Dakota 4	Air Freight Ltd.	
G–AMXL	D.H.C.I Chipmunk 22	W. C. C. Meyer	
G–AMYD	J/5L Aiglet Trainer	G. H. Maskell	
G–AMYI	J/8L Aiglet Trainer	D. S. Vernon	
G–AMYJ	Dakota 6	Intra Airways Ltd.	
G–AMZI	J/5F Aiglet Trainer	Surrey Aviation	
G–AMZT	J/5F Aiglet Trainer	A. H. Roscoe	
G–AMZU	J/5F Aiglet Trainer	P. J. Fish	
G–ANAF	*Dakota 4	IWM	
G–ANCF	Bristol 175 Britannia 308F	Monarch Airlines Ltd.	
G–ANCX	D.H.82A Tiger Moth	D. R. Wood	
G–ANDE	D.H.82A Tiger Moth	R. Sanders	
G–ANDP	D.H.82A Tiger Moth	A. H. Diver	
G–ANEF	D.H.82A Tiger Moth	RAF College Flying Club Co. Ltd.	
G–ANEL	D.H.82A Tiger Moth (N9238)	W. P. Maynall	
G–ANEW	D.H.82A Tiger Moth	A. L. Young	
G–ANEZ	D.H.82A Tiger Moth	J. W. Benson	
G–ANFC	D.H.82A Tiger Moth	London Gliding Club (Pty.) Ltd.	
G–ANFH	Westland S.55	Bristow Helicopters Ltd.	

* Historic aircraft, mostly preserved in non-flying condition.

Registration	Type	Owner or Operator	Where and when seen
G–ANFI	D.H.82A Tiger Moth (DE623)	Wallis & Son Ltd.	
G–ANFM	D.H.82A Tiger Moth	S. A. Brook, L. S. Mitton & J. Harthill	
G–ANFU	Auster 5	D. A. Gray & J. T. Sime	
G–ANFV	D.H.82A Tiger Moth	Strathallan Collection	
G–ANFW	D.H.82A Tiger Moth	G. M. Fraser	
G–ANHK	D.H.82A Tiger Moth	J. D. Iliffe	
G–ANHL	Auster 4	R. E. Webb	
G–ANHR	Auster 5	R. L. James, D. W. Mann & R. Gawler	
G–ANHS	Auster 4	P. S. Sturdgess	
G–ANHX	Auster 5D	M. P. Boulton	
G–ANHZ	Auster 5	A. Cornwell & D. J. Ronayne	
G–ANIE	Auster 5	H. O. Stibbard	
G–ANIJ	Auster 5D	Army Aviation Museum	
G–ANIS	Auster 5	J. Clark-Cockburn	
G–ANJA	D.H.82A Tiger Noth (N9389)	J. J. Young	
G–ANJK	D.H.82A Tiger Moth	Montgomeryshire Ultra Light Flying Club	
G–ANKK	D.H.82A Tiger Moth (T5854)	Birmingham Tiger Group	
G–ANKT	D.H.82A Tiger Moth (T6818)	The Shuttleworth Collection	
G–ANLW	W.B.I. Widgeon	Helicopter Hire Ltd.	
G–ANMZ	D.H.82A Tiger Moth	The Tiger Club	
G–ANNO	D.H.114 Heron IB/C	McDonald Aviation Ltd.	
G–ANOA	Hiller UH-12A	Bristow Helicopters Ltd.	
G–ANOD	D.H.82A Tiger Moth	D. R. & Mrs. M. Wood	
G–ANOH	D.H.82A Tiger Moth	S. J. Carr	
G–ANOK	S-91C Safir	A. F. Galt & Co. Ltd.	
G–ANON	D.H.82A Tiger Moth	R. Corry & D. Harrison	
G–ANOO	D.H.82A Tiger Moth	R.A.E. Bedford Aero Club	
G–ANOR	D.H.82A Tiger Moth	A. J. Cheshire	
G–ANOV	D.H.104 Dove 6	Civil Aviation Authority	
G–ANPE	D.H.82A Tiger Moth	R. W. & P. R. Budge	
G–ANPK	D.H.82A Tiger Moth	A. V. Horsey	
G–ANPP	P.34A Proctor 3	J. R. Batt	
G–ANRF	D.H.82A Tiger Moth	C. D. Cyster	
G–ANRN	D.H.82A Tiger Moth	Adamix (King's Cliff) Refractories	
G–ANRP	Auster 5	J. W. Weeks	
G–ANSM	D.H.82A Tiger Moth	Torbay Aviation Ltd.	
G–ANSZ	D.H.114 Heron IB	Peters' Aviation Ltd.	
G–ANTE	D.H.82A Tiger Moth	T. I. Sutton & B. J. Champion	
G–ANTK	*Avro 685 York	The Scout Association	
G–ANUO	D.H.114 Heron 2D	The GEC Co. Ltd.	
G–ANUT	D.H.104 Dove 6	Civil Aviation Authority	
G–ANUU	D.H.104 Dove 6	Civil Aviation Authority	
G–ANUW	D.H.104 Dove 6	Civil Aviation Authority	
G–ANVU	D.H.104 Dove IB	T. D. Keegan	
G–ANWB	D.H.C.I. Chipmunk 21	G. Briggs	
G–ANWX	J/5L Aiglet Trainer	Newcastle & Tees-side Gliding Club	
G–ANXA	D.H.114 Heron IB	Peters' Aviation Ltd.	
G–ANXB	D.H.114 Heron IB	Peters' Aviation Ltd.	
G–ANXR	P.31 Proctor 4 (RM221)	J. R. Batt	
G–ANYP	*P.31C Proctor 4	Torbay Aircraft Museum	
G–ANZJ	P.31C Proctor 4 (NP303)	Historic Aircraft Museum, Southend	
G–ANZR	D.H.82A Tiger Moth	D. R. & Mrs. M. Wood	
G–ANZU	*D.H.82A Tiger Moth (L6938)	P. A. Jackson	
G–ANZZ	D.H.82A Tiger Moth	The Tiger Club	
G–AOAA	D.H.82A Tiger Moth	The Tiger Club	
G–AOAR	P.31C Proctor 5 (NP181)	Historic Aircraft Preservation Society	

* Historic aircraft, mostly preserved in non-flying condition.

Registration	Type	Owner or Operator	Where and when seen
G–AOBN	Dakota 4	Eastlease Ltd.	
G–AOBO	D.H.82A Tiger Moth	T. J. Bolt & J. N. Moore	
G–AOBU	*P.84 Jet Provost	Shuttleworth Trust	
G–AOBV	J/5P Autocar	G. Lee	
G–AOBX	D.H. 82A Tiger Moth (T7187)	Leisure Sport Ltd.	
G–AOCR	Auster 5D	D. T. Cheetham	
G–AOCU	Auster 5	S. J. Ball	
G–AODR	D.H. 82A Tiger Moth	D. R. & Mrs. M. Wood	
G–AODT	D.H. 82A Tiger Moth	N. A. Brett & A. H. Warminger	
G–AOEG	D.H. 82A Tiger Moth	Midland Tiger Flying Group	
G–AOEH	Aeronca 7AC	M. Weeks, F. J. Burton & N. J. Fitton	
G–AOEI	D.H.82A Tiger Moth	Cambridge Flying Group	
G–AOEL	D.H.82A Tiger Moth	Capt. R. C. F. Bailey	
G–AOES	D.H.82A Tiger Moth	R. F. D. Vickers & D. R. Wood	
G–AOET	D.H.82A Tiger Moth	Jack W. Benson	
G–AOFE	D.H.C.I Chipmunk 22A	B. Webster	
G–AOFF	D.H.C.I Chipmunk 22	Bryant Bros. (Hauliers) Ltd.	
G–AOFJ	Auster 5	Miss P. M. Innocent	
G–AOFM	J/5P Autocar	R. M. Clarke	
G–AOFS	J/5L Aiglet Trainer	G. W. Howard	
G–AOFW	ATL-98 Carvair	British Air Ferries Ltd. *Big John*	
G–AOGA	M.75 Aries	R. E. Winn	
G–AOGE	P.34A Proctor 3	R. J. Sewell	
G–AOGM	J/5P Autocar	J. E. Stevens & Ptnrs.	
G–AOGO	D.H.114 Heron 2	E. S. & A. Robinson (Holdings) Ltd.	
G–AOGV	J/5R Alpine	A. B. H. Aviation	
G–AOHH	V.802 Viscount	British Airways	
G–AOHJ	V.802 Viscount	British Airways	
G–AOHK	V.802 Viscount	British Airways	
G–AOHL	V.802 Viscount	British Airways	
G–AOHM	V.802 Viscount	British Airways	
G–AOHO	V.802 Viscount	British Airways	
G–AOHT	V.802 Viscount	British Airways	
G–AOHV	V.802 Viscount	British Airways	
G–AOHZ	J/5P Autocar	G. J. Charlton & Ptnrs.	
G–AOIL	D.H.82A Tiger Moth	The Shuttleworth Collection	
G–AOIM	D.H.82A Tiger Moth	R. M. Wade & J. F. Terry	
G–AOIO	Thruxton Jackaroo	P. A. Gliddon	
G–AOIR	Thruxton Jackaroo	Stevenage Flying Club	
G–AOIS	D.H.82A Tiger Moth	V. B. & R.G. Wheele	
G–AOIT	Thruxton Jackaroo	Caledonian Flying Services Ltd.	
G–AOIY	J/5G Autocar	L. N. Garner	
G–AOJB	V.802 Viscount	British Airways	
G–AOJD	V.802 Viscount	British Airways	
G–AOJE	V.802 Viscount	British Airways	
G–AOJF	V.802 Viscount	British Airways	
G–AOJH	D.H.83C Fox Moth	J. S. Lewery	
G–AOIJ	D.H.82A Tiger Moth	M. W. Robinson	
G–AOKH	P.40 Prentice I	P. H. Louks	
G–AOKL	P.40 Prentice I (VS610)	J. R. Batt	
G–AOKO	P.40 Prentice I	J. F. Coggins	
G–AOLK	P.40 Prentice I	Hilton Aviation Ltd.	
G–AOLP	P.40 Prentice I	D. N. Downton & ptnrs.	
G–AOLU	P.40 Prentice I	Strathallan Collection	
G–AORD	V.802 Viscount	British Airways	
G–AORL	D.H.C.I Chipmunk 22	D. Gardner	
G–AOSE	D.H.104 Dove 6	Technical Hire & Consultancy Ltd.	
G–AOSK	D.H.C.I Chipmunk 22	F. H. Bateman	
G–AOSN	D.H.C.I Chipmunk 22	Spartan Flyers Ltd.	
G–AOSO	D.H.C.I Chipmunk 22	A. R. Lockyer	
G–AOSU	D.H.C.I Chipmunk 22	RAFGSA	
G–AOSY	D.H.C.I Chipmunk 22	J. A. W. Clowes	
G–AOSZ	D.H.C.I Chipmunk 22A	J. N. Russell	
G–AOTD	D.H.C.I Chipmunk 22	L. R. Vandome	

* Historic aircraft, mostly preserved in non-flying condition.

Registration	Type	Owner or Operator	Where and when seen
G–AOTF	D.H.C.I Chipmunk 23	RAF GSA Bicester	
G–AOTI	D.H.114 Heron 2D	Rolls-Royce (171) Ltd.	
G–AOTK	D.5 Turbi	The T. K. Flying Group	
G–AOTM	D.H.C.I Chipmunk 22A	Hawes Flying Group	
G–AOTV	D.H.C.I Chipmunk 23A	Sherwood Flying Group Ltd.	
G–AOTY	D.H.C.I Chipmunk 22A	West London Aero Services Ltd.*	
G–AOUG	D.H.104 Dove 6	Farihan Dajami	
G–AOUH	D.H.104 Dove 5	Farihan Dajami	
G–AOUJ	*Fairey Ultra-light	P. R. Swettenham (N.A.P.S.)	
G–AOUO	D.H.C.I Chipmunk 22	S. Gossip	
G–AOUP	D.H.C.I Chipmunk 22	Wessex Flying Group	
G–AOVF	B.175 Britannia 312	International Aviation Services	
G–AOVP	B.175 Britannia 312F	International Aviation Services	
G–AOVS	B.175 Britannia 312F	Westwing Aviation Services	
G–AOVW	Auster 5	B. Marriott	
G–AOXN	D.H.82A Tiger Moth	D. W. Mickleburgh	
G–AOXO	Tipsy Belfair	K. M. Bowen	
G–AOYG	V.806 Viscount	British Airways	
G–AOYH	V.806 Viscount	British Airways	
G–AOYI	V.806 Viscount	British Airways	
G–AOYJ	V.806 Viscount	British Airways	
G–AOYL	V.806 Viscount	British Airways	
G–AOYM	V.806 Viscount	British Airways	
G–AOYN	V.806 Viscount	British Airways	
G–AOYO	V.806 Viscount	British Airways	
G–AOYP	V.806 Viscount	British Airways	
G–AOYR	V.806 Viscount	British Airways	
G–AOYS	V.806 Viscount	British Airways	
G–AOZB	D.H.83A Tiger Moth	M. H. Reid	
G–AOZH	D.H.82A Tiger Moth	V. B. & R. G. Wheele	
G–AOZL	J/5Q Alpine	L. C. Cole	
G–AOZO	E.P.9 Prospector	Lancashire Aircraft Co., Ltd.	
G–AOZP	D.H.C.I Chipmunk 22	M. E. Darlington	
G–APAF	Auster 5	J. & Mrs. U. M. Pearce	
G–APAH	Auster 5 Alpha	Executive Flying Services Ltd.	
G–APAJ	Thruxton Jackaroo	E. W. Woods & R. B. Woods	
G–APAM	Thruxton Jackaroo	R. P. Williams	
G–APAO	Thruxton Jackaroo	A. T. Christian	
G–APAP	Thruxton Jackaroo	H. D. V. Leech	
G–APAV	Bristol 170 Mk. 32	Shackleton Aviation	
G–APBC	Dakota 4	Air Freight Ltd.	
G–APBD	PA-23 Apache 160	Channel Aviation Ltd.	
G–APBE	Auster 5	G. W. Clarke	
G–APBI	D.H.82A Tiger Moth	R. Devaney & ptnrs.	
G–APBO	Druine D.53 Turbi	Usworth Flying Group	
G–APBW	Auster 5	J. T. Wallis	
G–APCB	J/5Q Alpine	G. Jones	
G–APCX	J/5R Alpine	W. S. Ross, J. Gow & F. Gillian	
G–APCY	J/IN Alpha	J. R. Pearson	
G–APDB	D.H.106 Comet 4	IWM	
G–APDC	D.H.106 Comet 4	Dan-Air Services Ltd.	
G–APDG	D.H.106 Comet 4	Dan-Air Services Ltd.	
G–APDJ	D.H.106 Comet 4	Dan-Air Services Ltd.	
G–APDK	D.H.106 Comet 4	Dan-Air Services Ltd.	
G–APDO	D.H.106 Comet 4	Dan-Air Services Ltd.	
G–APDV	Hiller UH-12C	Nobby-Field Helicopters	
G–APEG	V.953 Vanguard	British Airways	
G–APEJ	V.953 Vanguard	British Airways	
G–APEK	V.953 Vanguard Merchantman	British Airways	
G–APEL	V.953 Vanguard Merchantman	British Airways	
G–APEM	V.953 Vanguard Merchantman	British Airways	
G–APEO	V.953C Vanguard Merchantman	British Airways	
G–APEP	V.953C Vanguard Merchantman	British Airways	

* Historic aircraft, mostly preserved in non-flying condition.

Registration	Type	Owner or Operator	Where and when seen
G–APES	V.953C Vanguard Merchantman	British Airways	
G–APET	V.953C Vanguard Merchantman	British Airways	
G–APEX	V.806 Viscount	Northeast Airlines	
G–APEY	V.806 Viscount	Northeast Airlines	
G–APFA	D.5 Turbi	Wolverhampton Ultra-light Flying Group	
G–APFB	Boeing 707-436	British Airtours	
G–APFD	Boeing 707-436	British Airtours	
G–APFF	Boeing 707-436	British Airtours	
G–APFG	Boeing 707-436	British Airtours	
G–APFI	Boeing 707-436	British Airways	
G–APFJ	Boeing 707-436	British Airways (leased to Malaysian Airline System)	
G–APFK	Boeing 707-436	British Airtours	
G–APFL	Boeing 707-436	British Airtours	
G–APFM	Boeing 707-436	British Airways	
G–APFN	Boeing 707-436	British Airways	
G–APFO	Boeing 707-436	British Airtours	
G–APHV	Avro 19 Srs. 2 (VM360)	Strathallan Collection	
G–APIE	Tipsy Belfair B	G. S. Whitley	
G–APIG	D.H.82A Tiger Moth	Westwick Distributors Ltd.	
G–APIK	J/IN Alpha	T. D. Howe	
G–APIM	V.806 Viscount	Cambrian Airways Ltd.	
G–APIT	P.40 Prentice I	J. R. Batt	
G–APIU	P.40 Prentice I	J. F. Coggins	
G–APJB	P.40 Prentice I	City Airways	
G–APJJ	*Fairey Ultra-light	Cranfield Institute of Technology	
G–APJN	Hiller UH-12B	Bristow Helicopters Ltd.	
G–APJO	D.H.82A Tiger Moth	D. R. & Mrs. M. Wood	
G–APJZ	J/IN Alpha	L. Goddard & E. Amey	
G–APKH	D.H.85 Leopard Moth	P. Franklin	
G–APKM	J/IN Alpha	K. C. Bachmann	
G–APKN	J/IN Alpha	Skegness Air Taxi Services Ltd.	
G–APKW	D.H.114 Heron IB	Peters' Aviation Ltd.	
G–APKY	Hiller UH-12B	Shackleton Aviation Ltd.	
G–APLG	J/5L Aiglet Trainer	D. H. Furnell	
G–APLK	M-100 Student	Miles Dufon Ltd.	
G–APMB	D.H.106 Comet 4B	Dan-Air Services Ltd.	
G–APMD	D.H.106 Comet 4B	Dan-Air Services Ltd.	
G–APME	D.H.106 Comet 4B	Dan-Air Services Ltd.	
G–APMF	D.H.106 Comet 4B	Dan-Air Services Ltd.	
G–APMG	D.H.106 Comet 4B	Dan-Air Services Ltd.	
G–APMH	J/IU Workmaster	R. E. Neal & S. R. Stevens	
G–APML	Dakota 6	Martin-Baker (Engineering) Ltd.	
G–APMP	Hiller UH-12C	M. T. Hynett	
G–APMR	Hiller UH-12C	Bristow Helicopters Ltd.	
G–APMS	Hiller UH-12C	Bristow Helicopters Ltd.	
G–APMX	D.H.82A Tiger Moth	Rollason Flying Group	
G–APMY	PA.23 Apache 160	Skyfotos Ltd.	
G–APNJ	Cessna 310	Yellow Bird Air Taxis Ltd.	
G–APNR	Hiller UH-12C	Bristow Helicopters Ltd.	
G–APNS	Garland-Bianchi Linnet	Mrs. P. B. Voice	
G–APNT	Currie Wot	L. W. Richardson & ptnrs.	
G–APNZ	D.31 Turbulent	The Tiger Club	
G–APOA	J/IN Alpha	Bristow Helicopters Ltd.	
G–APOD	Tipsy Belfair	R. J. Miller & C. A. Lock	
G–APOI	Saro Skeeter Srs. 8	E. Perry	
G–APOL	D.36 Turbulent	A. R. Leith	
G–APPA	D.H.C.I Chipmunk 22	R. N. Goode & D. Barr	
G–APPK	D.H.C.I Chipmunk 22	P. R. Spencer	
G–APPL	P.40 Prentice I	Miss S. J. Saggers	
G–APPM	D.H.C.I Chipmunk 22	L. T. Mersh	
G–APPX	V.702 Viscount	Field Aircraft Services Ltd.	
G–APRF	Auster 5	Vendair (London) Ltd.	
G–APRJ	*Avro 694 Lincoln B.2 (G-29-1)	Historic Aircraft Museum, Southend	

* Historic aircraft, mostly preserved in non-flying condition.

Registration	Type	Owner or Operator	Where and when seen
G–APRL	AW650 Argosy 101	Field Aircraft Services Ltd.	
G–APRN	AW650 Argosy 101	Air Bridge Carriers	
G–APRO	Auster 6A	A. H. Wheeler	
G–APRR	Super Aero 45	D. P. White	
G–APRT	Taylor Monoplane	C. J. Chambers & ptnrs.	
G–APRU	M.S.760 Paris	Cranfield Institute of Technology	
G–APSH	Hiller UH-12B	Bristow Helicopters Ltd.	
G–APSK	D.H.104 Dove 5	Severn Airways Ltd.	
G–APSO	D.H.104 Dove 5	Fairflight Charters Ltd.	
G–APST	D.31 Turbulent	K. E. Armstrong	
G–APSZ	Cessna 172	R. I. Cornes	
G–APTH	Agusta-Bell 47J	Tonrin Air Services	
G–APTM	Hiller UH-12B	Bristow Helicopters Ltd.	
G–APTP	PA-22 Tri-Pacer 150	D. M. Harbottle	
G–APTR	J/IN Alpha	John Pointon (Southern Transport) Ltd.	
G–APTS	D.H.C.1 Chipmunk 22A	B. R. Pickard	
G–APTU	Auster 5	B. G. F. King	
G–APTW	W.B.1 Widgeon	International Messengers Ltd.	
G–APTY	Beech G.35 Bonanza	T. G. Breakell & G. E. Brennand	
G–APTZ	D.31 Turbulent	G. Edmiston	
G–APUB	Beech 95 Travel Air	Gp Capt. D. R. S. Bader	
G–APUD	Bensen B.7M (modified)	Aeroplane Collection Ltd.	
G–APUE	L-40 Meta-Sokol	F. J. Nead	
G–APUK	J/1 Autocrat	P. L. Morley	
G–APUP	Sopwith Pup (Replica) (N5182)	K. C. D. St. Cyrien	
G–APUR	PA-22 Tri-Pacer 160	C. A. Harrop	
G–APUT	PA-22 Tri-Pacer 160	P. A. Crouch	
G–APUW	Auster J-5V-160	J. P. Webster	
G–APUY	D.31 Turbulent	S. P. Connatty	
G–APUZ	PA-24 Comanche 250	Bristol & Wessex Aeroplane Club Ltd.	
G–APVA	PA-22 Tri-Pacer 160	D. M. Whitham	
G–APVD	W.B.1 Widgeon	International Messengers Ltd.	
G–APVG	J/5L Aiglet Trainer	CIBA-Geigy (UK) Ltd.	
G–APVK	PA-23 Apache 160	IBC Civil Engineers	
G–APVN	D.31 Turbulent	R. Sherwin	
G–APVS	Cessna 170B	P. E. L. Lamyman	
G–APVU	L-40 Meta-Sokol	V. F. Wales	
G–APVV	Mooney M-20A	Arthur W. Clowes Ltd.	
G–APVW	Beech 35 Bonanza	J. E. & J. G. Powell	
G–APVY	PA-25 Pawnee 160	A.D.S. (Aerial) Ltd.	
G–APVZ	D.31 Turbulent	A. F. Bullock	
G–APWE	HPR-7 Herald 201	British Island Airways Ltd.	
G–APWF	HPR-7 Herald 201	British Island Airways Ltd.	
G–APWG	HPR-7 Herald 201	British Island Airways Ltd.	
G–APWH	HPR-7 Herald 201	British Island Airways Ltd.	
G–APWJ	HPR-7 Herald 201	British Island Airways Ltd.	
G–APWM	S.55 Whirlwind 1	Farihan Dajami	
G–APWR	PA-22 Tri-Pacer 160	West Lancashire Aero Club	
G–APWY	Piaggio P.166	The Marconi Co. Ltd.	
G–APXD	F8L Falco 1	Fine Stitchers Ltd.	
G–APXF	S.55 Whirlwind 1	Farihan Dajami	
G–APXJ	PA-24 Comanche 250	J. W. Quine & G. F. Lindsay	
G–APXM	PA-22 Tri-Pacer 160	Appleby Glade Ltd.	
G–APXP	PA-22 Tri-Pacer 160	G. H. Gledhill	
G–APXR	PA-22 Tri-Pacer 160	D. H. Rees & E. Hooton	
G–APXT	PA-22 Tri-Pacer 150	McKenzie & Tapp Ltd.	
G–APXU	PA-22 Tri-Pacer 125	R. C. Fleming	
G–APXY	Cessna 150	J. W. Barwell	
G–APYB	T.66 Nipper 2	B. O. Smith	
G–APYC	D.H.106 Comet 4B	Dan-Air Services Ltd.	
G–APYD	D.H.106 Comet 4B	Dan-Air Services Ltd.	
G–APYG	D.H.C.1 Chipmunk 22	Air Navigation & Trading Co. Ltd.	
G–APYI	PA-22 Tri-Pacer 135	Leith Air Ltd.	
G–APYN	PA-22 Tri-Pacer 160	W. D. Stephens & W. Heselton	
G–APYT	7FC Tri-Traveller	S. C. Luck & ptnrs.	

Registration	Type	Owner or Operator	Where and when seen
G–APYU	7FC Tri-Traveller	K. Collins	
G–APYW	PA-22 Tri-Pacer 150	J. D. Pett	
G–APYX	PA-23 Aztec 250	Holding and Barnes Ltd.	
G–APYZ	D.31 Turbulent	A. R. Lee	
G–APZE	PA-23 Apache 160	R. B. Tyler	
G–APZG	PA-24 Comanche 250	Steve Stephens Ltd.	
G–APZJ	PA-18 Super Cub 150	Southern Sailplanes	
G–APZK	PA-18 Super Cub 95	W. T. Knapton	
G–APZL	PA-22 Tri-Pacer 160	F. J. Holdcroft Ltd.	
G–APZM	D.H.106 Comet 4B	Dan-Air Services Ltd.	
G–APZR	Cessna 150	A. E. Clegg & ptnrs.	
G–APZS	Cessna 175A	Shackleton Aviation Ltd.	
G–APZU	D.H.104 Dove 6	Severn Airways Ltd.	
G–APZX	PA-22 Tri-Pacer 150	Clearways (Contracts) Ltd.	
G–ARAB	Cessna 150	Royal Artillery Aero Club	
G–ARAH	PA-22 Tri-Pacer 160	Skyfotos Ltd.	
G–ARAI	PA-22 Tri-Pacer 160	J. E. Fox	
G–ARAJ	PA-22 Tri-Pacer 160	Wearside Flying Group	
G–ARAM	PA-18 Super Cub 150	D. S. Morgan	
G–ARAN	PA-18 Super Cub 150	Yorkshire Gliding Club (Pty) Ltd.	
G–ARAO	PA-18 Super Cub 95	McAully Flying Group	
G–ARAP	7FC Tri-Traveller	R. B. Stratton	
G–ARAS	7FC Tri-Traveller	A. Bruniger	
G–ARAT	Cessna 180C	Peterborough Parachute Centre	
G–ARAU	Cessna 150	Cornwall Flying Club	
G–ARAW	Cessna 182C Skylane	M. Norton-Griffiths	
G–ARAX	PA-22 Tri-Pacer 150	S. W. Watkins	
G–ARAY	H.S. 748	Dan-Air Services Ltd.	
G–ARAZ	D.H.82A Tiger Moth	J. H. U. Mead	
G–ARBC	Cessna 310D	Airwork Services Ltd.	
G–ARBE	D.H.104 Dove 8	Hawker Siddeley Aviation Ltd.	
G–ARBG	T.66 Nipper 2	B. O. Smith	
G–ARBH	D.H.104 Dove I	International Travel Ltd.	
G–ARBL	D.31 Turbulent	J. D. Watt	
G–ARBN	PA-23 Apache 160	J. S. R. Kilby	
G–ARBO	PA-24 Comanche 250	T. Minocha & S. G. Bywater	
G–ARBP	T.66 Nipper 2	J. D. Watt	
G–ARBS	PA-22 Tri-Pacer 160	Stapleford Tripacer Group	
G–ARBT	PA-22 Tri-Pacer 150	E. H. Gould	
G–ARBV	PA-22 Tri-Pacer 150	A. L. Silcox	
G–ARBX	PA-18 Super Cub 95	A. A. Alderdice	
G–ARBY	V.708 Viscount	Alidair Ltd.	
G–ARBZ	D.31 Turbulent	D. G. H. Hilliard	
G–ARCC	PA-22 Tri-Pacer 150	PAG (Contracts) Ltd.	
G–ARCF	PA-22 Tri-Pacer 150	B. F. G. Lister	
G–ARCI	Cessna 310D	Airwork Services Ltd.	
G–ARCL	Cessna 175A	C. E. Sharp Plant Hire and Sales Ltd.	
G–ARCM	Cessna 172B Skyhawk	Moorland Concrete Ltd.	
G–ARCS	Auster D6/180	H. E. Smead	
G–ARCU	PA-22 Caribbean 150	M. A. G. Jack	
G–ARCV	Cessna 150	J. R. Moody	
G–ARCW	PA-23 Apache	E. M. Brain & R. Chew	
G–ARCZ	D.31 Turbulent	J. W. West	
G–ARDB	PA-24 Comanche 250	TAK Aviation	
G–ARDD	CP.301.C1 Emeraude	A. Mackintosh	
G–ARDE	D.H.104 Dove 6	Hunting Surveys & Consultants Ltd.	
G–ARDJ	Auster D.6/180	J. D. H. Radford	
G–ARDO	Jodel D.112	P. J. H. McCaig	
G–ARDP	PA-22 Tri-Pacer 150	G. M. Jones	
G–ARDS	PA-22 Caribbean 150	D. V. Asher	
G–ARDT	PA-22 Tri-Pacer 160	Luton Flying Club Ltd.	
G–ARDV	PA-22 Tri-Pacer 160	G. Clark	
G–ARDY	T.66 Nipper 2	Regional Security Services (Midlands) Ltd.	
G–ARDZ	D.140A Mousquetaire	W. R. Dryden	
G–AREA	D.H.104 Dove	Hawker Siddeley Aviation Leasing Ltd.	

Registration	Type	Owner or Operator	Where and when seen
G–AREB	Cessna 175B Skylark	P. J. Simpson	
G–ARED	PA-23 Apache 160	Alderney Publishers	
G–AREE	PA-23 Aztec 250	Montague Travel Ltd.	
G–AREF	PA-23 Aztec 250	Cambridge Aero Club Ltd.	
G–AREH	D.H.82A Tiger Moth	T. Pate	
G–AREI	Auster 3	A. L. Cogswell & R. C. West	
G–AREJ	Beechcraft 95 Travel Air	J. Grierson	
G–AREK	ATL.98 Carvair	Pauling (Middle East) Ltd.	
G–AREL	PA-22 Caribbean 150	Laarbruch Flying Club	
G–AREO	PA-18 Super Cub 150	Lasham Gliding Society Ltd.	
G–ARET	PA-22 Tri-Pacer 160	T. Haigh	
G–AREV	PA-22 Tri-Pacer 160	A. Walmsley & ptnrs.	
G–AREX	Aeronca 15AC Sedan	Blackbushe, Runfold Flying Group	
G–AREZ	D.31 Turbulent	C. M. D. Roberts	
G–ARFB	PA-22 Caribbean 150	Borrowash Estates Ltd.	
G–ARFD	PA-22 Tri-Pacer 160	C. Fergusson, J. Allan & W. F. McWhirter	
G–ARFF	Beech 65 Queen Air	Eagle Aircraft Services Ltd.	
G–ARFG	Cessna 175A Skylark	K. Lee & J. J. Francis	
G–ARFH	PA-24 Comanche 250	M. L. Press & Developments Ltd.	
G–ARFJ	Cessna 172B Skyhawk	Yorkshire Light Aircraft Ltd.	
G–ARFL	Cessna 175B Skylark	G. Evenington	
G–ARFM	Cessna 175B Skylark	Walter Edmundson (Haulage) Ltd.	
G–ARFO	Cessna 150A	J. C. Glynn	
G–ARFS	PA-22 Caribbean 150	M. H. Armstrong & C. McFadden	
G–ARFT	Jodel D.R. 1050 Ambassadeur	S. R. White	
G–ARFV	T.66 Nipper 2	D. M. Squires, P. A. Howell & E. M. Woodham	
G–ARGB	Auster 6A	A. M. Witt	
G–ARGC	Cessna 180D	P. M. Breton	
G–ARGG	D.H.C.I. Chipmunk 22	Air Navigation & Trading Co. Ltd.	
G–ARGI	Auster 6A	M. J. Kirk	
G–ARGK	Cessna 210	G. H. K. Rogers	
G–ARGL	PA-22 Tri-Pacer 160	D. Gabbitas	
G–ARGO	PA-22 Colt 108	Liverpool Aero Club Ltd.	
G–ARGR	V.708 Viscount	Alidair Ltd.	
G–ARGV	PA-18 Super Cub 150	Deeside Gliding Club (Aberdeenshire) Ltd.	
G–ARGW	Aero Commander 500B	Woods Management Services Ltd.	
G–ARGY	PA-22 Tri-Pacer 160	H. van de Worp	
G–ARGZ	D-31 Turbulent	C. J. Shaw	
G–ARHB	Forney F-1A Aircoupe	C. M. Robertson	
G–ARHC	Forney F-1A Aircoupe	Cornwall Flying Club	
G–ARHF	Forney F-1A Aircoupe	West London Aero Services Ltd.	
G–ARHI	PA-22 Comanche 180	J. L. Lewis	
G–ARHL	PA-23 Aztec 250	Aviation Investment Ltd.	
G–ARHN	PA-22 Caribbean 150	G. G. Foseberry	
G–ARHP	PA-22 Tri-Pacer 160	W. Wardle	
G–ARHR	PA-22 Caribbean 150	J. A. Hargroves	
G–ARHT	PA-22 Caribbean 150	J. S. Lewery	
G–ARHU	PA-22 Tri-Pacer 160	F. T. Metwan & ptnrs.	
G–ARHW	D.H.104 Dove 8	Hawker Siddeley Aviation Leasing Ltd.	
G–ARHX	D.H.104 Dove 8	Hill, Samuel & Co. Ltd.	
G–ARHZ	D.62 Condor	J. W. Spiers & P. B. Bolas	
G–ARIA	Bell 47G	Decca Navigator Co. Ltd.	
G–ARID	Cessna 172B	J. D. Prince & A. W. Morris	
G–ARIE	PA-24 Comanche 250	R. Rackwanski	
G–ARIF	O-H7 Coupe	A. W. J. G. Ord-Hume	
G–ARIH	Auster 6A	F. & H. (Aircraft) Ltd.	
G–ARIK	PA-22 Caribbean 150	C. A. Crane	
G–ARIL	PA-22 Caribbean 150	G. N. Richardson Motors	
G–ARIN	PA-24 Comanche 250	Miller Aerial Spraying Ltd.	

Registration	Type	Owner or Operator	Where and when seen
G–ARIU	Cessna 172B Skyhawk	P. A. Howell	
G–ARIV	Cessna 172B	T. P. W. Lineham	
G–ARIW	Rousseau CP.301B	N. R. Lowden & G. A. Hayward	
G–ARJB	D.H.104 Dove 8	J. C. Bamford (Excavators) Ltd.	
G–ARJC	PA-22 Colt 108	C. E. Holland	
G–ARJF	PA-22 Colt 108	J. E. Cummings & S. R. Reay	
G–ARJG	PA-22 Colt 108	Sqdn. Ldr. G. R. Sharp	
G–ARJH	PA-22 Colt 108	A. Walmsley	
G–ARJK	D.H.106 Comet 4B	Dan-Air Services Ltd.	
G–ARJN	D.H.106 Comet 4B	Dan-Air Services Ltd.	
G–ARJR	PA-23 Apache 160	Dom Air Services Ltd.	
G–ARJS	PA-23 Apache 160	Minerva Haulage Ltd.	
G–ARJT	PA-23 Apache 160	R. D. Dickson	
G–ARJU	PA-23 Apache 160	Surrey & Kent Flying Club Ltd.	
G–ARJV	PA-23 Apache 160	Gordon King (Aviation) Ltd.	
G–ARJW	PA-23 Apache 160	Business Air Travel Ltd.	
G–ARJZ	D.31 Turbulent	The Tiger Club	
G–ARKG	J/5G Autocar	C. Thompson	
G–ARKJ	Beech N35 Bonanza	G. A. M. Nisbett	
G–ARKK	PA-22 Colt 108	N. E. C. Day	
G–ARKM	PA-22 Colt 108	D. L. Maclean	
G–ARKN	PA-22 Colt 108	Shropshire Coachworks Ltd.	
G–ARKP	PA-22 Colt 108	C. J. & J. Freeman	
G–ARKR	PA-22 Colt 108	H. L. Crawley	
G–ARKS	PA-22 Colt 108	D. W. Mickleburgh	
G–ARLB	PA-24 Comanche 250	Stakehill Engineering Ltd.	
G–ARLD	Helio H-395	P. F. Hall	
G–ARLG	Auster D.4/108	P. E. Scott	
G–ARLI	PA-23 Apache 150	K. A. Learmonth	
G–ARLK	PA-24 Comanche 250	John Martin Construction Ltd.	
G–ARLL	PA-24 Comanche 250	L. S. Cooper & E. J. Spiers	
G–ARLO	A.61 Terrier	J. M. W. Howlett	
G–ARLP	A.61 Terrier	Herefordshire Gliding Club	
G–ARLR	A.61 Terrier	H. A. C. Worral & J. Park	
G–ARLT	Cessna 172B Skyhawk	John Potter & Associates	
G–ARLU	Cessna 172B Skyhawk	B. N. Turner	
G–ARLV	Cessna 172B Skyhawk	P. Rivas	
G–ARLW	Cessna 172B Skyhawk	Light Planes (Lancashire) Ltd.	
G–ARLX	Jodel D.140	M. J. Dunkerley	
G–ARLY	J/5P Autocar	J. W. Benson	
G–ARLZ	D.31A Turbulent	Usworth Flying Group	
G–ARMA	PA-23 Apache 160	Apache Aviation Ltd.	
G–ARMB	D.H.C.1 Chipmunk 22A	College of Air Training	
G–ARMC	D.H.C.1 Chipmunk 22A	West London Aero Services Ltd.	
G–ARMD	D.H.C.1 Chipmunk 22A	College of Air Training	
G–ARMF	D.H.C.1 Chipmunk 22A	College of Air Training	
G–ARMG	D.H.C.1 Chipmunk 22A	College of Air Training	
G–ARMH	PA-23 Aztec 250	Productivity & Manpower Ltd.	
G–ARMI	PA-23 Apache 160	E. W. Noakes	
G–ARMJ	Cessna 185	—	
G–ARML	Cessna 175B Skylark	Woolmer Aircraft Ltd.	
G–ARMM	Cessna 175B Skylark	A. R. German & M. E. Mottram	
G–ARMN	Cessna 175A	H. A. Claireaux	
G–ARMO	Cessna 172B Skyhawk	R. C. Beal & W. V. Mosgovoy	
G–ARMP	Cessna 172B	Park Hacking & Leigh Ltd.	
G–ARMR	Cessna 172B Skyhawk	J. Braithwaite	
G–ARMW	H.S.748 Srs. 1	Dan-Air Services Ltd.	
G–ARMX	H.S.748 Srs. 1	Dan-Air Services Ltd.	
G–ARMZ	D.31 Turbulent	Frederick A Shepherd	
G–ARNA	Mooney M.20B	D. A. Thomson	
G–ARNB	J/5G Autocar	M. T. Jeffrey	
G–ARNC	PA-22 Colt 108	M. Evans & M. NcCleary	
G–ARND	PA-22 Colt 108	Western Flying Services Ltd.	
G–ARNE	PA-22 Colt 108	T. W. Davies & ptnrs.	
G–ARNG	PA-22 Colt 108	West London Aero Services Ltd.	
G–ARNI	PA-22 Colt 108	A. Codling & L. Morris	
G–ARNJ	PA-22 Colt 108	Aeromart Flying Club Ltd.	
G–ARNK	PA-22 Colt 108	D. P. Golding	
G–ARNL	PA-22 Colt	Mr. J. A. & Miss J. A. Dodsworth	

Registration	Type	Owner or Operator	Where and when seen
G–ARNN	GC-1B Swift	K. E. Sword	
G–ARNO	A.61 Terrier	A. F. Butcher & ptnrs.	
G–ARNP	A.109 Airedale	K. A. Mancini	
G–ARNY	Jodel D.117	A. D. Henderson	
G–ARNZ	D.31 Turbulent	J. N. Eccott	
G–AROA	Cessna 172B Skyhawk	Margaret A. Gregory	
G–AROC	Cessna 175B Skylark	Yorkshire Flying Services Ltd.	
G–AROE	Aero 145	A. Harrison	
G–AROF	L.40 Meta-Sokol	B. G. Barber	
G–AROJ	A.109 Airedale	Cornish Gliding (& Flying) Club	
G–AROK	Cessna 310F	Airwork Services Ltd.	
G–ARON	PA-22 Colt 108	Warwickshire Aero Club Ltd.	
G–AROO	Forney F-1A Aircoupe	S. Clugston & ptnrs.	
G–AROR	Forney F-1A Aircoupe	Treswithick Air & Shipping Services Ltd.	
G–AROT	F.8L Falco	H. J. A. Morris	
G–AROV	D.H.106 Comet 4C	Dan-Air Services Ltd.	
G–AROW	Jodel D.140B	The Tiger Club	
G–AROY	Stearman A.75N.1	W. A. Jordan	
G–ARPA	H.S.121 Trident	British Airways	
G–ARPB	H.S.121 Trident	British Airways	
G–ARPC	H.S.121 Trident	British Airways	
G–ARPD	H.S.121 Trident	British Airways	
G–ARPE	H.S.121 Trident	British Airways	
G–ARPF	H.S.121 Trident	British Airways	
G–ARPG	H.S.121 Trident	British Airways	
G–ARPH	H.S.121 Trident	British Airways	
G–ARPJ	H.S.121 Trident	British Airways	
G–ARPK	H.S.121 Trident	British Airways	
G–ARPL	H.S.121 Trident	British Airways	
G–ARPM	H.S.121 Trident	British Airways	
G–ARPN	H.S.121 Trident	British Airways	
G–ARPO	H.S.121 Trident	British Airways	
G–ARPP	H.S.121 Trident	British Airways	
G–ARPR	H.S.121 Trident	British Airways	
G–ARPW	H.S.121 Trident	British Airways	
G–ARPX	H.S.121 Trident	British Airways	
G–ARPZ	H.S.121 Trident	British Airways	
G–ARRA	Boeing 707-436	British Airways	
G–ARRB	Boeing 707-436	British Airways	
G–ARRC	Boeing 707-436	British Airways	
G–ARRD	Jodel DR.1050	N. L. E. Dupee	
G–ARRE	Jodel DR.1050	Whitehouse Flying Group	
G–ARRF	Cessna 150A	Plymouth Aero Club	
G–ARRH	Cessna 175B Skylark	F. K. Parker	
G–ARRI	Cessna 175B Skylark	C. L. Thomas	
G–ARRP	PA-28 Cherokee	Dyce Flying Group	
G–ARRS	Piel CP.301A	J. Y. Paxton	
G–ARRT	Wallis WA-116-1	K. H. Wallis	
G–ARRW	H.S.748 Srs. 1	Dan-Air Services Ltd.	
G–ARRY	D.140B Mousquetaire	R. G. Andrews	
G–ARRZ	D.31 Turbulent	A. P. Docherty	
G–ARSB	Cessna 150A	Peterborough Aero Club Ltd.	
G–ARSC	PA-24 Comanche 180	Pasquale & Co. Ltd.	
G–ARSJ	Scintex CP.301-C2	R. H. Medler	
G–ARSK	PA-24 Comanche 250	Catani Aviation Ltd.	
G–ARSL	A.61 Terrier	J. D. Thompson	
G–ARSP	L.40 Meta-Sokol	K. K. Johnson	
G–ARSU	PA-22 Colt 108	P. E. Palmer	
G–ARSW	PA-22 Colt 108	G. W. Worley & G. K. Hare	
G–ARSX	PA-22 Tri-Pacer 160	J. S. Richardson	
G–ARTB	Mooney M.20B	M. P. Jackson	
G–ARTD	PA-23 Apache 160	Dr. D. A. Jones	
G–ARTG	Hiller UH-12C	E. C. Francis	
G–ARTH	Piper PA-12 Super Cruiser	R. I. & Mrs. J. O. Souch	
G–ARTL	D.H.82A Tiger Moth	Defford Aero Club (Worcestershire) Ltd.	
G–ARTN	Bensen Gyro-Copter	G. Whatley	
G–ARTS	D.H.104 Dove 6	Haywards Aviation Ltd.	
G–ARTT	M.S.880B Rallye Club	W. B. & Mrs. E. A. Swales	

G-EBWD. (Top) de Havilland D.H.60X Hermes Moth (105hp Cirrus Hermes I)/*Air Portraits*

G-APBC. (Centre) Douglas Dakota 4 (two 1,200hp Pratt & Whitney R-1830-90C)/*Peter J. Bish*

G-ASDC. (Above) Aviation Traders ATL-98 Carvair (four 1,450hp Pratt & Whitney R-2000-7M2)/
John Goring

Registration	Type	Owner or Operator	Where and when seen
G–ARTV	EP-9 Prospector	H. Best-Devereux	
G–ARUC	PA-22 Colt 108	Mrs. N. L. Howard	
G–ARUG	J/5G Autocar	K. G. W. Digby	
G–ARUH	DR.1050 Ambassadeur	N. H. Jones	
G–ARUI	A.61 Terrier	A. Macfarlane	
G–ARUL	Cosmic Wind	Walker Aviation Services & Plant Ltd.	
G–ARUM	D.H.104 Dove 8	National Coal Board	
G–ARUO	PA-24 Comanche	Uniform Oscar Group	
G–ARUP	PA-28 Cherokee 160	Garth Motors	
G–ARUR	PA-28 Cherokee 160	J. D. Rees	
G–ARUV	CP.301A Emeraude	C. A. Huxtable	
G–ARUW	PA-24 Comanche 250	J. P. I. Lloyd-Bostock	
G–ARUY	J/IN Alpha	A. J. Brown	
G–ARUZ	Cessna 175C	J. H. Hodder, D. W. Blake & J. Morris	
G–ARVB	V.1101 VC10	British Airways	
G–ARVE	V.1101 VC10	British Airways	
G–ARVF	V.1101 VC10	United Arab Emirates	
G–ARVH	V.1101 VC10	British Airways	
G–ARVJ	V.1101 VC10	British Airways	
G–ARVM	V.1101 VC10	British Airways	
G–ARVS	PA-28 Cherokee 160	M. Walker	
G–ARVT	PA-28 Cherokee 160	C. R. Knapton	
G–ARVU	PA-28 Cherokee 160	Alfred Smith & Son Ltd.	
G–ARVV	PA-28 Cherokee 160	F. W. Brown	
G–ARVW	PA-28 Cherokee 160	Victor Whiskey Group	
G–ARVZ	D.62A Condor	Rollason Aircraft & Engineering Ltd.	
G–ARWB	D.H.C.1 Chipmunk 22A	Aero Bonner Co. Ltd.	
G–ARWC	Cessna 150B	Light Aircraft Engineering Ltd.	
G–ARWD	Boeing 707-465	British Airways	
G–ARWH	Cessna 172C Skyhawk	Ferryfield School of Flying	
G–ARWM	Cessna 175C	Brenning Aviation	
G–ARWO	Cessna 172C Skyhawk	F. A. Abbey	
G–ARWR	Cessna 172C Skyhawk	Applied Cleaning Economics Ltd.	
G–ARWS	Cessna 175C	H. Tempest Ltd.	
G–ARWW	Bensen Gyro-Copter	R. L. E. Toms	
G–ARWY	Mooney M.20A	Rotherham Flying Group	
G–ARXC	A.109 Airedale	W. J. H. Lambert	
G–ARXD	A.109 Airedale	D. Howden	
G–ARXF	PA-23-250 Aztec B	Metals Research Ltd.	
G–ARXG	PA-24 Comanche 250	Star Trek Ltd.	
G–ARXH	Bell 47G	T. J. Druay	
G–ARXN	Tipsy Nipper 2	Griffon Flying Group	
G–ARXP	Luton L.A.4a Minor	W. C. Hymas	
G–ARXT	Jodel DR.1050	D. R. Skinner	
G–ARXU	Auster 5A	Bath & Wilts Gliding Club Ltd.	
G–ARXW	M.S.885 Super Rallye	M. K. Chester & E. Hall	
G–ARXX	M.S.880B Rallye Club	Beshcrest Motors Ltd.	
G–ARXY	M.S.880B Rallye Club	B. H. & N. D. Gaster	
G–ARYC	H.S.125	Rolls-Royce (1971) Ltd.	
G–ARYF	PA-23 Aztec 250	Webster Aviation	
G–ARYH	PA-22 Caribbean 160	Filtration (Water Treatment Engineers) Ltd.	
G–ARYI	Cessna 172C	J. T. Mirley & A. E. Wall	
G–ARYK	Cessna 172C	Mrs. K. M. & T. Hemsley	
G–ARYM	D.H.104 Dove 8	Volkswagen (GB) Ltd.	
G–ARYR	PA-28 Cherokee 180	D. J. Grant	
G–ARYS	Cessna 172B	K. J. Squires	
G–ARYU	Cessna 320	S. H. Aviation Ltd.	
G–ARYV	PA-24 Comanche 250	Chart Managements & ptnrs.	
G–ARYZ	A.109 Airedale	J. D. Reid	
G–ARZA	Wallis WA.116-1	N. D. Z. de Ferranti	
G–ARZB	Wallis WA.116	K. H. Wallis	
G–ARZD	Cessna 172C	Brooklands Aviation Ltd.	
G–ARZE	Cessna 172C	JBDR Flying Group Ltd.	
G–ARZF	Cessna 150B	M. Carragher	
G–ARZL	Bensen Gyro-Copter	C. H. Force	
G–ARZM	D.31 Turbulent	The Tiger Club	

Registration	Type	Owner or Operator	Where and when seen
G–ARZN	Beech N35 Bonanza	Beech Aircraft Ltd.	
G–ARZP	A.109 Airedale	C. Smith	
G–ARZW	Currie Wot	D. F. Faulkener-Bryant	
G–ARZX	Cessna 150B	Airwork Services Ltd.	
G–ASAA	Luton L.A.4a Minor	Four Counties Flying Syndicate	
G–ASAI	A.109 Airedale	G. J. Potts	
G–ASAJ	A.61 Terrier 2	Yorkshire Gliding Club Ltd.	
G–ASAK	A.61 Terrier 2	Rochford Hundred Flying Group	
G–ASAL	SAL Bulldog 120	Scottish Aviation (Bulldog) Ltd.	
G–ASAM	D.31 Turbulent	The Tiger Club	
G–ASAN	A.61 Terrier 2	R. G. Cooper	
G–ASAR	M.S.880B Rallye Club	J. W. Pearson	
G–ASAT	M.S.880B Rallye Club	H. R. Rowley	
G–ASAU	M.S.880B Rallye Club	J. D. Jewitt & A. C. Mercer	
G–ASAV	M.S.880B Rallye Club	A. W. Ramsey	
G–ASAX	A.61 Terrier 2	B. Rhodes	
G–ASAZ	Hiller UH-12 E4	Bell Fruit Ltd.	
G–ASBA	Currie Wot	M. A. Kaye	
G–ASBB	Beech 23 Musketeer	Ian Willis Publicity Ltd.	
G–ASBD	Hughes 269A	W. R. Finance Ltd.	
G–ASBG	HPR-7 Herald 203	British Island Airways Ltd.	
G–ASBH	A.109 Airedale	H. B. Fox & L. N. Hocking	
G–ASBN	Mooney M.20C Mark 21	R. A. Forward	
G–ASBS	CP.301A Emeraude	Abbey Glen Service Station	
G–ASBU	A.61 Terrier 2	W. M. D. McEvoy & M. McCluskey	
G–ASBY	A.109 Airedale	K. P. Donnan	
G–ASCC	Beagle E.3 AOP Mk. II	A. D. Heath & M. D. N. Fisher	
G–ASCH	A.61 Terrier 2	Enstone Eagles Flying Group	
G–ASCJ	PA-24 Comanche 250	R. H. P. & Mrs. Le Brocq	
G–ASCM	Isaacs Fury II	D. Toms, W. Hill & R. Williams	
G–ASCU	PA-18A Super Cub 150	Farm Aviation Services Ltd.	
G–ASCZ	CP.310A Emeraude	A. R. Turton	
G–ASDA	Beech 65–80 Queen Air	Parker & Heard Ltd.	
G–ASDC	ATL-98 Carvair	British Air Ferries Ltd. *Plain Jane*	
G–ASDD	D.H.104 Dove 5	Haywards Aviation Ltd.	
G–ASDI	PA-23 Apache 160	Apache Aircraft Services Ltd.	
G–ASDL	A.61 Terrier 2	C. P. Lockyer & C. E. Mason	
G–ASDN	PA-24 Comanche 250	J. W. Hodgson	
G–ASDO	Beech A.55 Baron	D. V. Beadon	
G–ASDY	Wallis WA-116/F	Wallis Autogyros Ltd.	
G–ASDZ	D.H.106 Comet 4C	Dan-Air Services Ltd.	
G–ASEA	Luton L.A.4a Minor	L. C. Mansfield	
G–ASEB	Luton L.A.4a Minor	Phoenix Aircraft Ltd.	
G–ASEC	H.S.125	Merlot International Aviation	
G–ASED	V.831 Viscount	Alida Cargo Ltd.	
G–ASEE	J/1N Alpha	H. C. J. & Sara L. G. Williams	
G–ASEG	A.61 Terrier	J. Surman	
G–ASEO	PA-24 Comanche 250	S. G. Nicholson	
G–ASEP	PA-23 Apache 235	V. H. Bellamy	
G–ASEU	D.62A Condor	The Tiger Club	
G–ASEV	PA-23 Aztec 250	West Bridgeford Machine Co.	
G–ASEY	A.61 Terrier 2	C. B. Ottaway & ptnrs.	
G–ASFA	Cessna 172D	R. A. Marven	
G–ASFB	Beech 23 Musketeer	Whiting Aviation Services	
G–ASFD	L-200A Morava	Dochin Industrial Buildings Ltd.	
G–ASFF	PA-23 Apache 235	International Air Charter Ltd.	
G–ASFG	PA-23 Aztec	Surrey & Kent Flying Club Ltd.	
G–ASFH	PA-24 Comanche 180	R. C. Hayes & F. J. C. Pole	
G–ASFJ	Beech P.35 Bonanza	Vanroy Ltd.	
G–ASFK	J/5G Autocar	North Denes Aerodrome Ltd.	
G–ASFL	PA-28 Cherokee 180	G. Capes & ptnrs.	
G–ASFO	Bo 208 Junior	H. F. J. Cheek	
G–ASFR	Bo 208 Junior	Sunderland Flying Club Ltd.	
G–ASFX	Turbulent	E. F. Clapham & W. B. S. Dobie	
G–ASFZ	PA-25 Pawnee 235	Skegness Air Taxi Service Ltd.	
G–ASGA	V.1151 Super VC10	British Airways	
G–ASGB	V.1151 Super VC10	British Airways	

Registration	Type	Owner or Operator	Where and when seen
G–ASGC	V.1151 Super VC10	British Airways	
G–ASGD	V.1151 Super VC10	British Airways	
G–ASGE	V.1151 Super VC10	British Airways	
G–ASGF	V.1151 Super VC10	British Airways	
G–ASGG	V.1151 Super VC10	British Airways	
G–ASGH	V.1151 Super VC10	British Airways	
G–ASGI	V.1151 Super VC10	British Airways	
G–ASGJ	V.1151 Super VC10	British Airways	
G–ASGK	V.1151 Super VC10	British Airways	
G–ASGL	V.1151 Super VC10	British Airways	
G–ASGM	V.1151 Super VC10	British Airways	
G–ASGP	V.1151 Super VC10	British Airways	
G–ASGR	V.1151 Super VC10	British Airways	
G–ASHA	Cessna 172D	R. Soar	
G–ASHB	Cessna 182F	Page and Moy Ltd.	
G–ASHH	PA-23 Aztec 250	Dewberry Printing Co.	
G–ASHJ	Brantly B.2B	A. G. Dean	
G–ASHK	Brantly B.2B	S. N. Cole	
G–ASHO	Cessna 182F	Chas W. Shelton Ltd.	
G–ASHR	Beech B35–33 Debonair	C. M. Fraser & E. A. Perry	
G–ASHS	Stampe SV.4B	The Tiger Club	
G–ASHU	PA-15 Vagabond	G. J. Romanes	
G–ASHV	PA-23 Aztec 250	R. F. Saywell Ltd.	
G–ASHW	D.H.104 Dove 8	Scottish Aviation Ltd.	
G–ASHX	PA-28 Cherokee 180	G. W. Barker & D. Mannix	
G–ASHZ	ATL-98A Carvair	British Air Ferries Ltd. *Fat Annie*	
G–ASIB	Cessna 172D	Eagle Adventure Sport Centre	
G–ASII	PA-28 Cherokee 180	N. I. Husband & B. J. Waller	
G–ASIJ	PA-28 Cherokee 180	W. Linskill	
G–ASIL	PA-28 Cherokee 180	F. W. Shaw & Sons (Worthing) Ltd.	
G–ASIO	Aero Commander 500A	R. B. Tyler (Plant) Ltd.	
G–ASIP	Auster 6A	British Airways Gliding Club	
G–ASIR	Beech D.95A Travel Air	Ranald Aviation Ltd.	
G–ASIT	Cessna 180	A. J. Spiller (Gt. Staughton) Ltd.	
G–ASIU	Beech B.65-80 Queen Air	J. D. M. Flyers Ltd.	
G–ASIY	PA-25 Pawnee 235	A.D.S. (Aerial) Ltd.	
G–ASJC	BAC One-Eleven 201	British Caledonian *City of Glasgow*	
G–ASJE	BAC One-Eleven 201	British Caledonian *City of Dundee*	
G–ASJF	BAC One-Eleven 201	British Caledonian *Burgh of Fort William*	
G–ASJG	BAC One-Eleven 201	British Caledonian *Burgh of Paisley*	
G–ASJH	BAC One-Eleven 201	British Caledonian *Burgh of Hawick*	
G–ASJI	BAC One-Eleven 201	British Caledonian *Royal Burgh of Nairn*	
G–ASJL	Beech H.35 Bonanza	J. D. Bingham	
G–ASJM	PA-30 Twin Comanche	J. T. Mirley	
G–ASJO	Beech B.23 Musketeer	D. W. Busby & K. H. Brend	
G–ASJR	Cessna 182F	Montague de Cartier Aviation	
G–ASJU	Aero Commander 520	Interflight Ltd.	
G–ASJV	V.S.361 Spitfire 9 (MH434)	Airborne Taxi Service	
G–ASJY	GY80 Horizon 160	A. D. Hemley	
G–ASJZ	Jodel D.117A	Wolverhampton Ultra-light Flying Group	
G–ASKB	D.H.98 Mosquito 35 (RS712)	Strathallan Collection	
G–ASKH	D.H.98 Mosquito T.3 (RR299)	Hawker Siddeley Aviation	
G–ASKJ	A.61 Terrier 2	Bristol & Gloucestershire Gliding Club	
G–ASKK	HPR-7 Herald 211	British Island Airways Ltd.	
G–ASKL	Jodel D.150A Mascaret	J. M. Graty	
G–ASKM	Beech B.65–80 Queen Air	All Seasons Aviation Ltd.	
G–ASKN	ATL-98A Carvair	British Air Ferries Ltd. *Big Bill*	

Registration	Type	Owner or Operator	Where and when seen
G–ASKP	D.H.82A Tiger Moth	The Tiger Club	
G–ASKS	Cessna 336 Skymaster	M. J. Godwin	
G–ASKT	PA-28 Cherokee 180	R. J. Cyster & ptnrs.	
G–ASKU	Cessna F.172E	G. H. Eaton & P. H. Dunlop	
G–ASKV	PA-25 Pawnee 235	Westwick Distributors Ltd.	
G–ASLA	PA-25 Pawnee 235	Westwick Distributors Ltd.	
G–ASLE	PA-30 Twin Comanche	Selflock Ltd.	
G–ASLF	Bensen Gyro-Copter	S. R. Hughes	
G–ASLH	Cessna 182F	Corbett Farms Ltd.	
G–ASLK	PA-25 Pawnee 235	Westwick Distributors Ltd.	
G–ASLL	Cessna 336 Skymaster	General Aviation Services Ltd.	
G–ASLN	F.1A Aircoupe	Cornwall Flying Club	
G–ASLO	Brantly B-2B	Miss A. B. Boardman	
G–ASLP	Bensen Gyro-Copter	R. Caygill	
G–ASLR	Agusta-Bell 47J-2	Twyford Moors (Helicopters) Ltd.	
G–ASLV	PA-28 Cherokee 235	C.S.E. (Aircraft Services) Ltd.	
G–ASLX	Piel CP.301A Emeraude	K. C. Green	
G–ASLY	Cessna F.172E	Westair Flying Services	
G–ASMA	PA-30 Twin Comanche	Finrad Ltd.	
G–ASMC	P.56 Provost T.I.	W. Walker	
G–ASME	Bensen Gyro-Copter	C. R. Papper & A. J. Tabenor	
G–ASMF	Beech D.95A Travel Air	Fenair Air Taxi	
G–ASMG	D.H.104 Dove 8	Hawker Siddeley Aviation Leasing Ltd.	
G–ASMH	PA-30 Twin Comanche	F. D. Barker & J. S. Selby	
G–ASMJ	Cessna F.172E	Congress Aviation Ltd.	
G–ASML	Luton L.A.4a Minor	R. Cole	
G–ASMM	D.31 Turbulent	Kenneth Browne	
G–ASMN	PA-23 Apache 160	West London Aero Services Ltd.	
G–ASMO	PA-23 Apache 160	Tyne Air Charter Ltd.	
G–ASMR	PA-30 Twin Comanche	P. S. Larner & D. B. Millbank	
G–ASMS	Cessna 150A	Thor Cryogenics Ltd.	
G–ASMT	Fairtravel Linnet 2	Dr. J. J. Bowen	
G–ASMU	Cessna 150D	—	
G–ASMV	Scintex CP1310-C3	W. A. Green	
G–ASMW	Cessna 150D	S. E. Ward	
G–ASMY	PA-23 Apache 160	Thurston Aviation Ltd.	
G–ASMZ	A.61 Terrier 2	Heron Flying Group	
G–ASNA	PA-23 Aztec 250	International Air Charter Ltd.	
G–ASNB	Auster 6A	West Wales Gliding Co. Ltd.	
G–ASNC	Beagle D.5/180 Husky	Airviews (Manchester) Ltd.	
G–ASND	PA-23 Aztec 250	H. K. Mitha	
G–ASNE	PA-28 Cherokee 180	W. T. Butcher	
G–ASNF	Ercoupe 415-CD	Charles Robertson (Developments) Ltd.	
G–ASNG	D.H.104 Dove 5	S. J. Filhol	
G–ASNH	PA-23 Aztec 250	Derek Crouch (Contractors) Ltd.	
G–ASNI	Scintex CP1310-C3	D. F. Redman	
G–ASNK	Cessna 205	James Fieldhouse Plastics	
G–ASNL	Sikorsky S-61N	BAH Orion	
G–ASNN	Cessna 182F	R. E. Bibby	
G–ASNO	Beech B55 Baron	Pex Aviation Ltd.	
G–ASNP	Mooney M.20C Mark 21	W. C. Smeaton	
G–ASNU	H.S.125 Srs. 1	Clarke Chapman & Co. Ltd.	
G–ASNV	Agusta-Bell 47J-2	S. W. Electricity Board	
G–ASNW	Cessna F.172E	Sir John A. P. Bagge	
G–ASNY	Bensen Gyro-Copter	D. L. Wallis	
G–ASNZ	Bensen Gyro-Copter	W. H. Turner	
G–ASOB	PA-30 Twin Comanche	G. L. Birch	
G–ASOC	Auster 6A	Banbury Plant Hire Ltd.	
G–ASOF	Beagle B.206	Northern Air Taxis Ltd.	
G–ASOH	Beech B.55 Baron	Metals & Methods	
G–ASOI	A.61 Terrier 2	Brooklands Flying Group	
G–ASOK	Cessna F.172E	R. J. Smith	
G–ASOM	A.61 Terrier 2	W. J. Dyer	
G–ASON	PA-30 Twin Comanche	Air Conditioning (Transport) Ltd.	
G–ASOO	PA-30 Twin Comanche	East Midlands Aviation	

Registration	Type	Owner or Operator	Where and when seen
G–ASOV	PA-25 Pawnee 235	A.D.S. (Aerial) Ltd.	
G–ASOX	Cessna 205A	Berrard Ltd.	
G–ASPA	D.H.104 Dove 8	Dowty Group Services Ltd.	
G–ASPF	Jodel D.120	G. H. Farr	
G–ASPI	Cessna F.172E	A. M. Castleton & ptnrs.	
G–ASPK	PA-28 Cherokee 140	A. F. Aviation Ltd.	
G–ASPL	H.S.748 Srs. I	Dan-Air Services Ltd.	
G–ASPS	J3C-65 Cub	A. J. Chalkley	
G–ASPT	Cessna 172D	C. H. Parker	
G–ASPU	D.31 Turbulent	P. A. Brook	
G–ASPX	Bensen B-8 Gyro-Copter	L. D. Goldsmith	
G–ASPY	SF 24A Motorspatz	P. Lloyd & K. Saddington	
G–ASRA	PA-24 Comanche 250	A. F. Sobey	
G–ASRB	D.62B Condor	Rollason Aircraft & Engines Ltd.	
G–ASRC	D.62B Condor	N. H. Jones	
G–ASRE	PA-23 Aztec 250	Air London (Executive Travel) Ltd.	
G–ASRF	Jenny Wren	G. W. Gowland	
G–ASRH	PA-30 Twin Comanche	Bigland Holdings Ltd.	
G–ASRI	PA-23 Aztec 250	Meridian Airmaps Ltd.	
G–ASRK	A.109 Airedale	A. C. Johnson	
G–ASRO	PA-30 Twin Comanche	A. G. Perkins	
G–ASRP	Jodel DR 1050	D. J. M. Edmondston	
G–ASRT	Jodel D.150 Mascaret	H. M. Kendall	
G–ASRU	PA-30 Twin Comanche 160	M. L. Sparks	
G–ASRW	PA-28 Cherokee 180	Shackleton Aviation Ltd.	
G–ASRX	Beech 65 A80 Queen Air	Seismograph Service (England) Ltd.	
G–ASSA	PA-30 Twin Comanche 160	D. W. Smith	
G–ASSB	PA-30 Twin Comanche 160	T. Brereton & Son Ltd.	
G–ASSE	PA-22 Colt 108	N. H. Reynolds	
G–ASSF	Cessna 182G	A. Newsham	
G–ASSI	H.S.125 Srs. I	Merlot International Aviation	
G–ASSM	H.S.125 Srs. I	Litchfield Co. Ltd.	
G–ASSO	Cessna 150D	Luton Flying Club Ltd.	
G–ASSP	PA-30 Twin Comanche	The Mastermix Engineering Co. Ltd.	
G–ASSR	PA-30 Twin Comanche	A. R. F. Bronson	
G–ASSS	Cessna 172E	D. H. N. Squires	
G–ASST	Cessna 150D	F. R. H. Parker	
G–ASSU	CP 301A Emeraude	H. M. A. Armstrong	
G–ASSW	PA-28 Cherokee 140	G. C. Starling	
G–ASSX	Cessna 172E	Fred Shoesmith & G. Firbank	
G–ASSY	D.31 Turbulent	G-ASSY Group	
G–ASTA	D.31 Turbulent	R. Jones	
G–ASTD	PA-23 Aztec 250	Air West Ltd.	
G–ASTG	Nord 1002	L. M. Walton	
G–ASTI	Auster 6A	M. Pocock	
G–ASTJ	BAC One-Eleven 201	British Caledonian Royal Burgh of Dumfirmline	
G–ASTL	Fairey Firefly I (Z2033)	Skyfame Museum	
G–ASTM	Hiller UH-12B	Bristow Helicopters Ltd.	
G–ASTP	Hiller UH-12C	Bristow Helicopters Ltd.	
G–ASTR	Hiller UH-12B	Bristow Helicopters Ltd.	
G–ASTV	Cessna 150D	Luton Flying Club Ltd.	
G–ASTZ	Hughes 269B	Twyford Moors (Helicopters) Ltd.	
G–ASUB	Mooney M.20E Super 21	T. J. Pigott	
G–ASUD	PA-28 Cherokee 180	D. W. Stivens	
G–ASUE	Cessna 150D	Luton Flying Club Ltd.	
G–ASUH	Cessna F.172E	C. G. M. Alington	
G–ASUI	A.61 Terrier 2	J. Knight	
G–ASUL	Cessna 182G	G. H. Reeve	
G–ASUP	Cessna F.172E	I. Williams & ptnrs.	
G–ASUR	Dornier Du 28A-1	Sheffair Ltd.	
G–ASUS	Jurca MJ 2B Tempete	D. G. Jones	
G–ASUW	Riley Dove I	Fairflight Charters Ltd.	

Registration	Type	Owner or Operator	Where and when seen
G–ASVE	Beech 65 A80 Queen Air	Short Brothers & Harland Ltd.	
G–ASVF	Cessna 150E	Luton Flying Club Ltd.	
G–ASVG	CP.301B Emeraude	K. R. Jackson	
G–ASVH	Hiller UH-12B	P. W. Hicks	
G–ASVI	Hiller UH-12B	Bristow Helicopters Ltd.	
G–ASVK	Hiller UH-12B	Bristow Helicopters Ltd.	
G–ASVL	Hiller UH-12B	Bristow Helicopters Ltd.	
G–ASVM	Cessna F.172E	J. White	
G–ASVN	Cessna 206	RAF Sport Parachute Association Ltd.	
G–ASVO	HPR-7 Herald 214	British Midland Airways	
G–ASVP	PA-25 Pawnee 235	A.D.S. (Aerial) Ltd.	
G–ASVR	PA-25 Pawnee 235	A.D.S. (Aerial) Ltd.	
G–ASVV	Cessna 310-1	A.I.R. Propafloor Ltd.	
G–ASVZ	PA-28 Cherokee 140	J. R. Everett	
G–ASWA	PA-28 Cherokee 140	Southend Light Aviation Centre Ltd.	
G–ASWB	A.109 Airedale	Tompa Metals Ltd.	
G–ASWE	Bo 208 Junior	F. M. Wallis	
G–ASWF	A.109 Airedale	D. W. Wastell	
G–ASWG	PA-25 Pawnee 235	A.D.S. (Aerial) Ltd.	
G–ASWH	Luton L.A.5 Major	J. J. Egerton	
G–ASWI	Wessex 60 Srs. 1	Bristow Helicopters Ltd.	
G–ASWL	Cessna F.172F	G. Read	
G–ASWM	A.61 Terrier 2	Parkers of Peterborough Ltd.	
G–ASWN	Bensen Gyro-Copter	D. R. Shepherd	
G–ASWO	Cessna 210D	R. S., R. R. & Mrs. K. G. Merrin	
G–ASWP	Beech A.23 Musketeer	Tenways Flying Group	
G–ASWS	Aero 145 Series 20	W. H. Grimes	
G–ASWT	Aero 145 Series 20	A. C. Frost	
G–ASWW	PA-30 Twin Comanche	Col. I. B. Baillie	
G–ASWX	PA-28 Cherokee 180	H. I. Jones (Whitby Garage) Ltd.	
G–ASXB	D.H.82A Tiger Moth	G. W. Bisshopp	
G–ASXC	Sipa 901	Waterside Flying Group	
G–ASXD	Brantly B.2B	Kebell Developments Ltd. & United Marine (1939) Ltd.	
G–ASXE	Brantly B.2B	Freemans of Bewdly (Aviation) Ltd.	
G–ASXF	Brantly 305	Express Aviation Services Ltd.	
G–ASXI	T.66 Nipper 2	Huddersfield Flying Group	
G–ASXJ	Luton L.A.4 Minor	P. D. Lea & E. A. Lingard	
G–ASXK	Aircopta	H. Dunmow & B. Coleman	
G–ASXR	Cessna 210	J. N. Scott	
G–ASXS	Jodel DR.1050	J. & B. Collins Ltd.	
G–ASXT	G.159 Gulfstream I	The Ford Motor Co. Ltd.	
G–ASXU	Jodel D.120A	P. M. Coulten	
G–ASXV	Beech B.65-A80 Queen Air	Ind Coope Ltd.	
G–ASXX	Avro 683 Lancaster 7 (NX611)	H.A.P.S.	
G–ASXY	Jodel D.117A	G. & G. D. Ward & L. Saffer	
G–ASXZ	Cessna 182G	W./Cdr. R. E. Stevenson	
G–ASYA	Aero Commander 560F	Valpoint Properties Ltd.	
G–ASYB	PA-23 Aztec 250	Edinburgh Flying Services Ltd.	
G–ASYD	BAC One-Eleven 475	B.A.C. (Holdings) Ltd.	
G–ASYG	A.61 Terrier 2	B. J. Guest	
G–ASYJ	Beech D.95A Travel Air	Crosby Aviation Ltd.	
G–ASYK	PA-30 Twin Comanche	G. F. L. Hill	
G–ASYL	Cessna 150E	K. & P. N. Shield & J. M. Morton	
G–ASYM	F.8L Super Falco	A. McNamara	
G–ASYN	A.61 Terrier 2	K. B. Holmes & ptnrs.	
G–ASYO	PA-30 Twin Comanche	M. R. Caustin	
G–ASYP	Cessna 105E	Yorkshire Flying Services Ltd.	
G–ASYV	Cessna 310G	Bifurcated Engineering Ltd.	
G–ASYW	Bell 47G-2	Bristow Helicopters Ltd.	
G–ASYY	Super Aero 45	J. & B. Shapero Ltd.	
G–ASYZ	Victa Airtourer 100	Rednal Polishing & Spraying Co. Ltd.	
G–ASZB	Cessna 150E	Shackleton Aviation Ltd.	

Registration	Type	Owner or Operator	Where and when seen
G—ASZD	Bo 208 Junior	D. H. C. Hull	
G—ASZE	A.61 Terrier 2	P. J. Moore	
G—ASZF	Boeing 707-336C	British Airways	
G—ASZG	Boeing 707-336C	British Airways	
G—ASZH	Jodel D.117	T. H. Charnley	
G—ASZJ	S.C.7 Skyvan 3	Short Bros & Harland Ltd.	
G—ASZR	Fairtravel Linnet	Blackbushe Aviation Ltd.	
G—ASZS	GY.80 Horizon 160	Shropshire Coachworks Ltd.	
G—ASZU	Cessna 150E	C. C. Dobson	
G—ASZV	T.66 Nipper 2	G. Thompson	
G—ASZW	Cessna F.172F	Luton Flying Club	
G—ASZX	A.61 Terrier	W. D. Hill	
G—ASZY	FRED Series 2	E. Clutton & E. W. Sherry	
G—ASZZ	Cessna 310J	Carl Ziegler Yacht Agency	
G—ATAA	PA-28 Cherokee 180	M. T. Furstenberg	
G—ATAD	Mooney M.20C	H. W. Walker	
G—ATAF	Cessna F.172F	J. O. Wallis	
G—ATAG	DR 1050 Ambassadeur	S. W. Brown & ptnrs.	
G—ATAI	D.H.104 Dove 8	Centrax Ltd.	
G—ATAK	Falco F.8L Srs. 3	A. Herdman	
G—ATAL	Dornier Do 28B–1	Richard Hayes Investments Ltd.	
G—ATAO	PA-24 Comanche 250	Botsford & Sons (Builders) Ltd.	
G—ATAS	PA-28 Cherokee 180	D. R. Wood	
G—ATAT	Cessna 150E	Warner Aircraft Services Ltd.	
G—ATAU	D.62B Condor	The Tiger Club	
G—ATAV	D.62C Condor	The Tiger Club	
G—ATAW	A.109 Airedale	M. J. Harvey	
G—ATAX	Auster 3	W. E. Roberts	
G—ATBF	*Sabre 4 (XB733)	Historic Aircraft Preservation Society	
G—ATBG	Nord 1002	L. M. Walton	
G—ATBH	Aero 145	S. Brod	
G—ATBI	Beech A.23 Musketeer	R. F. C. Dent	
G—ATBJ	Sikorsky S-61N	BAH	
G—ATBK	Cessna F.172F	F. W. Sherrell	
G—ATBL	D.H.60G Moth	A. Haigh-Thomas	
G—ATBN	PA-28 Cherokee 140	Stapleford Flying Club Ltd.	
G—ATBO	PA-28 Cherokee 140	R. F. C. Dent	
G—ATBP	Fournier RF3	I. Jamieson	
G—ATBS	D.31 Turbulent	J. A. Thomas	
G—ATBU	A.61 Terrier 2	P. R. Anderson	
G—ATBV	PA-23 Aztec 250	Eileen D. Goddard	
G—ATBX	PA-20 Pacer 135	R. I. Souch	
G—ATBZ	Westland Wessex 60	Bristow Helicopters Ltd.	
G—ATCC	A.109 Airedale	A. Robinson	
G—ATCD	D.5/180 Husky	Oxford Flying & Gliding Group	
G—ATCE	Cessna 206	D. M. Leonard	
G—ATCI	Victa Airtourer 100	G. A. Bamborough Ltd.	
G—ATCJ	Luton L.A.4a Minor	R. M. Sharphouse	
G—ATCL	Victa Airtourer 100	G. A. Bamborough Ltd.	
G—ATCN	Luton L.A.4a Minor	B. G. Pleasance	
G—ATCR	Cessna 310	Staverton Apache Ltd.	
G—ATCU	Cessna 337 Super Skymaster	University of Cambridge	
G—ATCX	Cessna 182H	I. H. Sugden	
G—ATCY	PA-23 Aztec 250	Eastern-Air Executive Ltd.	
G—ATDA	PA-28 Cherokee 160	Allesley Service Station	
G—ATDB	Nord 1101 Noralpha	J. B. Jackson	
G—ATDC	PA-23 Aztec 250	King Aviation Ltd.	
G—ATDG	GY.80 Horizon 160	J. Chappell	
G—ATDH	GY.80 Horizon 160	A. E. Langdon	
G—ATDL	Cessna 310J	D. M. Davies	
G—ATDN	A.61 Terrier 2	J. F. Moore	
G—ATDO	Bo 208C Junior	J. J. Williams	
G—ATDV	PA-24 Commanche 400	Walker Aviation Services & Plant Ltd.	
G—ATDZ	Z-326 Trener Master	M. D. Popoff	
G—ATED	Hiller UH-12E	North Scottish Helicopters Ltd.	

* Historic aircraft, mostly preserved in non-flying condition.

Registration	Type	Owner or Operator	Where and when seen
G–ATEF	Cessna 150E	Rimmer Aviation Ltd.	
G–ATEG	Cessna 150E	150 Group	
G–ATEM	PA-28 Cherokee 180	G. Wyles & W. Adams	
G–ATEN	PA-30 Twin Comanche	Air London (Executive Travel) Ltd.	
G–ATEP	EAA Biplane	E. L. Martin	
G–ATES	PA-32 Cherokee Six 260	Carlton Management Services Ltd.	
G–ATET	PA-30 Twin Comanche	Brenda Bayliss	
G–ATEV	DR.1050 Ambassadeur	J. E. Lewis	
G–ATEW	PA-30 Twin Comanche	Northumbria Group	
G–ATEX	Victa Airtourer 100	Condor Flying Club	
G–ATEZ	PA-28 Cherokee 140	M. K. Tuttey	
G–ATFA	Bensen B-8	J. Butler	
G–ATFD	DR 1051 Sicile Record	J. A. Booth	
G–ATFF	PA-23 Aztec 250	Air London	
G–ATFG	Brantly B.2B	B.E.A.S. Ltd.	
G–ATFH	Brantly B.2B	C. W. Udale (Plant) Ltd.	
G–ATFK	PA-30 Twin Comanche	I. Hall	
G–ATFL	Cessna F.172F	R. L. Beverley	
G–ATFM	Sikorsky S-61N	BAH Morning Star	
G–ATFR	PA-25 Pawnee 150	Air Tows Ltd.	
G–ATFS	PA-24 Comanche 180	T. A. G. Randell	
G–ATFU	D.H.85 Leopard Moth	J. W. Bensen	
G–ATFW	Luton L.A.4a Minor	G. W. Shield & ptnrs.	
G–ATFX	Cessna F.172G	Bristol & Wessex Aeroplane Club	
G–ATFY	Cessna F.172G	Richard (Menswear) Ltd.	
G–ATGC	Victa Airtourer 100	F. J. Laughlin	
G–ATGE	DR 1050 Ambassadeur	J. R. Roberts	
G–ATGF	M.S.892A Rallye Commodore 150	E. G. Bostock & R. A. Punter	
G–ATGG	M.S.885 Super Rallye	N. Turner & ptnrs.	
G–ATGH	Brantly B.2B	C. T. Lonsada	
G–ATGK	Riley Dove 1	Fairflight Charters Ltd.	
G–ATGN	Coal Gas Balloon	J. Thorn, R. A. Peak & P. G. Mulholland	
G–ATGO	Cessna F.172G	Bristol & Wessex Aeroplane Club Ltd.	
G–ATGP	DR 1050 Ambassadeur	F. Ryman	
G–ATGR	Beech 95-B55 Baron	Nathan Aircraft Ltd.	
G–ATGY	GY.80 Horizon	P. W. Gibberson	
G–ATGZ	GH-4 Gyroplane	G. Griffiths	
G–ATHA	PA-23 Apache 235	Spacedyers Ltd.	
G–ATHF	Cessna 150F	Cambridge Aero Club Ltd.	
G–ATHG	Cessna 150F	J. E. Dyson & T. E. O'Connor	
G–ATHH	Nord 1101 Noralpha	J. G. Kay	
G–ATHJ	PA-23 Aztec 250	Quinroy Ltd.	
G–ATHK	Aeronca 7AC Champion	B. Holland & A. T. Novak	
G–ATHL	Wallis WA-116/F	Wallis Autogyros Ltd.	
G–ATHM	Wallis WA-116/F	Wallis Autogyros Ltd.	
G–ATHN	Nord 1101 Noralpha	E. L. Martin	
G–ATHO	Beagle 206	E. Green & ptnrs.	
G–ATHR	PA-28 Cherokee 180	Rendex Transporters Ltd.	
G–ATHT	Victa Airtourer 115	M. A. Manning	
G–ATHU	A.61 Terrier 1	The Defford Aero Club (Worcs.) Ltd.	
G–ATHV	Cessna 150F	Yorkshire Flying Services Ltd.	
G–ATHW	Mooney Mk.21	F. J. L. Aran	
G–ATHX	Jodel DR 100A	C. E. Passmore	
G–ATHZ	Cessna 150F	Luton Flying Club	
G–ATIA	PA-24 Comanche 260	P. L. Builder	
G–ATIB	Bensen B.8M Gyro-Copter	A. Atkinson	
G–ATIC	DR 1050 Ambassadeur	M. J. Everard & H. Baker	
G–ATID	Cessna 337	Peter Darlington Ltd.	
G–ATIE	Cessna 150F	Staverton Flying School Ltd.	
G–ATIG	HPR-7 Herald	British Midland Airways	
G–ATII	Beech S.35 Bonanza	F. E. Cook	
G–ATIN	Jodel D.117	Mrs. M. J. Underhill	
G–ATIR	Stampe SV.4C	J. D. Iliffe	

Registration	Type	Owner or Operator	Where and when seen
G–ATIS	PA-28 Cherokee 160	N. F. Duke	
G–ATIU	Westland S.55 Srs. 3	Bristol Helicopter Ltd.	
G–ATIW	M.S.892A Rallye Commodore	Seven Flying Group Ltd.	
G–ATIX	Nord 1101 Noralpha	B. W. Homan	
G–ATIZ	Jodel D.117	N. Chandler	
G–ATJA	DR. 1050 Ambassadeur	The Tiger Club	
G–ATJC	Victa Airtourer 100	J. S. Coulson	
G–ATJD	PA-28 Cherokee 140	Chrismart Aviation Ltd.	
G–ATJE	PA-28 Cherokee 140	Lonmet (Aviation) Ltd.	
G–ATJF	PA-28 Cherokee 140	Keenair Services Ltd.	
G–ATJG	PA-28 Cherokee 140	D. E. Nixon	
G–ATJL	PA-24 Comanche 260	M. W. Webb	
G–ATJN	Jodel D.119	B. T. Price	
G–ATJP	PA-23 Apache 160	Lonmet (Aviation) Ltd.	
G–ATJR	PA-E23 Aztec 250	John Holmer & Sons Ltd.	
G–ATJT	GY.80 Horizon 160	Anderson Flying School Ltd.	
G–ATJU	Cessna 150F	W. D. Lincoln	
G–ATJW	Nord 1101 Noralpha	H. W. Elkin	
G–ATJX	Bucker Bu 131 Jungmann	J. E. Fricker & G. H. A. Bird	
G–ATJZ	PA-E23 Aztec 250	Baylee Air Holdings	
G–ATKC	Stampe S.V.4B	The Tiger Club	
G–ATKD	Cessna 150F	Cambridge Aero Club Ltd.	
G–ATKE	Cessna 150F	Skegness Air Taxi Services	
G–ATKF	Cessna 150F	Cambridge Aero Club Ltd.	
G–ATKG	Hiller UH-12B	Bristow Helicopters Ltd.	
G–ATKH	Luton L.A.4a Minor	L. Hepper	
G–ATKI	J3C-65 Cub	N. C. Netting	
G–ATKS	Cessna F.172G	Derek Crouch (Contractors) Ltd.	
G–ATKT	Cessna F.172G	N. Y. Souster	
G–ATKU	Cessna F.172G	G. A. Graham	
G–ATKW	PA-23 Aztec 250	Rene C. B. Boucher	
G–ATKX	Jodel D.140C	The Tiger Club	
G–ATKY	Cessna 150F	R. L. Beverley	
G–ATKZ	T.66-2 Nipper	M. W. Knights	
G–ATLA	Cessna 182J	H. R. A. Kidston	
G–ATLB	DR 1050-M1 Excellence	The Tiger Club	
G–ATLC	PA-23 Aztec 250	Shackleton Aviation Ltd.	
G–ATLD	Cessna 310K	W. H. & J. Rogers Group Ltd.	
G–ATLG	Hiller UH-12B	Bristow Helicopters Ltd.	
G–ATLH	Gyro-Glider	F. Fewsdale	
G–ATLM	Cessna F.172G	Yorkshire Flying Services Ltd.	
G–ATLN	Cessna F.172G	Miss P. M. H. Howard	
G–ATLO	Brantly 305	John Willment Properties Ltd.	
G–ATLP	Bensen B.8M	M. W. J. Whittaker	
G–ATLR	Cessna F.172G	R. W. M. & B. N. C. Mogg	
G–ATLT	Cessna U-206A	North Denes Aerodrome	
G–ATLV	D.120 Paris-Nice	D. Evernden & J. Nicholls	
G–ATLW	PA-28 Cherokee 180	Links Systems Ltd.	
G–ATMB	Cessna F.150F	P. Dodsworth & C. R. McNeil	
G–ATMC	Cessna F.150F	Cambridge Aero Club Ltd.	
G–ATMG	M.S.893 Rallye Commodore 180	F. W. Fay, C. W. Shard & J. S. A. Pritchard	
G–ATMH	Beagle D.5/180 Husky	The Tiger Club	
G–ATMI	H.S.748 Srs. 2A	Dan-Air Services Ltd.	
G–ATMJ	H.S.748	CAA (CAFU)	
G–ATMK	Cessna F.150F	Yorkshire Flying Services Ltd.	
G–ATMM	Cessna F.150F	P. M. Piccaver	
G–ATMN	Cessna F.150F	Ipswich School of Flying	
G–ATMP	Cessna 210F	Linwood Plant Ltd.	
G–ATMT	PA-30 Twin Comanche	Anglesey Air Charter Ltd.	
G–ATMU	PA-23 Apache 160	D. E. Nixon & C. Heathcote	
G–ATMW	PA-28 Cherokee 140	W. B. Bateson	
G–ATMX	Cessna 150F	Shropshire Aero Club Ltd.	
G–ATMY	Cessna 150F	Cox Aviation	
G–ATNB	PA-28 Cherokee 180	Parkright (Wisbech) Ltd.	
G–ATNE	Cessna F.150F	Bristol & Wessex Aeroplane Club	
G–ATNI	Cessna F.150F	Aerosport Ltd.	
G–ATNK	Cessna F.150F	Airwork Services Ltd.	

Registration	Type	Owner or Operator	Where and when seen
G–ATNL	Cessna F.150F	Airwork Services Ltd.	
G–ATNU	Cessna 182	Rogers Aviation Ltd.	
G–ATNV	PA-24 Commanche 260	A. S. M. McKinnon	
G–ATNW	Cessna F.150F	Flight One Ltd.	
G–ATNX	Cessna F.150F	Mooney Aviation Ltd.	
G–ATNY	Cessna 337A Super Skymaster	Skycabs	
G–ATOA	PA-23 Apache 160	Thurston Aviation Ltd.	
G–ATOC	Bo 208C Junior	Glamorgan Flying Club	
G–ATOD	Cessna F.150F	W. T. Tummon	
G–ATOE	Cessna F.150F	Aerosport Ltd.	
G–ATOG	Cessna F.150F	Airwork Services Ltd.	
G–ATOH	D.62B Condor	The Tiger Club	
G–ATOI	PA-28 Cherokee 140	D. E. Nixon	
G–ATOJ	PA-28 Cherokee 140	O. T. Kernahan	
G–ATOK	PA-28 Cherokee 140	Eurotec Ltd.	
G–ATOL	PA-28 Cherokee 140	Tamar Flying Group	
G–ATOM	PA-28 Cherokee 140	D. E. Nixon & C. G. C. Goate	
G–ATON	PA-28 Cherokee 140	P. R. Shanks & J. Earley	
G–ATOO	PA-28 Cherokee 140	H. I. Williams	
G–ATOP	PA-28 Cherokee 140	P. Hilton	
G–ATOR	PA-28 Cherokee 140	J. P. Taylor	
G–ATOS	PA-28 Cherokee 140	A. J. Hurst Securities Ltd.	
G–ATOT	PA-28 Cherokee 180	N. J. R. Installations Ltd.	
G–ATOU	Mooney M.20E Super 21	F. N. Husband	
G–ATOY	PA-24 Comanche 260	Lodge Flying Group	
G–ATPD	H.S. 125-1B	Shell Aircraft Ltd.	
G–ATPE	H.S. 125-1B	Shell Aircraft Ltd.	
G–ATPJ	BAC One-Eleven 301	Dan-Air Services Ltd.	
G–ATPK	BAC One-Eleven 301	Laker Airways Ltd.	
G–ATPL	BAC One-Eleven 301	Dan-Air Services Ltd.	
G–ATPM	Cessna F.150F	Dan-Air Services Ltd.	
G–ATPN	PA-28 Cherokee 140	Airways Aero Associations Ltd.	
G–ATPR	PA-E23 Aztec 250	P. T. Elmore & R. P. Cripps	
G–ATPT	Cessna 182J	M. J. Baird-Smith	
G–ATPU	Super Skymaster 337A	Brismo Finance Ltd.	
G–ATPV	JB.01 Minicab	R. Piddock & ptnrs.	
G–ATRC	Beech B.95A Travel Air	N. D. Howard	
G–ATRD	Cessna F.150F	Warwickshire Aero Club Ltd.	
G–ATRE	Cessna F.172G	D. M. Squires & R. E. Styles	
G–ATRG	PA-18 Super Cub 150	Air Tows Ltd.	
G–ATRH	PA-18 Super Cub 150	J. W. Benson	
G–ATRI	Bo 208C Junior	W. H. Jones	
G–ATRK	Cessna F.150F	Luton Flying Club Ltd.	
G–ATRL	Cessna F.150F	Peterborough Aero Club Ltd.	
G–ATRM	Cessna F.150F	P. H. Spring	
G–ATRN	Cessna F.150F	J. W. Flavell	
G–ATRO	PA-28 Cherokee 140	Associated Independent Recording (London) Ltd.	
G–ATRP	PA-28 Cherokee 140	T. R. E. Cook	
G–ATRR	PA-28 Cherokee 140	Woodgate Aviation	
G–ATRU	PA-28 Cherokee 180	Britannia Airways Ltd.	
G–ATRW	PA-32 Cherokee Six 260	Kent Messenger Ltd.	
G–ATRX	PA-32 Cherokee Six 260	A. Jacobs *Patricia*	
G–ATRY	Alon A-2 Aircoupe	West London Aero Services Ltd.	
G–ATSC	Wessex 60	Bristow Helicopters Ltd.	
G–ATSE	PA-30 Twin Comanche	Air London	
G–ATSI	Bo 208C Junior	T. M. H. Paterson	
G–ATSJ	Brantly 305	R. H. Ryan	
G–ATSL	Cessna F.172G	H. G. Le Cheminant	
G–ATSM	Cessna 337A Super Skymaster	Saldenhurst Ltd.	
G–ATSR	Beech M.35 Bonanza	T. F. Graham Ltd.	
G–ATST	M.S.893A Rallye Commodore	J. Lloyd	
G–ATSU	Jodel D. 140B Mousquetaire	J. S. Burnett Ltd.	
G–ATSV	Cessna 310C	Medburn Aviation Services Ltd.	
G–ATSX	Bo 208C Junior	Cotswold Aero Club Ltd.	

Registration	Type	Owner or Operator	Where and when seen
G-ATSY	Wassmer WA41 Super IV Baladou	A. J. Reid	
G-ATSZ	PA-30 Twin Comanche	B. P. Stein	
G-ATTB	Wallis WA.116-1	D. A. Wallis	
G-ATTD	Cessna 182J	Hancock & Roberts Ltd. & D. K. Nowill	
G-ATTF	PA-28 Cherokee 140	Mooney Aviation Ltd.	
G-ATTG	PA-28 Cherokee 140	J. F. Thurlow	
G-ATTI	PA-38 Cherokee 140	B.L.S. Aviation Ltd.	
G-ATTK	PA-28 Cherokee 140	Andrewsfield Flying Club	
G-ATTM	Jodel DR.250-160	H. Reis & J. B. Waterfield	
G-ATTN	Piccard Hot-Air Balloon	L. D. Goldsmith	
G-ATTP	BAC One-Eleven 207	Dan-Air Services Ltd.	
G-ATTR	Bo 208C Junior 3	E. B. Cox	
G-ATTU	PA-28 Cherokee 140	B.L.S. Aviation Ltd.	
G-ATTV	PA-28 Cherokee 140	Sherwood Flying Club	
G-ATTX	PA-28 Cherokee 180	L. W. Garner	
G-ATTY	PA-32 Cherokee Six 260	L. A. Dingemans & D. J. Everett	
G-ATUA	PA-25 Pawnee 235	A.D.S. (Aerial) Ltd.	
G-ATUB	PA-28 Cherokee 140	Airways Aero Associations Ltd.	
G-ATUC	PA-28 Cherokee 140	Airways Aero Associations Ltd.	
G-ATUD	PA-28 Cherokee 140	Airways Aero Associations Ltd.	
G-ATUE	V.812 Viscount	Alidair Cargo Ltd.	
G-ATUF	Cessna F.150F	G. C. McConnell & J. C. Mead	
G-ATUG	D.62B Condor	The Tiger Club	
G-ATUH	T.66 Nipper	V. H. Hallam	
G-ATUI	Bo 208C Junior	Cotswold Aero Club	
G-ATUL	PA-28 Cherokee 180	Hanbrair Ltd.	
G-ATVC	PA-32 Cherokee Six 260	Fosters Farlington Ltd.	
G-ATVF	D.H.C.I Chipmunk 22	J. A. Simms	
G-ATVG	Hiller UH-12E	Management Aviation Ltd.	
G-ATVH	BAC One-Eleven 207	Dan-Air Services Ltd.	
G-ATVI	Sipa 903	J. Martin	
G-ATVK	PA-28 Cherokee 140	Southend Light Aviation Centre Ltd.	
G-ATVL	PA-28 Cherokee 140	West London Aero Services	
G-ATVO	PA-28 Cherokee 140	Herts & Essex Aero Club	
G-ATVP	*F.B.5 Gunbus (2345)	RAF Museum	
G-ATVS	PA-28 Cherokee 180	Webster Aviation Ltd.	
G-ATVW	D.62B Condor	The Tiger Club	
G-ATVX	Bo 208C Junior	Laarbruch Flying Club	
G-ATWA	DR.1050 Ambassadeur	K. Dubrow	
G-ATWE	M.S.892A Rallye Commodore	D. I. Murray	
G-ATWG	PA-30 Twin Comanche 160	L. R. Davies	
G-ATWH	H.S.125-1B/R	GKN Group Services Ltd.	
G-ATWJ	Cessna F.172F	D. J. G. Poole & K. Cameron	
G-ATWL	Jodel D.120	PFA Flying Group 272	
G-ATWN	Aero Commander 680F	Elliott Brothers (London) Ltd.	
G-ATWO	PA-28 Cherokee 180	P.B.C. European Transport Ltd.	
G-ATWP	Alon A-2 Aircoupe	Cornwall Flying Club	
G-ATWR	PA-30 Twin Comanche 160	C. Phillips	
G-ATWS	Luton L.A.4a Minor	K. J. Hazelwood	
G-ATWV	Boeing 707-336C	British Airways	
G-ATWZ	M.S.892 Rallye Commodore	R. G. Allen & K. F. Olivier	
G-ATXA	PA-22 Tri-Pacer 150	D. R. Jones	
G-ATXD	PA-30 Twin Comanche 160	Southwark Estates Ltd.	
G-ATXF	GY-80 Horizon 150	J. G. Hornsby & ptnrs.	
G-ATXG	PA-E23 Aztec 250	Luton Flying Club	
G-ATXM	PA-28 Cherokee 180	J. Khan	
G-ATXN	Mitchell-Proctor Kittiwake	D. W. Kent	
G-ATXO	Sipa 903	M. Hillam	
G-ATXR	Free Balloon	Mrs. C. M. Bulmer	
G-ATXW	McCandless M.4	W. H. Ekin	

* Historic aircraft, mostly preserved in non-flying condition.

Registration	Type	Owner or Operator	Where and when seen
G-ATXY	McCandless M.4/T.1	W. H. Ekin (Engineering) Ltd.	
G-ATXZ	Bo 208C Junior	J. A. Taylor	
G-ATYA	PA-25 Pawnee 235	Skegness Air Taxi Services Ltd.	
G-ATYE	Beagle B.206 Srs. 2	Maidenhead Organ Studies Ltd.	
G-ATYF	PA-30 Twin Comanche 160	Arrow Air Services *Brunflug*	
G-ATYM	Cessna F.150G	Wycombe Air Centre Ltd.	
G-ATYN	Cessna F.150G	Skegness Air Taxi Services Ltd.	
G-ATYP	Bo 208C Junior	Shackleton Aviation Ltd.	
G-ATYS	PA-28 Cherokee 180	K. R. Cox	
G-ATYV	Bell 47G	K. McDonald	
G-ATYW	Beagle B.206-1	Northern Air Taxis Ltd.	
G-ATYZ	M.S.880B Rallye Club	Nylo Flying Group	
G-ATZA	Bo 208C Junior	W. C. Roberts	
G-ATZB	Hiller UH-12B	Bristow Helicopters Ltd.	
G-ATZC	Boeing 707-365C	British Caledonian *County of Stirling*	
G-ATZD	Boeing 707-365C	British Airways	
G-ATZG	Free Balloon	RAF Abingdon Free Balloon Club	
G-ATZH	Canadair CL-44D	Transmeridian Air Cargo Ltd.	
G-ATZJ	PA-23 Aztec 250	C.S.E. Aviation Ltd.	
G-ATZK	PA-28 Cherokee 180	Drumgate Ltd.	
G-ATZL	Jodel DR.250	D. A. Hood	
G-ATZM	Piper Cub J3C-65	B. Brooks	
G-ATZO	Beagle B.206 Srs. 1	Skyliner Services Ltd.	
G-ATZS	Wassmer WA41 Super IV Baladou	R. K. Gambell	
G-ATZU	PA-30 Twin Comanche 160	Air Navigation & Trading Co. Ltd.	
G-ATZV	PA-30 Twin Comanche 160	Quickflight Airservices Ltd.	
G-ATZY	Cessna F.150G	Airwork Services Ltd.	
G-ATZZ	Cessna F.150G	Airwork Services Ltd.	
G-AVAA	Cessna F.150G	Airwork Services Ltd.	
G-AVAC	Cessna F.150G	Airwork Services Ltd.	
G-AVAI	H.S.125 Srs. 3B	Brown and Root (U.K.) Ltd.	
G-AVAJ	Hiller UH-12B	Bristow Helicopters Ltd.	
G-AVAO	PA-30 Twin Comanche 160	Heath Street Car Hire Ltd.	
G-AVAP	Cessna F.150G	G. J. Foreman	
G-AVAR	Cessna F.150G	West Wales Flying Club	
G-AVAS	Cessna F.172H	Birmingham Aviation Ltd.	
G-AVAU	PA-30 Twin Comanche 160	Lenair Aviation Ltd.	
G-AVAW	D.62B Condor	The Tiger Club	
G-AVAX	PA-28 Cherokee 180	College of Air Training	
G-AVAY	PA-28 Cherokee 180	College of Air Training	
G-AVAZ	PA-28 Cherokee 180	College of Air Training	
G-AVBA	PA-28 Cherokee 180	College of Air Training	
G-AVBB	PA-28 Cherokee 180	College of Air Training	
G-AVBC	PA-28 Cherokee 180	College of Air Training	
G-AVBE	PA-28 Cherokee 180	College of Air Training	
G-AVBG	PA-28 Cherokee 180	College of Air Training	
G-AVBH	PA-28 Cherokee 180	College of Air Training	
G-AVBJ	PA-28 Cherokee 180	College of Air Training	
G-AVBK	SF-25 Motorfalke	C. W. Vigar	
G-AVBL	PA-30 Twin Comanche 160	F. J. Wells	
G-AVBP	PA-28 Cherokee 140	Croft Precision Products Ltd.	
G-AVBS	PA-28 Cherokee 180	British Freehold Investments Ltd.	
G-AVBT	PA-28 Cherokee 180	Airways Aero Associations	
G-AVBU	PA-32 Cherokee Six	Wilford Aviation Ltd.	
G-AVBW	BAC One-Eleven 320	Laker Airways	
G-AVBX	BAC One-Eleven 320	Laker Airways	
G-AVBY	BAC One-Eleven 320	Laker Airways	
G-AVBZ	Cessna F.172H	J. Seville	
G-AVCA	Brantly B.2B	Lusair Ltd.	
G-AVCB	DR.1051 Sicile	J. W. West	

Registration	Type	Owner or Operator	Where and when seen
G–AVCC	Cessna F.172H	Rogers Aviation Ltd.	
G–AVCD	Cessna F.172H	Toonghose Aviation Ltd.	
G–AVCE	Cessna F.172H	Cleco Electrical Industries Ltd.	
G–AVCG	Beagle B.206 Srs. 2	March Engineering Ltd.	
G–AVCI	Beagle B.206 Srs. 2	Kattan (GB) Ltd.	
G–AVCJ	Beagle B.206 Srs. 2	Lowland Aero Service Co. Ltd.	
G–AVCM	PA-24 Comanche 260	Express Aviation Services Ltd.	
G–AVCN	BN-2 Islander	Aurigny Air Services	
G–AVCP	PA-30 Twin Comanche 160	Airways Aviation Ltd.	
G–AVCS	A.61 Terrier I	J. Nicoll & R. Andrews	
G–AVCT	Cessna F.150G	Dorset Flying Club & Aviation Centre Ltd.	
G–AVCU	Cessna F.150G	Parker Aviation Services	
G–AVCV	Cessna 182J	J. A. Moores	
G–AVCW	PA-30 Twin Comanche 160	Seagull Aircraft Ltd.	
G–AVCX	PA-30 Twin Comanche 160	Edinburgh Flying Services	
G–AVCY	PA-30 Twin Comanche 160	R. J. Fisher	
G–AVCZ	D.62B Condor	Experimental Flying Group	
G–AVDA	Cessna 182	J. W. Grant	
G–AVDB	Cessna 310L	Airwork Services Ltd.	
G–AVDE	Turner Giroglider Mk. I	J. S. Smith	
G–AVDG	Wallis WA-116 Srs. I	Wallis Autogyros Ltd.	
G–AVDI	PA-23 Apache 150	R. B. Smith	
G–AVDT	Champion 7AC	W. R. Prescott	
G–AVDU	Champion 7EC	J. E. Wilson	
G–AVDV	PA-22 Tri-Pacer	Horsted Aviation Ltd.	
G–AVDW	D.62B Condor	N. H. Jones	
G–AVDX	H.S. 125 Srs. 3B	Civil Aviation Authority	
G–AVDY	Luton L.A.4a Minor	D. E. Evans, W. J. A. Huxley & A. G. Fowles	
G–AVDZ	PA-25 Pawnee 235	Skegness Air Taxi Services Ltd.	
G–AVEB	Morane MS 230 Et 2	Hon. P. Lindsay	
G–AVEC	Cessna F.172H	Clarke Engineering & Construction Co. Ltd.	
G–AVEF	D150 Mascaret	The Tiger Club	
G–AVEG	SIAI-Marchetti S.205	Rousted Ltd.	
G–AVEH	SIAI-Marchetti S.205	Cecil M. Yuill	
G–AVEK	Cessna 411A	Welltrade Ltd.	
G–AVEL	Cessna F.150G	Pegasus Aviation Ltd.	
G–AVEM	Cessna F.150G	Airwork Services Ltd.	
G–AVEN	Cessna F.150G	Airwork Services Ltd.	
G–AVEO	Cessna F.150G	Airwork Services Ltd.	
G–AVER	Cessna F.150G	Plymouth Aero Club Ltd.	
G–AVET	Beech C55 Baron	Peters Aviation Ltd.	
G–AVEU	WA.41 Baladou	Baladou Flying Group	
G–AVEX	D.62B Condor	N. H. Jones	
G–AVEY	Super Wot	A. Eastelow	
G–AVEZ	HPR-7 Herald 210	British Island Airways Ltd.	
G–AVFA	H.S.121 Trident Two	British Airways	
G–AVFC	H.S.121 Trident Two	British Airways	
G–AVFD	H.S.121 Trident Two	British Airways	
G–AVFE	H.S.121 Trident Two	British Airways	
G–AVFF	H.S.121 Trident Two	British Airways	
G–AVFG	H.S.121 Trident Two	British Airways	
G–AVFH	H.S.121 Trident Two	British Airways	
G–AVFI	H.S.121 Trident Two	British Airways	
G–AVFJ	H.S.121 Trident Two	British Airways	
G–AVFK	H.S.121 Trident Two	British Airways	
G–AVFL	H.S.121 Trident Two	British Airways	
G–AVFM	H.S.121 Trident Two	British Airways	
G–AVFN	H.S.121 Trident Two	British Airways	
G–AVFO	H.S.121 Trident Two	British Airways	
G–AVFP	PA-28 Cherokee 140	Charmian Huggins (Aviation) Ltd.	
G–AVFR	PA-28 Cherokee 140	C. Grear	
G–AVFS	PA-32 Cherokee Six	F. D. Gales	
G–AVFU	PA-32 Cherokee Six	S. L. H. Construction Ltd.	

Registration	Type	Owner or Operator	Where and when seen
G–AVFW	PA-30 Twin Comanche 160	J. T. R. Baines	
G–AVFX	PA-28 Cherokee 140	M. Gorensweigh	
G–AVFY	PA-28 Cherokee 140	A. J. & Mrs. J. M. Meston	
G–AVFZ	PA-28 Cherokee 140	Keenair Services Ltd.	
G–AVGA	PA-24 Comanche 260	Morgan Hemingway & Co. Ltd.	
G–AVGB	PA-28 Cherokee 140	G. Abbot	
G–AVGC	PA-28 Cherokee 140	J. H. Kimber	
G–AVGD	PA-28 Cherokee 140	Douglas Metcalf	
G–AVGE	PA-28 Cherokee 140	A. G. Brauch Contractors Ltd.	
G–AVGH	PA-28 Cherokee 140	Mooney Aviation Ltd.	
G–AVGI	PA-28 Cherokee 140	W. B. Bateson	
G–AVGJ	Jodel DR 1050	G. D. H. Crawford	
G–AVGK	PA-28 Cherokee 180	Liverpool Aero Club	
G–AVGL	Cessna F.150G	G. B. & F. N. Claridge	
G–AVGM	Cessna F.150G	Luton Flying Club Ltd.	
G–AVGN	PA-24 Comanche 260	Viscount Chelsea	
G–AVGP	BAC One-Eleven 408	Cambrian Airways	
G–AVGT	PA-30 Twin Comanche 160	Chart Managements & Partners	
G–AVGU	Cessna F.150G	J. A. & Mrs. J. M. C. Pothecary	
G–AVGV	Cessna F.150G	G. Hull	
G–AVGX	Bo 208C Junior	R. J. Pascoe	
G–AVGY	Cessna 182K	H. E. Peacock	
G–AVGZ	DR.1050 Ambassadeur	W. H. Gilchrist & A. T. Howarth	
G–AVHC	Brooklands Mosquito II	R. H. Ryan	
G–AVHF	Beech A.23 Musketeer	Foyle Aviation Ltd.	
G–AVHH	Cessna F.172H	Webster Aviation Ltd.	
G–AVHJ	WA.41 Baladou	G. N. Carr-Glyn	
G–AVHL	Jodel DR.105A	Girls Venture Corps	
G–AVHM	Cessna F.150G	Municipal Product and Services Ltd.	
G–AVHN	Cessna F.150G	Bristol and Wessex Aero Club Ltd.	
G–AVHO	Beagle B.206 Srs. 2	BAC (Holdings) Ltd.	
G–AVHT	E.3 Auster 9M (WZ711)	H. Somerton-Rayner	
G–AVHW	PA-30 Twin Comanche 160	The Hon. J. R. Dawnay	
G–AVHY	Fournier RF.4	R. Swinn & J. Conolly	
G–AVHZ	PA-30 Twin Comanche	Express Aviation Services Ltd.	
G–AVIA	Cessna F.150G	L. Richards	
G–AVIB	Cessna F.150G	Warwickshire Aero Club	
G–AVIC	Cessna F.172H	W. B. Llewellyn	
G–AVID	Cessna 182J	Inch Farming Co. Ltd.	
G–AVIE	Cessna F.172D	Air Anglia	
G–AVIG	A-B 206A JetRanger	Bristow Helicopters Ltd.	
G–AVII	A-B 206A JetRanger	Bristow Helicopters Ltd.	
G–AVIL	Alon A.2 Aircoupe	Vernonair Ltd.	
G–AVIN	M.S.880B Rallye Club	F. M. F. Cox & ptnrs.	
G–AVIO	M.S.880B Rallye Club	Highwood Flying Group	
G–AVIP	Brantly B.2B	Cosworth Engineering Ltd.	
G–AVIR	Cessna F.172H	West Lancashire Aero Club Ltd.	
G–AVIS	Cessna F.172H	Shropshire Aero Club Ltd.	
G–AVIT	Cessna F.150G	Shropshire Aero Club Ltd.	
G–AVIU	Jodel DR 1050	P. R. Cremer	
G–AVIX	Cessna 337B	Skycab (Europe) Northampton Ltd.	
G–AVIZ	SF.25 Motorfalke	J. McBeth	
G–AVJB	V.815 Viscount	British Midland Airways	
G–AVJE	Cessna F.150G	Ipswich School of Flying	
G–AVJF	Cessna F.172H	W. R. & Mrs. B. M. Young	
G–AVJG	Cessna 337B	Shackleton Aviation Ltd.	
G–AVJH	D.62 Condor	E. W. Osbourn	
G–AVJI	Cessna F.172H	R. A. Aero Club Ltd.	
G–AVJJ	PA-30 Twin Comanche 160	Peregrine Air Services Ltd.	
G–AVJK	Jodel DR 1050 M.1 Excellence	J. H. B. Urmston	
G–AVJN	Brantly B.2B	Dickson Motors (Perth) Ltd.	

Registration	Type	Owner or Operator	Where and when seen
G–AVJO	Fokker E.III Replica	Personal Plane Services Ltd.	
G–AVJR	Free Balloon	G. F. Turnbull	
G–AVJS	Nord 1002	F. R. Brown	
G–AVJT	PA-30 Twin Comanche	Seel-Pak (Household Products) Ltd.	
G–AVJU	PA-24 Comanche 260	Progressive Identification Systems Ltd.	
G–AVJV	Wallis WA-117 Srs. 1	K. H. Wallis	
G–AVJW	Wallis WA-118 Srs. 2	K. H. Wallis	
G–AVKB	MB.50 Pipistrelle	C. Hamilton & W. Overy	
G–AVKC	BN-2A-21 Islander	Fairey Britten-Norman Air Services Ltd.	
G–AVKD	Fournier FR.4D	Lasham RF4 Group	
G–AVKE	Gadfly HDW.1	Gadfly Aircraft Ltd.	
G–AVKF	Cessna F.172H	R. E. Husband & T. Widdows	
G–AVKG	Cessna F.172H	P. Newsham	
G–AVKI	Nipper T.66 Srs. 3	K. D. G. Courtney & ptnrs.	
G–AVKJ	Nipper T.66 Srs. 3	I. M. Kirkwood	
G–AVKK	Nipper T.66 Srs. 3	Westcountry Aircraft Servicing Ltd.	
G–AVKM	D.62B Condor	N. H. Jones	
G–AVKN	Cessna 401	Coltex Ltd. *Courier Coltina*	
G–AVKO	Gloster Non-Rigid Airship	M. J. Rynick	
G–AVKP	A.109 Airedale	St. Pirans Flying Group	
G–AVKR	Bo 208C Junior	D. H. T. Bain	
G–AVKS	Bell 47G-2	Bristow Helicopters Ltd.	
G–AVKU	WA41 Baladou	Altair Aviation & General Trading Co.	
G–AVKX	Hiller UH-12E	Management Aviation Ltd.	
G–AVKY	Hiller UH-12E	T. M. Sloan	
G–AVKZ	PA-23 Aztec 250	The British Oxygen Co. Ltd.	
G–AVLA	PA-28 Cherokee 140	Aerosport Ltd.	
G–AVLB	PA-28 Cherokee 140	D. C. Tyne & ptnrs.	
G–AVLC	PA-28 Cherokee 140	Swansea & District Flying School & Club Ltd.	
G–AVLD	PA-28 Cherokee 140	B.L.S. Aviation Ltd.	
G–AVLE	PA-28 Cherokee 140	Sherwood Flying Group	
G–AVLF	PA-28 Cherokee 140	West London Aero Services Ltd.	
G–AVLG	PA-28 Cherokee 140	Lonmet (Aviation) Ltd.	
G–AVLH	PA-28 Cherokee 140	Air Tours	
G–AVLI	PA-28 Cherokee 140	Pace Developments	
G–AVLJ	PA-28 Cherokee 140	Barbers Animal Products Ltd.	
G–AVLN	B.121 Pup 2	C. B. G. Masefield	
G–AVLO	Bo 208C Junior	J. Limberg Ltd.	
G–AVLP	PA-23 Aztec 250	Survey Flights Ltd.	
G–AVLR	PA-28 Cherokee 140	Keenair Services Ltd.	
G–AVLS	PA-28 Cherokee 140	F. B. Spriggs	
G–AVLT	PA-28 Cherokee 140	Southend Light Aviation Centre	
G–AVLU	PA-28 Cherokee 140	London Transport (Central Road Services) Sports Association Flying Club	
G–AVLV	PA-23 Aztec 250	T. M. Lupton	
G–AVLW	Fournier RF.4D	Sir Hugo Sebright	
G–AVLY	Jodel D.120	D. I. Anson	
G–AVMA	GY.80 Horizon 180	B. R. & S. Hildick	
G–AVMB	D.62B Condor	N. H. Jones	
G–AVMD	Cessna 150G	Pegasus Aviation Ltd.	
G–AVME	PA-28 Cherokee 140	R. V. H. Butters	
G–AVMF	Cessna F.150G	J. D. Palfreman	
G–AVMH	BAC One-Eleven 510	British Airways	
G–AVMI	BAC One-Eleven 510	British Airways	
G–AVNJ	BAC One-Eleven 510	British Airways	
G–AVMK	BAC One-Eleven 510	British Airways	
G–AVML	BAC One-Eleven 510	British Airways	
G–AVMM	BAC One-Eleven 510	British Airways	
G–AVMN	BAC One-Eleven 510	British Airways	
G–AVMO	BAC One-Eleven 510	British Airways	
G–AVMP	BAC One-Eleven 510	British Airways	

Registration	Type	Owner or Operator	Where and when seen
G–AVMR	BAC One-Eleven 510	British Airways	
G–AVMS	BAC One-Eleven 510	British Airways	
G–AVMT	BAC One-Eleven 510	British Airways	
G–AVMU	BAC One-Eleven 510	British Airways	
G–AVMV	BAC One-Eleven 510	British Airways	
G–AVMW	BAC One-Eleven 510	British Airways	
G–AVMX	BAC One-Eleven 510	British Airways	
G–AVMY	BAC One-Eleven 510	British Airways	
G–AVMZ	BAC One-Eleven 510	British Airways	
G–AVNB	Cessna F.150G	G. A. J. Bowles	
G–AVNC	Cessna F.150G	J. W. Parker	
G–AVNG	Beech A80 Queen Air	Vernair Ltd.	
G–AVNI	PA-30 Twin Comanche	C. D. A. Jones Contractors Ltd.	
G–AVNK	PA-23 Aztec 250	Luton Flying Club Ltd.	
G–AVNL	PA-23 Aztec 250	T. M. Lupton	
G–AVNM	PA-28 Cherokee 180	College of Air Training	
G–AVNN	PA-28 Cherokee 180	College of Air Training	
G–AVNO	PA-28 Cherokee 180	College of Air Training	
G–AVNP	PA-28 Cherokee 180	College of Air Training	
G–AVNR	PA-28 Cherokee 180	College of Air Training	
G–AVNS	PA-28 Cherokee 180	College of Air Training	
G–AVNT	PA-28 Cherokee 180	College of Air Training	
G–AVNU	PA-28 Cherokee 180	College of Air Training	
G–AVNV	PA-28 Cherokee 180	College of Air Training	
G–AVNW	PA-28 Cherokee 180	College of Air Training	
G–AVNX	Fournier RF.4D	N. W. Fox	
G–AVNY	Fournier RF.4D	A. N. Mavrogordato	
G–AVNZ	Fournier RF.4D	Cobra Group	
G–AVOA	Jodel DR 1050 Ambassadeur	I. MacPherson	
G–AVOD	Beagle D5/180 Husky	Turiff Construction Corporation Ltd.	
G–AVOE	BAC One-Eleven 416	Cambrian Airways	
G–AVOF	BAC One-Eleven 416	Cambrian Airways	
G–AVOH	D.62B Condor	N. H. Jones	
G–AVOI	H.S.125 Srs. 3B	Fortes (Publicity) Services Ltd.	
G–AVOM	Jodel DR. 221	K. E. Nicholas	
G–AVON	Luton LA.5 Major	G. R. Mee	
G–AVOO	PA-18 Super Cub 150	T. A. McMullin & R. C. Stafford-Allen	
G–AVOR	Land Development Aircraft	D. Lockspeiser	
G–AVOZ	PA-28 Cherokee 180	A. P. Baker, W. J. Golden & R. T. J. Holmes	
G–AVPA	Sopwith Pup Replica	C. J. Warrilow	
G–AVPB	Boeing 707-336C	British Airways	
G–AVPC	D.31 Turbulent	J. Sharp	
G–AVPD	D.92 Bebe	S. W. McKay	
G–AVPE	H.S.125 Srs. 3B	BAC Ltd.	
G–AVPF	PA-30 Twin Comanche	Ewbank & Son	
G–AVPH	Cessna F.150G	Air Touring Shops	
G–AVPI	Cessna F.172H	W. R. Boyce	
G–AVPJ	D.H.82A Tiger Moth	The Barnstormers Ltd.	
G–AVPK	M.S.892A/150 Rallye Commodore	J. H. Spanton	
G–AVPL	M.S.892 Rallye Commodore	J. H. Atkinson	
G–AVPM	Jodel D.117	H. T. Blakeston	
G–AVPN	HPR.7 Herald 203	British Island Airways	
G–AVPR	PA-30 Twin Comanche 160	L. O. Choundley	
G–AVPS	PA-30 Twin Comanche 160	S. E. Marples & A. Wilson	
G–AVPT	PA-18 Super Cub 150	N. H. Jones	
G–AVPU	PA-18 Super Cub 150	T. Docherty Ltd.	
G–AVPV	PA-28 Cherokee 180	Southend Light Aviation Centre	
G–AVPX	Taylor Monoplane	T. E. Jones-Griffiths	
G–AVPY	PA-25 Pawnee 235	Farm Aviation Services Ltd.	
G–AVRC	BN-2A-26 Islander	Fairey Britten-Norman Air Services Ltd.	

Registration	Type	Owner or Operator	Where and when seen
G–AVRF	H.S.125 Srs. 3B	BAC Ltd.	
G–AVRG	H.S.125 Srs. 3A	Court Line Aviation	
G–AVRK	PA-28 Cherokee 180	M. L. P. Aviation	
G–AVRL	Boeing 737-204	Britannia Airways Ltd.	
G–AVRM	Boeing 737-204	Britannia Airways Ltd.	
G–AVRN	Boeing 737-204	Britannia Airways Ltd.	
G–AVRO	Boeing 737-204	Britannia Airways Ltd.	
G–AVRP	PA-28 Cherokee 140	Air Navigation & Trading Co.	
G–AVRS	GY.80 Horizon 180	K. F. Plummer	
G–AVRT	PA-28 Cherokee 140	Tawney Flying Group	
G–AVRU	PA-28 Cherokee 140	Fenland Tractors Ltd.	
G–AVRW	GY-20 Minicab	R. B. Pybus	
G–AVRX	PA-23 Aztec 250	Central Air Services (Air Envoy) Ltd.	
G–AVRY	PA-28 Cherokee 180	Roses Flying Group	
G–AVRZ	PA-28 Cherokee 180	Briglea Engineering Ltd.	
G–AVSA	PA-28 Cherokee 180	J. M. A. Gunn	
G–AVSB	PA-28 Cherokee 180	White House Garage Ltd.	
G–AVSC	PA-28 Cherokee 180	West London Aero Services Ltd.	
G–AVSD	PA-28 Cherokee 180	A. J. Currie	
G–AVSE	PA-28 Cherokee 180	S E Aviation Ltd.	
G–AVSF	PA-28 Cherokee 180	Goodwood Terrena Ltd.	
G–AVSG	PA-28 Cherokee 180	Howard Cundey & Co.	
G–AVSH	PA-28 Cherokee 180	Woodgate Aviation Ltd.	
G–AVSI	PA-28 Cherokee 140	C. S. Mckenzie	
G–AVSK	Bell 47-G4A	Autair Helicopter Services Ltd.	
G–AVSN	A-B 206A JetRanger	Ferranti Helicopters Ltd.	
G–AVSO	PA-23 Aztec 250	Edinburgh Flying Services Ltd.	
G–AVSP	PA-28 Cherokee 180	Goodwood Terrena Ltd.	
G–AVSR	Beagle D 5/180 Husky	A. L. Young	
G–AVTB	Nipper RA45 Srs. 3	J. S. A. Pritchard	
G–AVTC	Nipper RA45 Srs. 3	I. MacLennan & ptnrs.	
G–AVTE	Bell 206A JetRanger	W. R. Finance Ltd.	
G–AVTH	Jodel DR 1051	B. A. Bennett	
G–AVTI	PA-30 Twin Comanche 160	Pastel Ltd.	
G–AVTJ	PA-32 Cherokee Six 260	J. Jacobs	
G–AVTK	PA-32 Cherokee Six 260	R. W. Budge	
G–AVTL	HAG 1/4 Free Balloon	T. A. Adams	
G–AVTM	Cessna F.150H	K. A. Learmonth	
G–AVTN	Cessna F.150H	I. R. Hamilton	
G–AVTO	Cessna F.150H	Norfolk & Norwich Aero Club Ltd.	
G–AVTP	Cessna F.172H	Western Air Training Ltd.	
G–AVTS	PA-23 Aztec 250	Bristol Air Taxis Ltd.	
G–AVTT	Ercoupe 415D	A. H. Cullimore	
G–AVTV	M.S.893 Rallye Commodore	A. Lister	
G–AVTX	Taylor Monoplane	P. Lockwood	
G–AVUA	Cessna F.172A	P. Blamire	
G–AVUD	PA-30 Twin Comanche	F. M. Aviation	
G–AVUF	Cessna F.172A	Rogers Aviation Ltd.	
G–AVUG	Cessna F.150H	Hornet Aviation Ltd.	
G–AVUH	Cessna F.150H	Cadby Engineering Ltd.	
G–AVUI	Cessna F.150H	Peter S. King (Aviation) Ltd.	
G–AVUJ	F.8L Falco 4	E. Dawson	
G–AVUK	Enstrom F-28	G. A. Dommett	
G–AVUL	Cessna F.172A	J. A. Blythe, D. R. Calo & D. H. Stephens	
G–AVUM	Hughes 296B	P. Berriman	
G–AVUN	PA-30 Twin Comanche	Overseas Aero Leasing	
G–AVUS	PA-28 Cherokee	T. H. Conway & R. F. Fox	
G–AVUT	PA-28 Cherokee	Shackleton Aviation Ltd.	
G–AVUU	PA-28 Cherokee	Goodwood Estate Co. Ltd.	
G–AVUV	Cessna 310N	Airwork Services Ltd.	
G–AVUX	Cessna F.172A	Steel Plant Services (Rotherham) Ltd.	
G–AVUZ	PA-32 Cherokee Six 300	Willow Vale Electronics Ltd.	
G–AVVB	H.S.125 Srs. 3B	Beecham-Imperial Aviation Ltd.	
G–AVVC	Cessna F.172H	T. G. Fielding	

Registration	Type	Owner or Operator	Where and when seen
G–AVVE	Cessna F.150H	J. A. Bassett & ptnrs.	
G–AVVF	D.H.104 Dove 8	Martin Baker (Engineers) Ltd.	
G–AVVG	PA-28 Cherokee 180	604 Squadron Flying Club	
G–AVVI	PA-30 Twin Comanche	W. Linskill	
G–AVVJ	M.S.893 Rallye Commodore	F. A. O. Gaze	
G–AVVL	Cessna F.150H	Urban Airways Ltd.	
G–AVVM	Jodel D.117	J. G. Hornsby, D. Potter, R. Pine, J. M. Arthurs, J. W. Hall & E. Donnelly	
G–AVVN	D.62C Condor	H.N. Jones	
G–AVVO	Avro 652A Anson 19 Srs. 2	Tippers Air Transport Ltd.	
G–AVVS	Hughes 269B	W. Holmes	
G–AVVT	PA-23 Aztec 250	Western Air Training Ltd.	
G–AVVU	Beech A.23A Musketeer	Oldcastle Aviation Ltd.	
G–AVVV	PA-28 Cherokee 180	J. M. Henderson	
G–AVVW	Cessna F.150H	Bristol & Wessex Aeroplane Club Ltd.	
G–AVVX	Cessna F.150H	R. B. Sandell & Co. Ltd.	
G–AVVY	Cessna F.150H	J. Turnbull	
G–AVVZ	Cessna F.172H	Travel Centre (Norwich) Ltd.	
G–AVWA	PA-28 Cherokee 140	Syrod Aviation Services Ltd.	
G–AVWB	PA-28 Cherokee 140	Surrey & Kent Flying Club Ltd.	
G–AVWD	PA-28 Cherokee 140	Apache Aircraft Services	
G–AVWE	PA-28 Cherokee 140	W. C. C. Meyer	
G–AVWF	PA-28 Cherokee 140	Liverpool Aero Club Ltd.	
G–AVWG	PA-28 Cherokee 140	W. B. Bateson	
G–AVWH	PA-28 Cherokee 140	Rimmer Aviation	
G–AVWI	PA-28 Cherokee 140	J. C. Smith & Miss L. M. Veitch	
G–AVWJ	PA-28 Cherokee 140	E.F.G. Flying Services Ltd.	
G–AVWL	PA-28 Cherokee 140	Dovecraft Ltd.	
G–AVWM	PA-28 Cherokee 140	B.L.S. Aviation Ltd.	
G–AVWN	PA-28R Cherokee Arrow	Berna Industries Ltd.	
G–AVWO	PA-28R Cherokee Arrow	Jackson Aviation Ltd.	
G–AVWR	PA-28R Cherokee Arrow	Mono-Construction Ltd.	
G–AVWT	PA-28R Cherokee Arrow	Unibrass Holdings Ltd.	
G–AVWU	PA-28R Cherokee Arrow	Delta Aviation Ltd.	
G–AVWV	PA-28R Cherokee Arrow	Mapair Ltd.	
G–AVWW	Mooney M.20F	A. & J. & G. Cullen	
G–AVWY	Fournier RF.4D	T. G. Hoult	
G–AVWZ	Fournier RF.4D	Lazenby Garages Ltd.	
G–AVXA	PA-25 Pawnee 235	W. P. Miller	
G–AVXC	Nipper T.66 Srs. 3	W. G. Wells, R. R. Lockwood & P. A. J. Winney	
G–AVXD	Nipper T.66 Srs. 3	S. Russell	
G–AVXF	PA-28R Cherokee Arrow	Allzones Travel Ltd.	
G–AVXG	Luton LA.5 Major	R. G. Kellett	
G–AVXI	H.S.748 Srs. 2	Civil Aviation Authority	
G–AVXJ	H.S.748 Srs. 2	Civil Aviation Authority	
G–AVXK	H.S.125 Srs. 3B-RA	Shell Aircraft Ltd.	
G–AVXL	H.S. 125 Srs. 3B	McAlpine Aviation Ltd.	
G–AVXV	Bleriot XI	L. D. Goldsmith	
G–AVXW	D.62B Condor	N. H. Jones	
G–AVXX	Cessna FR. 172E	J. F. McClory, W. K. Haggie & H. Sadler	
G–AVXY	Auster AOP.9	R. J. Moody	
G–AVYB	H.S.121 Trident 1E-140	Northeast Airlines	
G–AVYC	H.S.121 Trident 1E-110	Northeast Airlines	
G–AVYD	H.S.121 Trident 1E-110	Northeast Airlines	
G–AVYE	H.S.121 Trident 1E-140	Northeast Airlines	
G–AVYF	Beech A.23-24 Musketeer	Guernsey Flying Group Ltd.	
G–AVYK	A.61 Terrier 3	F. Pickett	
G–AVYL	PA-28 Cherokee 180	P. T. Johnson	
G–AVYM	PA-28 Cherokee 180	L. Wood & A. G. Watson	
G–AVYO	PA-28 Cherokee 140	Goodwood Estate Co. Ltd.	
G–AVYP	PA-28 Cherokee 140	Enniskillen Flying Club	
G–AVYR	PA-28 Cherokee 140	B.L.S. Aviation Ltd.	
G–AVYS	PA-28R Cherokee Arrow	G. Montague (Southern) Ltd.	
G–AVYT	PA-28R Cherokee Arrow	Business Flying Group	
G–AVYU	A.61 Terrier 3	J. A. Simms	

Registration	Type	Owner or Operator	Where and when seen
G–AVYV	Jodel D.120	J. B. J. Berrow	
G–AVYW	Brookland Mosquito II	E. Brooks	
G–AVYX	Agusta-Bell 206 JetRanger	S.W. Electricity Board	
G–AVYZ	BAC One-Eleven 320L	Laker Airways	
G–AVZA	IMCO Callair A-9	Arable & Bulb Chemicals Ltd.	
G–AVZB	Aero Z-37 Cmelak	ADS (Aerial) Ltd.	
G–AVZC	Hughes 269	Twyford Moors (Helicopters) Ltd.	
G–AVZE	Druine D.62B Condor	N. H. Jones	
G–AVZF	Bell 47G-2	Autair International Ltd.	
G–AVZG	AB 206A JetRanger	Ben Turner & Sons (Helicopters) Ltd.	
G–AVZI	Bo 208C Junior	C. F. Rogers	
G–AVZM	Beagle B.121 Pup 1	ARAZ Group	
G–AVZN	Beagle B.121 Pup 1	G. H. & Mrs. T. Willson	
G–AVZO	Beagle B.121 Pup 1	Ferryfield School of Flying	
G–AVZP	Beagle B.121 Pup 1	Brooklands Aviation Ltd.	
G–AVZR	PA-28 Cherokee 180	G. Knowles & ptnrs.	
G–AVZS	Cessna 310B	Jax Garage Ltd.	
G–AVZT	PA-31 Navajo	Cabair Ltd.	
G–AVZU	Cessna F.150H	Continental Cars (Stansted) Ltd.	
G–AVZV	Cessna F.172H	Oldment Ltd.	
G–AVZW	EAA Model P Biplane	R. G. Mainment & G. R. Edmundson	
G–AVZX	M.S.880B Rallye Club	L. Clutton & ptnrs.	
G–AVZY	M.S.880B Rallye Club	M. H. Dooher & J. H. Morgan	
G–AVZZ	Boeing 707-138B	Laker Airways	
G–AWAA	M.S.880B Rallye Club	Miss R. M. M. Ross	
G–AWAC	Gardan GY-80 Horizon 180	P. J. Collis & A. E. Chapman	
G–AWAD	Beech D 55 Baron	College of Air Training	
G–AWAE	Beech D 55 Baron	College of Air Training	
G–AWAF	Beech D 55 Baron	College of Air Training	
G–AWAG	Beech D 55 Baron	College of Air Training	
G–AWAH	Beech D 55 Baron	College of Air Training	
G–AWAI	Beech D 55 Baron	College of Air Training	
G–AWAJ	Beech D 55 Baron	College of Air Training	
G–AWAK	Beech D 55 Baron	College of Air Training	
G–AWAL	Beech D 55 Baron	College of Air Training	
G–AWAM	Beech D 55 Baron	College of Air Training	
G–AWAN	Beech D 55 Baron	College of Air Training	
G–AWAO	Beech D 55 Baron	College of Air Training	
G–AWAP	Sud SE 3180 Alouette III	Helicopter Hire Ltd.	
G–AWAT	Druine D.62B Condor	N. H. Jones	
G–AWAU	*Vickers F.B.27A Vimy (replica) (F8614)	RAF Museum	
G–AWAV	Cessna F.150F	Ipswich School of Flying	
G–AWAW	Cessna F.150F	Herefordshire Aero Club Ltd.	
G–AWAX	Cessna 150D	Dr. E. W. Duck	
G–AWAZ	PA-28R Cherokee Arrow 180	Gill Aviation Ltd.	
G–AWBA	PA-28R Cherokee Arrow 180	The Viscount Bledisloe	
G–AWBB	PA-28R Cherokee Arrow 180	Lt. Col. G. L. Wathen	
G–AWBC	PA-28R Cherokee Arrow 180	Eric Thurston Group Management Co. Ltd.	
G–AWBD	PA-28 Cherokee 140	Mossair Ltd.	
G–AWBE	PA-28 Cherokee 140	H. Gill	
G–AWBG	PA-28 Cherokee 140	Waltham Publications Ltd.	
G–AWBH	PA-28 Cherokee 140	Southend Light Aviation Centre Ltd.	
G–AWBJ	Fournier RF.4D	R. J. Hardy	
G–AWBK	Cessna 421	Northair Aviation Ltd.	
G–AWBL	BAC One-Eleven 416	Cambrian Airways	
G–AWBM	Druine D.31 Turbulent	W. B. Gunn & W. B. Paige	

* Preserved in non-flying condition.

Registration	Type	Owner or Operator	Where and when seen
G–AWBN	PA-30 Twin Comanche 160	Stourfield Investments Ltd.	
G–AWBP	Cessna 182L	R. Q. Whiteman & H. J. Walker	
G–AWBS	PA-28 Cherokee 140	West London Aero Services Ltd.	
G–AWBT	PA-30 Twin Comanche 160	C.S.E. (Aircraft Services) Ltd.	
G–AWBU	Morane-Saulnier N (replica)	Personal Plane Services Ltd.	
G–AWBV	Cessna 182L	J. O. Wilson & A. A. Hunter	
G–AWBX	Cessna F.150H	Western Air Training Ltd.	
G–AWCD	DR.253 Regent	M. L. Desoutter & Scoba Ltd.	
G–AWCH	Cessna F.172H	M. Bua	
G–AWCJ	Cessna F.150H	Wycombe Air Centre Ltd.	
G–AWCK	Cessna F.150H	Wycombe Air Centre Ltd.	
G–AWCL	Cessna F.150H	Strathspey Aviation Co. Ltd.	
G–AWCM	Cessna F.150H	Peterborough Aero Club Ltd.	
G–AWCN	Cessna FR.172E	LEC Refrigeration Ltd.	
G–AWCO	Cessna F.150H	K. A. Learmonth	
G–AWCP	Cessna F.150H	Herefordshire Aero Club Ltd.	
G–AWCR	Piccard Ax6 Balloon	The London Balloon Club	
G–AWCW	Beech E.95 Travel Air	H. W. Astor	
G–AWCX	PA-32 Cherokee Six 260	G.T.E. Aviation Ltd.	
G–AWCY	PA-32 Cherokee Six 260	Mrs. D. & C. R. Whyham	
G–AWCZ	PA-32 Cherokee Six 260	K. A. Learmonth	
G–AWDA	Nipper T.66 Srs. 3	C. T. Storey & ptnrs.	
G–AWDD	Nipper T.66 Srs. 3	T. R. Whitlam	
G–AWDG	Boeing 707-138B	Laker Airways	
G–AWDH	D.31 Turbulent	J. H. Tetley	
G–AWDI	PA-23 Aztec 250	Luton Flying Club Ltd.	
G–AWDJ	Cessna 411	Dr. M. A. Hession	
G–AWDK	Canadair CL-44D4	Tradewinds Airways Ltd.	
G–AWDL	PA-25 Pawnee 235	Peter Charles (Airfarmers) Ltd.	
G–AWDO	D.31 Turbulent	R. Watling-Greenwood	
G–AWDP	PA-28 Cherokee 180	J. R. Thursby & M. W. Priest	
G–AWDR	Cessna FR.172E	Largoair Ltd.	
G–AWDU	Brantly B.2B	A. & B. Car (Distributors) Ltd.	
G–AWDW	Bensen B.8 Gyro-Copter	M. R. Langton	
G–AWDX	Beagle B.121 Pup 1	W. M. Beverley	
G–AWDZ	Beagle B.121 Pup 1	L. M. Harper	
G–AWED	PA-31 Navajo	Whitbread & Co. Ltd.	
G–AWEF	Stampe SV.4B	N. H. Jones	
G–AWEG	Cessna 172G	A. D. Watt	
G–AWEI	D.62B Condor	N. H. Jones	
G–AWEK	Fournier RF.4D	M. R. Carlton	
G–AWEL	Fournier RF.4D	A. B. Clymo	
G–AWEM	Fournier RF.4D	B. J. Griffin	
G–AWEN	Jodel DR.1050	J. A. Bray & R. J. W. Wood	
G–AWEO	Cessna F.150H	Sir W. G. Armstrong Whitworth Flying Group	
G–AWEP	GY-20 Minicab	F. S. Jackson	
G–AWER	PA-23 Aztec 250	Woodgate Aviation	
G–AWES	Cessna 150G	Lowland Aero Service Co. Ltd.	
G–AWET	PA-28 Cherokee 180	Zitair Flying Club Ltd.	
G–AWEU	PA-28 Cherokee 140	Liverpool Aero Club Ltd.	
G–AWEV	PA-28 Cherokee 140	Glasgow Air Services Ltd.	
G–AWEX	PA-28 Cherokee 140	K. Fletcher	
G–AWEZ	PA-28R Cherokee Arrow 180	Diagnostic Reagents Ltd.	
G–AWFB	PA-28R Cherokee Arrow 180	Luke Aviation Ltd.	
G–AWFC	PA-28R Cherokee Arrow 180	B. R. Le Marquand & F. H. Walker	
G–AWFD	PA-28R Cherokee Arrow 180	J. E. Fricker & G. H. A. Bird	
G–AWFE	Jodel D.140E	Airscooters Ltd.	
G–AWFF	Cessna F.150H	Herefordshire Aero Club Ltd.	
G–AWFH	Cessna F.150H	Norfolk & Norwich Aero Club Ltd.	
G–AWFI	PA-30 Twin Comanche 160	Edinburgh Flying Services Ltd.	

Registration	Type	Owner or Operator	Where and when seen
G–AWFJ	PA-28R Cherokee Arrow 180	H. W. Preiskel & P. Gardner	
G–AWFK	PA-28R Cherokee Arrow 180	J. A. Rundle (Holdings) Ltd.	
G–AWFM	D.H.104 Dove 6	Fairflight Charters Ltd.	
G–AWFN	D.62B Condor	N. H. Jones	
G–AWFO	D.62B Condor	N. H. Jones	
G–AWFP	D.62B Condor	N. H. Jones	
G–AWFR	D.31 Turbulent	S. W. Usherwood	
G–AWFT	Jodel D.9 Bebe	W. H. Cole	
G–AWFW	Jodel D.117	F. H. Greenwell	
G–AWFX	Sikorsky S-61N	BAH	
G–AWFY	SA.318C Alouette Astazou	Dean Aviation Ltd. & BEAS Ltd.	
G–AWFZ	Beech A23-19A Musketeer	R. Sweet & B. D. Corbett	
G–AWGA	A.109 Airedale	A. P. Chapman & S. L. & D. Coates	
G–AWGC	Cessna F.172H	Surrey & Kent Flying Club Ltd.	
G–AWGD	Cessna F.172H	A. A. Mattacks	
G–AWGE	Cessna F.172H	R. A. Gray	
G–AWGJ	Cessna F.172H	J. Freeman & C. J. Freeman	
G–AWGK	Cessna F.150H	BBC Club	
G–AWGM	Mitchell-Proctor Kittiwake 2	Arkle Research & Development	
G–AWGN	Fournier RF.4D	Sportair Flying Club	
G–AWGP	Cessna T210N	R. Woods & ptnrs.	
G–AWGR	Cessna F.172H	P. Bushell	
G–AWGS	Canadair CL-44-D4	Tradewinds Airways Ltd.	
G–AWGT	Canadair CL-44-D4	Tradewinds Airways Ltd.	
G–AWGU	Agusta-Bell 206A JetRanger II	BAH	
G–AWGW	Cessna F.172H	James Fieldhouse Plastics	
G–AWGX	Cessna F.172H	Aberdeen Aero Club	
G–AWGY	Cessna F.172H	G. B. & F. N. Claridge	
G–AWGZ	Taylor Monoplane	J. Morris	
G–AWHB	*CASA 2.111 (6J+PR)	Historic Aircraft Museum	
G–AWHF	Hispano HA-1112-MIL	Spitfire Productions Ltd.	
G–AWHU	Boeing 707-379C	British Airways	
G–AWHV	Rollason Beta B.2	Rollason Aircraft & Engines Ltd.	
G–AWHW	Rollason Beta B.4	C. E. Bellhouse	
G–AWHX	Rollason Beta B.2	Rollason Aircraft & Engines Ltd.	
G–AWHY	Falconair F-11-3	W. M. Greenwood	
G–AWIF	Brookland Mosquito	L. Chiappi	
G–AWIG	Jodel D.112	P. Cawkwell & G. Firth	
G–AWIH	Mooney M.20C Ranger	J. E. Dixon	
G–AWII	V.S. Spitfire Vc (AR501)	Shuttleworth Trust	
G–AWIJ	V.S. Spitfire IIIA (P7350)	RAF Museum	
G–AWIK	Beech 23 Musketeer	D. J. Bateman	
G–AWIN	Campbell-Bensen B.8MC	M. J. Cuttell & J. Deane	
G–AWIO	Brantly B.2B	G. J. Ward & E. J. Roche	
G–AWIP	Luton L.A.4a Minor	J. G. Plews & K. P. Ricketts	
G–AWIR	Midget Mustang	A. F. Jarman & K. E. Sword	
G–AWIT	PA-28 Cherokee 180	South Lodge Flying Group	
G–AWIV	Storey TSR.3	T. M. Storey	
G–AWIW	Stampe SV.4B	Rothmans Aerobatic Team	
G–AWIX	PA-30 Twin Comanche 160	T. D. Keegan	
G–AWIY	PA-23 Aztec 250	Northern Executive Aviation Ltd.	
G–AWJA	Cessna 182L	L. Berney	
G–AWJC	Free Balloon (gas)	P. D. Furlong	
G–AWJD	Campbell-Bensen B.8M	Campbell Aircraft Ltd.	
G–AWJE	Nipper T.66 Srs. 3	N. H. Jones	
G–AWJF	Nipper T.66 Srs. 3	D. Shrimpton	
G–AWJH	Nipper T.66 Srs. 3	K. A. Learmonth	
G–AWJI	M.S.880B Rallye Club	Thames Estuary Flying Services	
G–AWJK	M.S.880B Rallye Club	J. Berry	
G–AWJN	Tigercraft Tiger Mk. II	Frederick Fewsdale	

*Preserved in non-flying condition.

Registration	Type	Owner or Operator	Where and when seen
G–AWJO	Tigercraft Tiger Mk. II	Frederick Fewsdale	
G–AWJP	Tigercraft Tiger Mk. III	Frederick Fewsdale	
G–AWJR	Tigercraft Tiger Mk. I	Frederick Fewsdale	
G–AWJS	Tigercraft Mosquito Mk. I	Frederick Fewsdale	
G–AWJT	Tigercraft Tiger Mk. I	J. H. Turner	
G–AWJV	*D.H.98 Mosquito TT Mk. 35 (TA634)	Hawker Siddeley	
G–AWJW	Agusta-Bell 206B JetRanger II	Ferranti Helicopters Ltd.	
G–AWJX	Z.526 Akrobat	Aerobatics International Ltd.	
G–AWJY	Z.526 Akrobat	Ello Manufacturing Co.	
G–AWJZ	Cessna F.150H	Firm Flights Co. Ltd.	
G–AWKB	M.J.5 Sirocco F.2 39	G. D. Claseton	
G–AWKC	Hughes 269B	Shackleton Aviation Ltd.	
G–AWKD	Piper PA-17 Vagabond	A. Corran & A. T. Dowie	
G–AWKE	Cessna 337C Skymaster	Ewart & Co. (Studio) Ltd.	
G–AWKF	PA-30 Twin Commanche 160	Gill Aviation Ltd.	
G–AWKG	Hiller UH-12B	Stewarts Construction Equipment Ltd.	
G–AWKN	B.121 Pup I	Aerosport Ltd.	
G–AWKO	B.121 Pup I	East Air Travel Ltd.	
G–AWKP	Jodel DR.253 Regent	R. C. Chandless	
G–AWKS	M.S.880B Rallye Club	Colthorpe Group Services	
G–AWKT	M.S.880B Rallye Club	D. C. Strain	
G–AWKW	PA-24 Comanche 180	J. & T. M. Greeves Ltd.	
G–AWKX	Beech A65 Queen Air	Vernair Transport Services	
G–AWKZ	PA-23 Apache 160	E. A. Clack & T. Pritchard	
G–AWLA	Cessna F.150H	J. W. Erswell	
G–AWLB	Druine Turbulent	A. E. Shoulder	
G–AWLE	Cessna F.172H	G. A. Bamborough Ltd.	
G–AWLF	Cessna F.172H	Fairey Britten-Norman Air Services Ltd.	
G–AWLG	SIPA 903	T. G. Turner	
G–AWLJ	Cessna F.150H	A. R. Ashley	
G–AWLL	Agusta-Bell 206A JetRanger	Dickson Motors (Perth) Ltd.	
G–AWLM	Bensen B.8MS	G. & G. D. Ward	
G–AWLP	Mooney M.20F	Siminco Ltd.	
G–AWLR	Nipper T.66 Srs. 3	J. D. Lowther	
G–AWLS	Nipper T.66 Srs. 3	R. E. R. Wilks & W. Wells	
G–AWLW	Hawker Hurricane IIB (P3308)	Strathallan Collection	
G–AWLY	Cessna F.150H	Coventry (Civil) Aviation Ltd.	
G–AWLZ	Fournier RF.4D	J. Edge	
G–AWMA	PA-25 Pawnee 235	Miller Aerial Spraying Co.	
G–AWMC	Campbell-Bensen B.8M2	M. E. Sykes Hankinson	
G–AWMD	Jodel D.11	D. A. Lord	
G–AWMF	PA-18 Super Cub	Airways Aero Association Ltd.	
G–AWMI	Glos-Airtourer 115	Bernell Aviation Ltd.	
G–AWMJ	Cessna F.172H	Gold Star Publications Ltd.	
G–AWMM	M.S.893A Rallye Commodore 180	G. Nixon	
G–AWMN	Luton L.A.4a Minor	R. E. R. Wilks	
G–AWMP	Cessna F.172H	Leicestershire Aero Club Ltd.	
G–AWMR	Druine D.31 Turbulent	S. J. Hargreaves	
G–AWMS	H.S.125 Srs. 3B	Rio Tinto Zinc Services Ltd.	
G–AWMT	Cessna F.150H	Cheshire Air Training School Ltd.	
G–AWMU	Cessna F.172H	C. J. Leonard	
G–AWMZ	Cessna F.172H	Security Centres (UK) Ltd.	
G–AWNA	Boeing 747-36	British Airways	
G–AWNB	Boeing 747-36	British Airways	
G–AWNC	Boeing 747-36	British Airways	
G–AWND	Boeing 747-36	British Airways	
G–AWNE	Boeing 747-36	British Airways	
G–AWNF	Boeing 747-36	British Airways	
G–AWNG	Boeing 747-36	British Airways	

* Preserved in non-flying condition.

Registration	Type	Owner or Operator	Where and when seen
G–AWNH	Boeing 747-36	British Airways	
G–AWNI	Boeing 747-36	British Airways	
G–AWNJ	Boeing 747-36	British Airways	
G–AWNK	Boeing 747-36	British Airways	
G–AWNL	Boeing 747-36	British Airways	
G–AWNM	Boeing 747-36	British Airways	
G–AWNN	Boeing 747-36	British Airways	
G–AWNO	Boeing 747-36	British Airways	
G–AWNP	Boeing 747-36	British Airways	
G–AWNR	BN-2A Islander	Loganair Ltd.	
G–AWNT	BN-2A Islander	Survey Flights Ltd.	
G–AWNU	BN-2A Islander	Herts and Essex Aero Club (1946) Ltd.	
G–AWOA	M.S.880B Rallye Club	Oakley Motor Units Ltd.	
G–AWOB	M.S.880B Rallye Club	T. G. H. Stakes	
G–AWOE	Aero Commander 680E	Elstree Flying Club	
G–AWOF	PA-15 Vagabond	Dr. D. A. Jones	
G–AWOH	PA-17 Vagabond	J. K. Jones	
G–AWOJ	Cessna F.172H	Wycombe Air Centre Ltd.	
G–AWOK	Free Balloon (gas)	University of Sussex Ballooning Society	
G–AWOL	Bell 206A JetRanger	Darmead Ltd.	
G–AWOT	Cessna F.150H	Cadby Engineering Ltd.	
G–AWOU	Cessna 170B	North Denes Aerodrome	
G–AWOV	Canadair CL-44D	Tradewinds Airways Ltd.	
G–AWOW	PA-31 Navajo	Bristol Air Taxis Ltd.	
G–AWOX	Wessex 60 Srs. I	Bristow Helicopters Ltd.	
G–AWPA	D.31A Turbulent	Usworth Flying Group	
G–AWPG	Z.526 Akrobat	H. Foulds	
G–AWPH	P.56 Provost T Mk. I	J. A. D. Bradshaw	
G–AWPJ	Cessna F.150H	Parker (Farms)	
G–AWPK	PA-23 Aztec 250	Vernair Transport Services	
G–AWPL	Bensen B-8	N. F. Higgins	
G–AWPM	Beech A.90 King Air	Eagle Aircraft Services	
G–AWPN	Shield Xyla	G. W. Shield	
G–AWPP	Cessna F.150H	Urban Airways Ltd.	
G–AWPS	PA-28 Cherokee 140	Miles Dufon Ltd.	
G–AWPU	Cessna F.150J	Light Planes (Lancashire) Ltd.	
G–AWPV	Cessna F.172H	Northwest Flying School	
G–AWPW	PA-12 Super Cruiser	P. Ligertwood	
G–AWPX	Cessna 150E	W. R. Emberton	
G–AWPY	Bensen B.8M	J. M. Deane	
G–AWPZ	Andreasson BA-4B	S. E. & P. J. C. Phillips	
G–AWRB	Beagle B.121 Pup I	P. O. P. Pulvermacher	
G–AWRI	Bell 206 JetRanger	Trident Management Ltd.	
G–AWRJ	Cessna 421	Shackleton Aviation Ltd. & Aslav (Engineering) Ltd.	
G–AWRK	Cessna F.150J	Civil Services Flying Club	
G–AWRL	Cessna F.172H	Vectaphone	
G–AWRM	Beagle B.206 Srs. 2	Jersey Fisheries Ltd.	
G–AWRO	Beagle B.206 Srs. 2	E. Crabtree	
G–AWRP	Grasshopper CR.LBH-I	Cierva Rotorcraft Ltd.	
G–AWRS	Avro 19 Srs. 2 (TX213)	Strathallan Collection	
G–AWRT	Glos-Airtourer 115	Hollybush Investments Ltd.	
G–AWRV	Bell 206 JetRanger	W. L. Howes (Contractors) Ltd.	
G–AWRW	B.121 Pup Srs. 2	Vaughan Association Ltd.	
G–AWRZ	Bell 47G-5	Yellow Bird Air Services Ltd.	
G–AWSD	Cessna F.150	W. G. R. Wunderlich	
G–AWSF	Cessna 401	Con-Mech Engineers Ltd.	
G–AWSH	Z.526 Akrobat	Aerobatics International Ltd.	
G–AWSJ	Agusta-Bell 47G-2	Alan Mann Helicopters Ltd.	
G–AWSK	Agusta-Bell 47G-2	Bristow Helicopters Ltd.	
G–AWSL	PA-28 Cherokee 180D	Fascia Ltd.	
G–AWSM	PA-28 Cherokee 235	C.S.E. Aviation Ltd.	
G–AWSN	D.62B Condor	N. H. Jones	
G–AWSO	D.62B Condor	N. H. Jones	
G–AWSP	D.62B Condor	N. H. Jones	
G–AWSR	D.62B Condor	N. H. Jones	
G–AWSS	D.62B Condor	N. H. Jones	
G–AWST	D.62B Condor	South Yorks Flying Club	

Registration	Type	Owner or Operator	Where and when seen
G—AWSU	F.8L Falco Srs. 4	G. W. Connolly & M. Slazenger	
G—AWSV	Skeeter 12 (XM553)	Maj. M. Somerton-Rayner	
G—AWSX	Scheibe SF-27M	Gordon & T. S. L. Mackie	
G—AWSY	Boeing 737-204	Britannia Airways Ltd.	
G—AWSZ	M.S.894A Rallye Minerva 220	M. J. Powell	
G—AWTA	Cessna 310N	David Berry (Bonded) Ltd.	
G—AWTJ	Cessna F.150J	Shemain Ltd.	
G—AWTL	PA-28 Cherokee 180D	Leston Aviation	
G—AWTM	PA-28 Cherokee 140	Richard Flint Publicity Ltd.	
G—AWTR	Beech A.23-19A Musketeer	M. W. Robinson	
G—AWTT	Beech A.23-19A Musketeer	Spencer Aviation Ltd.	
G—AWTV	Beech A.23-19A Musketeer	D. J. Chapman	
G—AWTW	Beech B.55 Baron	Forecourt Services Ltd.	
G—AWTX	Cessna F.150J	Tango X Flying Group	
G—AWUA	Cessna P.206D	G. B. Grant & Sons (Farmers) Ltd.	
G—AWUB	GY.20 Minicab	H. P. Burrill	
G—AWUE	Jodel DR. 1050	G. R. Fountain & D. F. Mann	
G—AWUF	H.S.125 Srs. 1B	Lamport & Holt Line Ltd.	
G—AWUG	Cessna F.150H	Norfolk & Norwich Aero Club Ltd.	
G—AWUH	Cessna F.150H	K. A. Learmonth	
G—AWUI	Cessna F.150H	Wells Chartair Ltd.	
G—AWUJ	Cessna F.150H	Learmonth Aviation Ltd.	
G—AWUL	Cessna F.150H	M. Cairns, W. Linskill and G. B. Pyle	
G—AWUM	Cessna F.150H	Western Air Training Ltd.	
G—AWUN	Cessna F.150H	K. A. Learmonth	
G—AWUO	Cessna F.150H	W. Todd	
G—AWUP	Cessna F.150H	Western Air Training Ltd.	
G—AWUR	Cessna F.150J	K. A. Learmonth	
G—AWUS	Cessna F.150J	Cheshire Air Training School	
G—AWUT	Cessna F.150J	Western Air Training Ltd.	
G—AWUU	Cessna F.150J	Woodgate Aviation Ltd.	
G—AWUV	Cessna F.150J	R. C. May	
G—AWUW	Cessna F.172H	Norfolk & Norwich Aero Club Ltd.	
G—AWUX	Cessna F.172H	Warm Air Ventilating & Engineering Ltd.	
G—AWUY	Cessna F.172H	D. Livesey	
G—AWUZ	Cessna F.172H	L. H. Norris	
G—AWVA	Cessna F.172H	E. V. & D. H. Aylott	
G—AWVB	Jodel D.117	Lynn A. Williams	
G—AWVC	B.121 Pup 1	Lincoln Aero Club Ltd.	
G—AWVE	Jodel DR.1050M.1	D. J. Leo, D. W. Morris & M. Jest	
G—AWVF	P.56 Provost T.1.	J. R. Walgate	
G—AWVH	Glos-Airtourer 115	Plessey (Southern) Flying Group	
G—AWVK	H.P.137 Jetstream	Decca Navigation Co. Ltd.	
G—AWVN	Aeronca 7AC Champion	Bowker Air Services	
G—AWVP	Gyroflight Hornet	Gyroflight Ltd.	
G—AWVR	Skyship non-rigid Airship	Skyships Ltd.	
G—AWVS	Cessna 337D	Cowick Hall Aviation Ltd.	
G—AWVY	BN-2A Islander	Brinsop Farms Ltd.	
G—AWVZ	Jodel D.112	D. O. A. Elmer	
G—AWWD	Boeing 707-349C	British Caledonian County of Argyle	
G—AWWE	B.121 Pup 2	Arkle R. & D.	
G—AWWF	B.121 Pup 1	Three Counties Aero Club Ltd.	
G—AWWI	Jodel D.117	J. H. Kirkham	
G—AWWK	Beech B90 King Air	Winster Engineering Ltd.	
G—AWWL	H.S.125 Srs. 3B-RA	McAlpine Aviation Ltd.	
G—AWWM	GY-201 Minicab	J. S. Bryshaw	
G—AWWN	DR 1051 Sicile	A. V. Orchard	
G—AWWO	DR 1050 Ambassadeur	W. Galley	
G—AWWP	Woody Pusher Mk. 1	M. S. Bird & Mrs. R. D. Bird	

LAAS
INTERNATIONAL

Making assumptions can be dangerous!

But we're going to assume, since you've bought Civil Aircraft Markings, that you are an enthusiast or spotter.

We're going to stick our necks out even further and assume that you'd like to be kept fully up to date every month on what is going on in the aviation world.

If we're right in both cases, then we think you'll be more than interested in LAAS International and our monthly journal, AVIATION NEWS and REVIEW.

Join LAAS International and you will receive 12 copies of our magazine each year. Every issue is packed with information and illustrated too. Regular features include International Register Review, Airlines and Operators, and we believe that in two sections—Touchdown and Ports of Call—we have the most comprehensive lists of airport movements and airfield news published in Britain today.

Members of LAAS receive other benefits too. These include:

sharply reduced prices for all our many other publications (registers and monographs).

the chance to travel with the Society to air shows throughout Britain and abroad.

the opportunity to join us on our exciting and ambitious excursions programme this year.

For all this, we only ask you to part with—

Membership fee including VAT	11p
Subscription to Aviation News and Review	£1·89
	£2·00

Doesn't that seem a small price to pay?

If despite all this you still need convincing further, then send 20p for a sample magazine.

Rates quoted at time of going to press.

Please send all remittances to:

LAAS INTERNATIONAL Dept C.76,
10 Devon Road,
Luton,
Beds LU2 0RH.

LAAS INTERNATIONAL—
Europe's largest aviation enthusiasts Society

G-ATHM. (Top) Wallis WA-116/F (60hp Franklin 2A-120) with underfuselage tank for long-distance record flights

G-AWOX. (Centre) Westland Wessex 60 (two 1,350shp Bristol Siddeley Gnome 660)/*Peter J. Bish*

G-AXNX. (Above) Cessna 182N Skylane (230hp Continental O-470-R) /*Austin J. Brown*

Registration	Type	Owner or Operator	Where and when seen
G–AWWT	D.31 Turbulent	F. S. Merriday	
G–AWWU	Cessna FR.172E	Dowdeswell Engineering Co. Ltd.	
G–AWWV	Cessna FR.172E	Mrs. B. D. Porter	
G–AWWW	Cessna 401	G. Myerson	
G–AWWX	BAC One-Eleven 509	Dan-Air Services Ltd.	
G–AWWZ	BAC One-Eleven 509	British Caledonian	Isle of Eriskay
G–AWXA	Cessna 182M	Rogers Aviation Ltd.	
G–AWXH	Cessna F.150H	V. Bernard	
G–AWXM	Cessna 401	Dalebridge Properties Ltd.	
G–AWXO	H.S.125 Srs. 400B	McAlpine Aviation Ltd.	
G–AWXR	PA-28 Cherokee 180D	J. D. Williams	
G–AWXS	PA-28 Cherokee 180D	Herefordshire Aero Club Ltd.	
G–AWXT	M.S.880B Rallye Club	P. H. Johnson	
G–AWXU	Cessna F.150J	Mona Aviation Ltd.	
G–AWXV	Cessna F.172H	Aero Associations Flying Group	
G–AWXW	PA-23 Aztec 250D	M. Darlington (Ongar) Ltd.	
G–AWXY	M.S.885 Super Rallye	J. & B. Fowler	
G–AWXZ	SNCAN SV-4C	Personal Planes Service Ltd.	
G–AWYB	Cessna FR.172E	C. W. Larkin	
G–AWYE	H.S.125 Srs. 1B	Rolls-Royce (1971) Ltd.	
G–AWYF	G.159 Gulfstream	Ford Motor Co. Ltd.	
G–AWYH	Aero Commander 200D	W. J. D. Roberts	
G–AWYJ	B.121 Pup 1	Cameron Rainwear Ltd.	
G–AWYL	Jodel DR.253 Regent	Clarville Ltd.	
G–AWYO	B.121 Pup 1	T. A. Cox & N. E. Goff	
G–AWYR	BAC One-Eleven 501	British Caledonian	Isle of Tiree
G–AWYS	BAC One-Eleven 501	British Caledonian	Isle of Bute
G–AWYT	BAC One-Eleven 501	British Caledonian	Isle of Barra
G–AWYU	BAC One-Eleven 501	British Caledonian	Isle of Colonsay
G–AWYV	BAC One-Eleven 501	British Caledonian	Isle of Harris
G–AWYX	M.S.880B Rallye Club	P. A. Crawford	
G–AWYY	Sopwith Camel replica	Universal Pictures Ltd.	
G–AWYZ	H.S.121 Trident Three	British Airways	
G–AWZA	H.S.121 Trident Three	British Airways	
G–AWZB	H.S.121 Trident Three	British Airways	
G–AWZC	H.S.121 Trident Three	British Airways	
G–AWZD	H.S.121 Trident Three	British Airways	
G–AWZE	H.S.121 Trident Three	British Airways	
G–AWZF	H.S.121 Trident Three	British Airways	
G–AWZG	H.S.121 Trident Three	British Airways	
G–AWZH	H.S.121 Trident Three	British Airways	
G–AWZI	H.S.121 Trident Three	British Airways	
G–AWZJ	H.S.121 Trident Three	British Airways	
G–AWZK	H.S.121 Trident Three	British Airways	
G–AWZL	H.S.121 Trident Three	British Airways	
G–AWZM	H.S.121 Trident Three	British Airways	
G–AWZN	H.S.121 Trident Three	British Airways	
G–AWZO	H.S.121 Trident Three	British Airways	
G–AWZP	H.S.121 Trident Three	British Airways	
G–AWZR	H.S.121 Trident Three	British Airways	
G–AWZS	H.S.121 Trident Three	British Airways	
G–AWZT	H.S.121 Trident Three	British Airways	
G–AWZU	H.S.121 Trident Three	British Airways	
G–AWZV	H.S.121 Trident Three	British Airways	
G–AWZW	H.S.121 Trident Three	British Airways	
G–AWZX	H.S.121 Trident Three	British Airways	
G–AWZZ	H.S.121 Trident Three	British Airways	
G–AXAA	Canadair CL-44D-4	Transmeridian Air Cargo Ltd.	
G–AXAB	PA-28 Cherokee 140	W. B. Bateson	
G–AXAH	SIAI-Marchetti F.260	The Hon. J. C. Baring	
G–AXAI	ATL.98 Carvair	British Air Ferries Ltd.	Fat Albert
G–AXAJ	Glos-Airtourer 150	E. N. Struys	
G–AXAK	M.S.880B Rallye Club	R. L. & Mrs. C. Stewart	
G–AXAN	D.H.82A Tiger Moth	A. J. Cheshire	
G–AXAO	Omega 56 Free Balloon	P. D. Furlong	
G–AXAS	Wallis WA-116T	K. H. Wallis	

49

Registration	Type	Owner or Operator	Where and when seen
G–AXAT	Jodel D.117A	G. R. French & J. H. Kimber	
G–AXAU	PA-30 Twin Comanche 160C	Shackleton Aviation Ltd.	
G–AXAV	PA-30 Twin Comanche 160C	Webster Aviation	
G–AXAW	Cessna 421A	British Steel Corporation	
G–AXAX	PA-23 Aztec 250D	Alexandra Aviation Ltd.	
G–AXAZ	PA-31 Navajo	Meridian Airmaps Ltd.	
G–AXBC	PA-32 Cherokee Six 300B	Valley Motors (Norwich) Ltd.	
G–AXBD	PA-25 Pawnee 235C	Farm Aviation Ltd.	
G–AXBG	Bensen B.8M	R. Curtis	
G–AXBH	Cessna F.172H	Wycombe Air Centre	
G–AXBJ	Cessna F.172H	Sussex Marine Aviation Charters Ltd.	
G–AXBU	Cessna FR. 172F	Sir P. Grant-Suttie	
G–AXBW	D.H.82A Tiger Moth (T5879)	R. Venning	
G–AXBY	Cessna 401A	H. A. Coward	
G–AXBZ	D.H.82A Tiger Moth	D. H. McWhir	
G–AXCA	PA-28R Cherokee Arrow 200	G. R. Brown	
G–AXCG	Jodel D.117	G. M. Jones & J. J. Pratt	
G–AXCJ	Beech A.23 Musketeer	D. D. Moss	
G–AXCK	BAC One-Eleven 401	Dan-Air Services Ltd.	
G–AXCL	M.S.880B Rallye Club	A. Cope & F. Ratcliffe	
G–AXCM	M.S.880B Rallye Club	Mid Wales Flying Group	
G–AXCN	M.S.880B Rallye Club	Severn Valley Auto Group	
G–AXCP	BAC One-Eleven 401	Dan-Air Services Ltd.	
G–AXCX	B.121 Pup 2	Executive Air	
G–AXCY	Jodel D.117	Dr. M. T. Moore	
G–AXCZ	Stampe SV-4C	D. Toms	
G–AXDB	Piper J3C-65 Cub	N. D. Norman	
G–AXDC	PA-23 Aztec 250D	Eastlease Ltd.	
G–AXDD	PA-31 Navajo 300	Tanmill Ltd.	
G–AXDE	Bensen B.8	T. J. Harwell	
G–AXDH	BN-2A Islander	Parachute Regiment Free Fall Club	
G–AXDI	Cessna F.172H	Jim Russell International Racing Drivers Ltd.	
G–AXDJ	Cessna F.150H	Wycombe Air Centre	
G–AXDK	Jodel DR.315 Petit Prince	Thomas Pay & Sons Ltd.	
G–AXDL	PA-30 Twin Comanche 160C	Northern Executive Aviation Ltd.	
G–AXDM	H.S.125 Srs. 400B	Wavertree Ltd.	
G–AXDN	BAC-Sud Concorde 01	D.T.I.	
G–AXDU	B.121 Pup 2	Deltair Ltd.	
G–AXDV	B.121 Pup 1	R. A. Chappell & B. J. Dunford	
G–AXDW	B.121 Pup 1	Cranfield Institute of Technology	
G–AXDX	Wassmer Jodel D 120	G. D. Pybus	
G–AXDY	Falconar F-11	G. K. Ellis	
G–AXDZ	Cassutt Racer Srs. 111M	E. P. Sadler	
G–AXEA	Cassutt Racer Srs. 111M	F. S. Gathercole	
G–AXEB	Cassutt Racer Srs. 111M	T. M. Storey	
G–AXEC	Cessna 182M	Miss M. J. Freeman	
G–AXED	PA-25 Pawnee 235	Bowker Air Services Ltd.	
G–AXEH	B.125 Srs. 1 Bulldog	Scottish Aviation (Bulldog) Ltd.	
G–AXEJ	Hughes 500	F. J. Wallis Ltd.	
G–AXEO	Scheibe SF.25B Falke	D. Collinson	
G–AXER	PA-30 Twin Comanche 160C	HPP Ltd.	
G–AXET	B.121 Pup 2	Dungenair Ltd.	
G–AXEU	B.121 Pup 2	T. Saveker Ltd.	
G–AXEV	B.121 Pup 2	J. A. Old	
G–AXEW	B.121 Pup 1	Surrey & Kent Flying Club Ltd.	
G–AXEX	B.121 Pup 1	Dr. W. P. Stevens & Mrs. S. J. Stevens	
G–AXFA	PA-23 Aztec 250D	Herts & Essex Aero Club	
G–AXFD	PA-25 Pawnee 235	Westwick Distributors Ltd.	

Registration	Type	Owner or Operator	Where and when seen
G–AXFE	Beech B.90 King Air	GKN Group Services Ltd.	
G–AXFF	Cessna A.188 Agwagon	Yellow Bird Air Services Ltd.	
G–AXFG	Cessna 337D Super Skymaster	Margate Motors Plant & Aircraft Hire Ltd.	
G–AXFH	D.H.114 Heron 1B	Peters Aviation Ltd.	
G–AXFK	Cessna F.172H	Skyfotos Ltd.	
G–AXFM	Servotec Grasshopper 3	Cierva Rotorcraft Ltd.	
G–AXFN	Jodel D.119	R. O. Harper	
G–AXGA	PA-18 Super Cub	Felthorpe Flying Group	
G–AXGC	M.S.880B Rallye Club	Berkshire Aviation Services Ltd.	
G–AXGD	M.S.880B Rallye Club	Kathleen Boutland, R. C. Smith & E. M. Fadyen	
G–AXGE	M.S.880B Rallye Club	P. D. Higgs	
G–AXGG	Cessna F.150J	Lowland Aero Services Co. Ltd.	
G–AXGJ	Cessna 337D Super Skymaster	This England Ltd.	
G–AXGO	Bell 206B JetRanger	Tradewinds Helicopters Ltd.	
G–AXGP	Piper J-3C-65 Cub	W. K. Butler	
G–AXGR	Luton L.A.4a Minor	R. Spall & D. W. Spall	
G–AXGS	D.62B Condor	N. H. Jones	
G–AXGU	D.62B Condor	N. H. Jones	
G–AXGV	D.62B Condor	N. H. Jones	
G–AXGW	Boeing 707-336C	British Airways	
G–AXGX	Boeing 707-336C	British Airways	
G–AXGZ	D.62B Condor	N. H. Jones	
G–AXHA	Cessna 337A Super Skymaster	Barman Industrial Developments	
G–AXHC	Stampe SV-4C	R. J. Guess	
G–AXHE	BN-2A Islander	Rhine Army Parachute Association	
G–AXHG	M.S.880B Rallye Club	Froggat Bower Ltd.	
G–AXHI	M.S.880B Rallye Club	J. Scott	
G–AXHO	B.121 Pup 2	Harvair Ltd.	
G–AXHP	Piper J3C-65 Cub	W. F. Barnes & P. W. Griffin	
G–AXHR	Piper J3C-65 Cub	D. R. Elphick	
G–AXHS	M.S.880B Rallye Club	M. E. Stone	
G–AXHT	M.S.880B Rallye Club	Air Touring Services Ltd.	
G–AXHV	Jodel D.117A	D. M. Cashmore & K. R. Payne	
G–AXHW	Agusta-Bell 47G-4	Autair Hellicopter Services Ltd.	
G–AXHX	H.S.892 Rallye Commodore	Lord Davies	
G–AXIA	B.121 Pup 1	Cranfield Institute of Technology	
G–AXID	B.121 Pup 2	Sussex Marine Aviation Charters	
G–AXIE	B.121 Pup 2	L. Whitehouse	
G–AXIF	B.121 Pup 2	Aerosport Ltd.	
G–AXIG	B.125 Bulldog 104	Scottish Aviation (Bulldog) Ltd.	
G–AXIH	Bu 133 Jungmeister	R. E. Legg	
G–AXIO	PA-28 Cherokee 140B	G. Montague (Southern) Ltd.	
G–AXIP	PA-28 Cherokee 140B	Pegasus School of Flying	
G–AXIR	PA-28 Cherokee 140B	Group 45	
G–AXIT	M.S.893A Rallye Commodore 180	J. Grehan	
G–AXIV	PA-23 Aztec 250D	Cabair Ltd.	
G–AXIW	Scheibe SF-25B Falke	Herefordshire Gliding Club Ltd.	
G–AXIX	Glos-Airtourer 150	Glos-Air Ltd.	
G–AXIY	Bird Gyrocopter	Gerald Bird	
G–AXJA	Omega 56 Free Balloon	Omega Aerostatics	
G–AXJB	Omega 84 Free Balloon	Hot-Air Group	
G–AXJH	B.121 Pup 2	Lapwing Flying Group	
G–AXJI	B.121 Pup 2	Southend Light Aviation Centre	
G–AXJJ	B.121 Pup 2	E. F. Orchard	
G–AXJK	BAC One-Eleven 501	British Caledonian Isle of Staffa	
G–AXJL	BAC One-Eleven 501	British Caledonian Isle of Mingulay	
G–AXJM	BAC One-Eleven 501	British Caledonian Isle of Islay	
G–AXJN	B.121 Pup 2	Toon Ghose Aviation Ltd.	
G–AXJO	B.121 Pup 2	Lowe (Paddock Wood) Ltd.	

Registration	Type	Owner or Operator	Where and when seen
G–AXJR	Scheibe SF-25B Falke	A. W. Gough	
G–AXJV	PA-28 Cherokee 140B	Border Piper Group Ltd.	
G–AXJW	PA-28 Cherokee 140B	G. I. Cooper	
G–AXJX	PA-28 Cherokee 140B	Apache Aircraft Services	
G–AXJY	Cessna U-206D Super Skywagon	A. I. Walgate & Son	
G–AXKB	BN-2A Islander	Loganair Ltd.	
G–AXKD	PA-23 Aztec 250D	Aviation Beauport	
G–AXKF	Bell 206A JetRanger	Bristow Helicopters	
			Golden Hind
G–AXKH	Luton L.A.4a Minor	M. E. Vaisey	
G–AXKI	Jodel D.9	P. L. Cyster	
G–AXKJ	Jodel D.9	B. G. Pleasance	
G–AXKK	Westland Bell 47G-4A	Bristow Helicopters Ltd.	
G–AXKL	Westland Bell 47G-4A	Bristow Helicopters Ltd.	
G–AXKM	Westland Bell 47G-4A	Bristow Helicopters Ltd.	
G–AXKN	Westland Bell 47G-4A	Bristow Helicopters Ltd.	
G–AXKO	Westland Bell 47G-4A	Bristow Helicopters Ltd.	
G–AXKR	Westland Bell 47G-4A	Bristow Helicopters Ltd.	
G–AXKS	Westland Bell 47G-4A	Bristow Helicopters Ltd.	
G–AXKT	Westland Bell 47G-4A	Bristow Helicopters Ltd.	
G–AXKU	Westland Bell 47G-4A	Bristow Helicopters Ltd.	
G–AXKV	Westland Bell 47G-4A	Bristow Helicopters Ltd.	
G–AXKW	Westland Bell 47G-4A	Bristow Helicopters Ltd.	
G–AXKX	Westland Bell 47G-4A	Bristow Helicopters Ltd.	
G–AXKY	Westland Bell 47G-4A	Bristow Helicopters Ltd.	
G–AXKZ	Westland Bell 47G-4A	Bristow Helicopters Ltd.	
G–AXLA	Westland Bell 47G-4A	Bristow Helicopters Ltd.	
G–AXLG	Cessna 310K	Smiths (Outdrives) Ltd.	
G–AXLI	Nipper T.66 RA.45 Srs. 3	C. J. L. Wilkinson	
G–AXLS	Jodel DR 105A	G. S. Claybourn	
G–AXLX	H.S.125 Srs. 400B	Turbo-Union Ltd.	
G–AXLZ	Piper PA-18 Super Cub 95	J. C. Quantrell	
G–AXMA	PA-24 Comanche 180	Tegrel Products Ltd.	
G–AXMB	Slingsby Motor Cadet	I. G. Smith	
G–AXMD	Omega Hot Air Balloon	Nimble Bread Ltd.	
G–AXMG	BAC One-Eleven 518	Lloyds Associated Air Leasing	
G–AXMM	Bell 206/A JetRanger	W. Holmes	
G–AXMN	Auster J/5B	I. R. F. Hammond	
G–AXMP	PA-28 Cherokee 180	Brent Aviation Ltd.	
G–AXMR	PA-31 Navajo 300	Burch (Engineering) Ltd.	
G–AXMS	PA-30 Twin Comanche	R. C. Simon & A. R. Wershat	
G–AXMT	Bu 133 Jungmeister	S. R. Flack	
G–AXMW	B.121 Pup 1	Surrey & Kent Flying Club Ltd.	
G–AXMX	B.121 Pup 2	Susan A. Jones	
G–AXMY	PA-30 Twin Comanche	Ringway Lighting Ltd.	
G–AXNB	Boeing 737-204	Britannia Airways Ltd.	
G–AXNC	Boeing 737-204	Britannia Airways Ltd.	
G–AXNI	Bu 133 Jungmeister	M. W. Stow	
G–AXNJ	Wassmer Jodel D.120	A. G. Thelwall &	
			G. R. Gladstone
G–AXNK	Cessna F.150J	Nona Aviation Ltd.	
G–AXNL	B.121 Pup 1	A. A. C. Dingle & ptnrs.	
G–AXNM	B.121 Pup 1	Gardner & White	
G–AXNN	B.121 Pup 2	Knights Aviation Ltd.	
G–AXNO	B.121 Pup 2	Richmond Optical Co. Ltd.	
G–AXNP	B.121 Pup 2	Executive Air	
G–AXNR	B.121 Pup 2	Audley End Developments Ltd.	
G–AXNS	B.121 Pup 2	R. Light, D. Bonsall & R. Gibbs	
G–AXNW	Nord SV-4C	M. J. Coburn &	
			C. C. G. Hughes
G–AXNX	Cessna 182N	Air Tows Ltd.	
G–AXNY	Fixter Pixie	J. van Geest	
G–AXNZ	Pitts S.1C Special	P. E. Cadbury	
G–AXOG	PA-23 Aztec 250D	R. W. Diggens	
G–AXOH	M.S.894 Rallye Minerva	Bristol Cars Ltd.	
G–AXOI	Jodel B.9	G. K. Penson & P. M. Bowden	
G–AXOJ	B.121 Pup 2	D. Pollard	
G–AXOL	Currie Wot	J. A. Espin	
G–AXOO	V.952 Vanguard	Invicta International	

Registration	Type	Owner or Operator	Where and when seen
G–AXOR	PA-28 Cherokee 180D	J. A. Butterfield & ptnrs.	
G–AXOS	M.S.894A Rallye Minerva	Hereford Farmplan Ltd.	
G–AXOT	M.S.893 Rallye Commodore 180	Col. J. F. Williams-Wynne	
G–AXOV	Beech B55A Baron	Pen Aviation Ltd.	
G–AXOW	PA-23 Aztec 250D	N. G. M. Williams	
G–AXOZ	B.121 Pup I	Morris & Hinton Transport	
G–AXPA	B.121 Pup I	Surrey & Kent Flying Club Ltd.	
G–AXPB	B.121 Pup I	D. Smith	
G–AXPD	B.121 Pup I	Surrey & Kent Flying Club Ltd.	
G–AXPF	Cessna F.150K	Pegasus Aviation Ltd.	
G–AXPG	Mignet HM-293	W. H. Cole	
G–AXPI	Cessna F172D	Oldham & Crowther (Spares) Ltd.	
G–AXPM	B.121 Pup I	D. Taylor	
G–AXPN	B.121 Pup 2	Starline Elms Coaches	
G–AXPT	SC.7 Skyvan Srs. 3M	Short Bros & Harland Ltd.	
G–AXPU	H.S.125 Srs. 3B/RA	McAlpine Aviation Ltd.	
G–AXPW	Nord SV-4C	Robinson Aircraft Ltd.	
G–AXRA	Campbell Cricket	Campbell Aircraft Ltd.	
G–AXRB	Campbell Cricket	J. C. P. Thomas	
G–AXRC	Campbell Cricket	E. N. Simmons	
G–AXRD	Campbell Cricket	Glyndwr Rees	
G–AXRK	Sprite 115	E. G. Thale	
G–AXRL	PA-28 Cherokee 160	A. T. Tyler	
G–AXRN	BN-2A Islander	Fairey Britten-Norman Air Services Ltd.	
G–AXRO	PA-30 Twin Comanche 160C	C.S.E. (Aircraft Services) Ltd.	
G–AXRP	Nord,SV-4C	M. D. Tweedie & ptnrs.	
G–AXRS	Boeing 707-355C	British Caledonian *County of Caithness*	
G–AXRT	Cessna FA.150	Peterborough Aero Club Ltd.	
G–AXRU	Cessna FA.150	Brymon Aviation Ltd.	
G–AXRX	Cessna Super-Skymaster 337D	Unimetrics Ltd.	
G–AXSC	B.121 Pup 2	Surrey & Kent Flying Club Ltd.	
G–AXSD	B.121 Pup 2	Cranfield Institute of Technology	
G–AXSF	Proctor Petrel	Proctor Aircraft Associates	
G–AXSG	PA-28 Cherokee 180	Shopshire Aero Club Ltd.	
G–AXSH	PA-28 Cherokee 140B	Brailey & Co. (Aviation) Ltd.	
G–AXSI	Cessna F.172H	Denham Flying Training School Ltd.	
G–AXSJ	Cessna FA.150	Staverton Flying School Ltd.	
G–AXSL	Cessna 310P	Time (Jersey) Ltd.	
G–AXSM	DR.1051 Sicile	C. Woods	
G–AXSP	PA-30 Twin Comanche 160C	Universal Computers Ltd.	
G–AXSR	Brantly B.2B	B.E.A.S. Ltd.	
G–AXSS	BN-2A Islander	Loganair Ltd.	
G–AXSV	Jodel DR.340 Major	Staverton Flying School Ltd.	
G–AXSW	Cessna FA.150	Lowland Aero Service Ltd.	
G–AXSX	Beech C.23 Musketeer	S. W. G. Bullen	
G–AXSZ	PA-28 Cherokee 140B	A. R. Powley	
G–AXTA	PA-28 Cherokee 140B	C.S.E. (Aircraft Services) Ltd.	
G–AXTB	PA-28 Cherokee 140B	Stapleford Flying Club	
G–AXTC	PA-28 Cherokee 140B	C.S.E. (Aircraft Services) Ltd.	
G–AXTD	PA-28 Cherokee 140B	G. H. Kilby	
G–AXTE	PA-28 Cherokee 140B	N. Clayton	
G–AXTF	PA-28 Cherokee 140B	Adserve Computing Ltd.	
G–AXTG	PA-28 Cherokee 140B	Shemain Ltd.	
G–AXTH	PA-28 Cherokee 140B	G. Montague (Southern) Ltd.	
G–AXTI	PA-28 Cherokee 140B	P. E. Eglington	
G–AXTJ	PA-28 Cherokee 140B	C.S.E. (Aircraft Services) Ltd.	
G–AXTK	PA-28 Cherokee 140B	EHB Aviation Group	
G–AXTL	PA-28 Cherokee 140B	A. Compagnone	
G–AXTM	PA-28 Cherokee 140B	H. Michael & R. J. Connolly	
G–AXTN	PA-28 Cherokee 140B	Shemain Ltd.	
G–AXTO	PA-24 Comanche 260C	Micro Metalsmiths Ltd.	
G–AXTP	PA-28 Cherokee 180	D. I. L. Butler	

Registration	Type	Owner or Operator	Where and when seen
G–AXTU	H.S.125 Srs. 400B	Bellway Holdings Ltd.	
G–AXTX	Jodel D.112	J. J. Penney	
G–AXUA	B.121 Pup I	F. R. Blennerhassett & ptnrs.	
G–AXUC	PA-12 Super Cruiser	V. N. Mukaloff	
G–AXUE	Jodel DR.105A	Carlton Flying Group	
G–AXUF	Cessna FA.150	Airwork Services Ltd.	
G–AXUI	H.P.137 Jetstream I	Cranfield Institute of Technology	
G–AXUJ	J/I Autocrat	R. G. Earp	
G–AXUK	Jodel DR.1050	P. A. Ellway & ptnrs.	
G–AXUL	Canadair CL-44D	Transmeridian Air Cargo Ltd.	
G–AXUM	H.P.137 Jetstream I	Cranfield Institute of Technology	
G–AXUV	Cessna F.172K	W. C. Prosser	
G–AXUW	Cessna FA.150	Leicestershire Aero Club	
G–AXUX	Beech B95 Travel Air	J. H. Southern	
G–AXUY	Jodel DR.100A	Light Planes (Lancashire) Ltd.	
G–AXUZ	Sprite 125	C. B. Healey	
G–AXVB	Cessna F.172H	Watts Aviation Services	
G–AXVC	Cessna FA.150	Light Planes (Lancashire) Ltd.	
G–AXVG	H.S.748 Srs. 2	Dan-Air Services Ltd.	
G–AXVK	Campbell Cricket	Campbell Aircraft Ltd.	
G–AXVM	Campbell Cricket	M. M. Cobbold	
G–AXVN	McCandless M.4	R. McCandless	
G–AXVR	BN-2A Islander	Loganair Ltd.	
G–AXVS	DR.1050 Ambassadeur	F. W. Tilley	
G–AXVU	Omega 84 free balloon	Brede Balloons Ltd.	
G–AXVV	Piper J.3C-65 Cub	J. Daniel	
G–AXVW	Cessna F.150K	W. H. & J. Rogers Group Ltd.	
G–AXVX	Cessna F.172H	Lonmet (Aviation) Ltd.	
G–AXWA	Auster AOP.9	T. Platt	
G–AXWB	Omega 65 (Hot Air Balloon)	M. J. Moore & A. W. S. Robinson	
G–AXWD	Jurca MJ 10	F.P.A. Group	
G–AXWE	Cessna F.150D	Westair Flying Services Ltd.	
G–AXWF	Cessna F.172H	D. K. Aviation Ltd.	
G–AXWP	BN-2A Islander	Aurigny Air Services	
G–AXWR	BN-2A Islander	Aurigny Air Services	
G–AXWT	Jodel D.11	C. King & R. Owen	
G–AXWV	DR.253 Regent	Avions Robin (U.K.) Ltd.	
G–AXWY	Taylor Titch	S. E. O. Tomlinson	
G–AXWZ	PA-28R Cherokee Arrow 200	Walker Wright & Co. Ltd.	
G–AXXA	PA-28 Cherokee 180E	Lonmet (Aviation) Ltd.	
G–AXXB	PA-31 Navajo 300	A.B. Munro	
G–AXXC	Piel CP.301B Emeraude	J. R. R. Gale	
G–AXXD	Hughes H.269B	Twyford Moors (Helicopters) Ltd.	
G–AXXG	BN-2A Islander	G.K.N. Group Services Ltd.	
G–AXXH	BN-2A Islander	Northern Executive Aviation Ltd.	
G–AXXJ	BN-2A Islander	Brymon Aviation Ltd.	
G–AXXM	Piel CP.301A Emeraude	Mrs. P. H. Wren	
G–AXXN	WHE Airbuggy	W. H. Ekin	
G–AXXP	Hot-Air Balloon	R. F. D. Bradshaw	
G–AXXR	Beech 95-B55A Baron	Bumbles Ltd.	
G–AXXV	D.H.82A Tiger Moth (DE992)	D. R. Lawrence	
G–AXXW	Jodel D.117	D. A. Young & S. J. Booth	
G–AXXY	Boeing 707-336B	British Airways	
G–AXXZ	Boeing 707-336B	British Airways	
G–AXYA	PA-31 Navajo 300	C.S.E. (Aircraft Services) Ltd.	
G–AXYB	PA-31 Navajo 300	C.S.E. (Aircraft Services) Ltd.	
G–AXYC	PA-31 Navajo 300	C.S.E. (Aircraft Services) Ltd.	
G–AXYD	BAC One-Eleven 509	British Caledonian	Isle of Arran
G–AXYK	Taylor Monoplane	C. Oakins	
G–AXYO	PA-25 Pawnee 235	Westwick Distributors Ltd.	
G–AXYU	Jodel D.9 Bebe	J. A. Littlechild	
G–AXYV	Taylor Titch	D. G. Wiggins	
G–AXYW	SNCAN SV-4B	Aerobatic Associates Ltd.	

Registration	Type	Owner or Operator	Where and when seen
G–AXYX	WHE Airbuggy	W. H. Beevers	
G–AXYY	WHE Airbuggy	W. H. Ekin	
G–AXYZ	WHE Airbuggy	W. H. Ekin	
G–AXZA	WHE Airbuggy	W. H. Ekin	
G–AXZB	WHE Airbuggy	W. H. Ekin	
G–AXZC	PA-28 Cherokee 180E	College of Air Training	
G–AXZD	PA-28 Cherokee 180E	College of Air Training	
G–AXZE	PA-28 Cherokee 180E	College of Air Training	
G–AXZF	PA-28 Cherokee 180E	College of Air Training	
G–AXZJ	Cessna F.172H	M. W. P. Cripps & K. C. Warner	
G–AXZM	Nipper Mk. III	S. J. Booth & D. A. Young	
G–AXZO	Cessna 180	R.S.A. Parachute Club Ltd.	
G–AXZP	PA-23 Aztec 250	Enterprise Hotels Ltd.	
G–AXZR	Taylor Titch	A. J. Fowler & D. F. Evands	
G–AXZT	Jodel D.117	H. W. Baines	
G–AXZU	Cessna 182N	L. H. & J. C. Riddell	
G–AXZV	Mooney M.20F	R. F. Wanbon	
G–AXZW	Ercoupe 415C	K. Savidge	
G–AYAA	PA-28 Cherokee 180E	College of Air Training	
G–AYAB	PA-28 Cherokee 180E	College of Air Training	
G–AYAC	PA-28R Cherokee Arrow 200	Graynish Investment Holdings Ltd.	
G–AYAD	PA-30 Twin Comanche 160C	Primco Ltd.	
G–AYAE	Bell 47G-4A	Helicopter Hire Ltd.	
G–AYAF	PA-30 Twin Commanche 160C	Arrow Air Services (Charter) Ltd.	
G–AYAH	Beechcraft D.185	Eastern Seaboard Ltd.	
G–AYAI	Fournier RF-5	Exeter RF Group	
G–AYAJ	Cameron O-84 Hot-Air Balloon	E. T. Hall	
G–AYAK	Yak-11	Mann & Son (London) Ltd.	
G–AYAL	Omega 56 free balloon	Nimble Bread Ltd.	
G–AYAN	Motor Cadet Mk. 3	I. Stevenson & J. D. Chapman	
G–AYAO	Cessna F.172D	Transmatic Fyllan Ltd.	
G–AYAP	PA-28 Cherokee 180E	College of Air Training	
G–AYAR	PA-28 Cherokee 180E	College of Air Training	
G–AYAS	PA-28 Cherokee 180E	College of Air Training	
G–AYAT	PA-28 Cherokee 180E	College of Air Training	
G–AYAU	PA-28 Cherokee 180E	College of Air Training	
G–AYAV	PA-28 Cherokee 180E	College of Air Training	
G–AYAW	PA-28 Cherokee 180E	College of Air Training	
G–AYBD	Cessna F.150K	F. D. Forbes	
G–AYBE	AB-206A JetRanger	United Marine (1939) Ltd.	
G–AYBF	Mooney M.20F	E. Perrin Ltd.	
G–AYBG	Scheibe SF.25B Falke	British Gliding Association Ltd.	
G–AYBJ	Boeing 707-321	British Midland Airways	
G–AYBK	PA-28 Cherokee 180E	College of Air Training	
G–AYBO	PA-23 Aztec 250D	Rowntree Mackintosh Ltd.	
G–AYBP	Jodel D.112	M. J. Coburn & C. C. G. Hughes	
G–AYBT	PA-28 Cherokee 180E	College of Air Training	
G–AYBU	Omega 84 free balloon	D. R. Gibbons	
G–AYBV	Chasle Tourbillon	B. A. Mills	
G–AYCC	Campbell Cricket	Campbell Aircraft Ltd.	
G–AYCE	CP.301C Emeraude	K. Webb	
G–AYCF	Cessna FA.150K	Messenger Aviation Services	
G–AYCG	SNCAN SV-4C	SBV Aero Services Ltd.	
G–AYCJ	Cessna TP.206D	Brymon Aviation Ltd.	
G–AYCK	SNCAN SV-4C	K. Knight & J. M. D. Llewelyn	
G–AYCL	Cessna T.210K	Modern Tube Developments Ltd.	
G–AYCM	AB-206A JetRanger	Fras-Air Ltd.	
G–AYCN	Piper J3C-65 Cub	R. H. Heath	
G–AYCO	DR.360 Chevalier	L. M. Gould	
G–AYCP	Jodel D.112	W. Hutchings	
G–AYCT	Cessna F.172K	Lowland Aero Services Co. Ltd.	
G–AYDD	SIAI-Marchetti SF-260	J. W. Cousins & Son	
G–AYDG	M.S.894A Rallye Minerva	P. H. Johnson & H. G. Proctor	

Registration	Type	Owner or Operator	Where and when seen
G–AYDI	D.H.82A Tiger Moth	M. J. Coburn & C. C. G. Hughes	
G–AYDJ	Campbell Cricket	A van Preussen	
G–AYDT	PA-28 Cherokee 140C	West London Aero Services Ltd.	
G–AYDU	Wittman W.9 Tailwind	A. J. E. Perkins	
G–AYDV	Swalesong SA.11 Srs. 1	J. R. Coates	
G–AYDW	A.61 Terrier 2	J. S. Harwood	
G–AYDX	A.61 Terrier 2	T. MacDonald & ptnrs.	
G–AYDY	Luton L.A.4a Minor	L. J. E. Goldfinch	
G–AYDZ	Jodel DR.200	Don Martin (Car Sales) Ltd.	
G–AYEB	Jodel D.112	M. W. Rice & N. J. Mathias	
G–AYEC	CP.301A Emeraude	W. Carter	
G–AYED	PA-24 Comanche 260	Patgrove Ltd.	
G–AYEE	PA-28 Cherokee 180E	College of Air Training	
G–AYEF	PA-28 Cherokee 180E	College of Air Training	
G–AYEG	Falconar F-9	A. G. Thelwall	
G–AYEH	DR.1050 Ambassadeur	E. J. Horsfall	
G–AYEI	PA-31 Navajo 300	R. C. Furze & A. J. Hayden	
G–AYEJ	DR.1050 Ambassadeur	G. Weaver	
G–AYEK	DR.1050 Ambassadeur	Farm Supply Co. (Thirsk) Ltd.	
G–AYEL	Bell 47G-5	B.E.A.S. Ltd.	
G–AYEM	PA-23 Aztec 250D	Air Charter Scotland	
G–AYEN	Piper J3C-65 Cub	P. Warde & C. F. Morris	
G–AYEP	H.S.125 Srs. 400B	British Steel Corporation	
G–AYES	M.S.892A Rallye Commodore 150	Waveney Flying Group	
G–AYET	M.S.892A Rallye Commodore 150	Eglinton Flying Group	
G–AYEU	Brookland Hornet	Gyroflight Ltd.	
G–AYEV	DR.1050 Ambassadeur	Dr. A. R. Worters	
G–AYEW	DR.1051 Sicile	C. G. Burden	
G–AYEX	Boeing 707-355C	British Caledonian	
G–AYEY	Cessna F.150K	Skyfotos Ltd.	
G–AYFA	SA Twin Pioneer CC Mk 2	Scottish Aviation Ltd.	
G–AYFC	D.62B Condor	N. H. Jones	
G–AYFD	D.62B Condor	N. H. Jones	
G–AYFE	D.62C Condor	N. H. Jones	
G–AYFF	D.62B Condor	N. H. Jones	
G–AYFG	D.62C Condor	N. H. Jones	
G–AYFH	D.62B Condor	N. H. Jones	
G–AYFI	PA-39 Twin Comanche C/R	American Airspeed Inc. Ltd.	
G–AYFJ	M.S.880B Rallye Club	K. Hutson & ptnrs.	
G–AYFM	H.S.125 Srs. 400B	Ford Motor Co.	
G–AYFP	D.140 Mousquetaire	J. W. O'Sullivan	
G–AYFS	Brookland Hornet	Gyroflight Ltd.	
G–AYFT	PA-39 Twin Comanche C/R	Apache Aircraft Services Ltd.	
G–AYFU	Crosby BA-4B	Crosby Aviation Ltd. & J. R. Frampton	
G–AYFV	Crosby BA-4B	W. B. Limb	
G–AYFW	Crosby BA-4B	Crosby Aviation Ltd.	
G–AYFX	AA/1 Yankee	J. E. Moody	
G–AYFY	EAA Biplane	H. Kuehling	
G–AYFZ	PA-31 Navajo 300	Bayswater Services Ltd.	
G–AYGA	Jodel D.117	R. M. Long & D. H. Reay	
G–AYGB	Cessna 310Q	Airwork Services Ltd.	
G–AYGC	Cessna F.150K	Light Planes (Lancashire) Ltd.	
G–AYGD	DR.1051 Sicile	L. H. Oakins	
G–AYGE	SNCAN SV-4C	S. C. D. Ward	
G–AYGG	D.120 Paris-Nice	M. A. T. Mountford	
G–AYGM	Cessna T.210D	Industrial Pharmaceutical Service Ltd.	
G–AYGN	Cessna T.210D	Westair Flying Services Ltd.	
G–AYGO	Cessna FR.172G	R. Jones	
G–AYGP	PA-25 Pawnee 235	Skegness Air Taxi Service	
G–AYGX	Cessna FR.172E	Fairoaks Aviation Services Ltd.	
G–AYGY	Beech King Air 100	The Distillers Co. Ltd.	
G–AYGZ	Beech 58 Baron	Eagle Aircraft Services	
G–AYHA	AA/1 Yankee	M. J. Coleman	

Registration	Type	Owner or Operator	Where and when seen
G–AYHF	Campbell Cricket	D. W. Friend	
G–AYHH	Campbell Cricket	D. S. McGillivray	
G–AYHI	Campbell Cricket	K. J. Rickards	
G–AYHN	AB-206A JetRanger	Chromecourt Ltd.	
G–AYHW	Cessna F.337E Super Skymaster	Four T Engineering Ltd.	
G–AYHX	Jodel D.117A	R. K. G. Hanington	
G–AYHY	Fournier RF-4D	N. J. Jones	
G–AYHZ	PA-28R Cherokee Arrow 200	Hub & Gillespie Tubes Ltd.	
G–AYIA	Hughes 500	D. A. George	
G–AYIB	Cessna 182N	Sir G. P. Grant-Suttle	
G–AYIF	PA-28 Cherokee 140C	C.S.E. (Aircraft Services) Ltd.	
G–AYIG	PA-28 Cherokee 140C	C.S.E. (Aircraft Services) Ltd.	
G–AYIH	PA-28 Cherokee 140C	C.S.E. (Aircraft Services) Ltd.	
G–AYII	PA-28R Cherokee Arrow 200	Devon Growers Ltd.	
G–AYIJ	SNCAN SV-4C	Amberley Aviation & Supply Co.	
G–AYIL	Scheibe SF-25B Falke	RAF Gliding & Soaring Association	
G–AYIO	PA-28 Cherokee 140	Arthur Maiden Ltd.	
G–AYIP	PA-39 Twin Comanche C/R	P. D. Lees & G. Pinkus	
G–AYIT	D.H.82A Tiger Moth	R. L. H. Alexander & ptnrs.	
G–AYIU	Cessna 182N	Moatair Service Ltd.	
G–AYJA	DR.1050 Ambassadeur	D. B. Ward & J. H. Burge	
G–AYJB	SNCAN SV-4C	R. A. Blech	
G–AYJC	Stinton-Warren S.31–2	Sqn. Ldr. Darrol Stinton	
G–AYJD	Alpavia-Fournier RF-3	S. R. Beck	
G–AYJP	PA-28 Cherokee 140C	C.S.E. (Aircraft Services) Ltd.	
G–AYJR	PA-28 Cherokee 140C	C.S.E. (Aircraft Services) Ltd.	
G–AYJS	PA-28 Cherokee 140C	Thames Estuary Flying Services Ltd.	
G–AYJT	PA-28 Cherokee 140 C	C.S.E. (Aircraft Services) Ltd.	
G–AYJU	TP-206A Super Skylane	Thorpe Aviation Ltd.	
G–AYJW	Cessna FR.172E	Alpine Press Ltd.	
G–AYJX	Cessna FA.150L Aerobat	South London Aero Club	
G–AYJY	Isaacs Fury II	A. V. Francis	
G–AYKA	Beech 95-B55A Baron	Fenair Ltd.	
G–AYKB	Bede BD-4	K. Bywater	
G–AYKC	D.H.82A Tiger Moth	G. Freeman & ptnrs.	
G–AYKD	DR.1050 Ambassadeur	J. B. Laines	
G–AYKE	M.S.880B Rallye Club	W. E. Taylor & Son Ltd.	
G–AYKF	M.S.880B Rallye Club	G. H. G. Bishop & ptnrs.	
G–AYKJ	Jodel D.117A	G. D. M. Wynne	
G–AYKK	Jodel D.117	P. Cawhwell & ptnrs.	
G–AYKL	Cessna F.150L	A. & J. Argyle Ltd.	
G–AYKM	Cessna FA.150L	Warren Aviation Ltd.	
G–AYKS	Leopoldoff L-7	G. A. & Mrs. D. E. Mason	
G–AYKT	Jodel D.117	J. N. Gladish	
G–AYKU	PA-23 Aztec 250D	H. W. B. Knitwear Ltd.	
G–AYKV	PA-28 Cherokee 140C	C.S.E. (Aircraft Services) Ltd.	
G–AYKW	PA-28 Cherokee 140C	C.S.E. (Aircraft Services) Ltd.	
G–AYKX	PA-28 Cherokee 140C	C.S.E. (Aircraft Services) Ltd.	
G–AYKY	PA-28 Cherokee 140C	C.S.E. (Aircraft Services) Ltd.	
G–AYKZ	SAI KZ-8	R. E. Mitchell	
G–AYLA	Glos-Airtourer 115	Vagabond Flying Group	
G–AYLB	PA-39 Twin Comanche C/R	E. A. Radnall & Co. Ltd.	
G–AYLC	DR.1051 Sicile	E. W. B. Trollope	
G–AYLE	M.S.880B Rallye Club	S. W. O. Ivermee	
G–AYLF	DR.1051 Sicile	M. G. Iles	
G–AYLG	H.S.125 Srs. 400B	British Steel Corporation	
G–AYLJ	PA-31 Navajo	Vickers Ltd.	
G–AYLK	Stampe SV-4C	R. W. & P. R. Budge	
G–AYLL	DR.1050 Ambassadeur	V. E. Hanning-Lee	
G–AYLM	AA-1 Yankee	Eastern Aviation Ltd.	
G–AYLN	AA-1 Yankee	R. Gilkes	
G–AYLO	AA-1 Yankee	First National City Bank (C.I.) Ltd.	

Registration	Type	Owner or Operator	Where and when seen
G–AYLP	AA-1 Yankee	C. R. Snelling	
G–AYLT	Boeing 707-336C	British Airways	
G–AYLU	Pitts S-1 Special	J. E. Randall	
G–AYLV	Jodel D.120	R. E. Wray	
G–AYLW	Beech King Air 100	T.I. (Group Services) Ltd.	
G–AYLX	Hughes 269C	Medminster Ltd.	
G–AYLY	PA-23 Aztec 250	Peregrine Air Services Ltd.	
G–AYLZ	Super Aero 45 Srs. 2	K. M. C. Brooksbank	
G–AYMA	Stolp Starduster Too	P. J. Leggo	
G–AYME	Fournier RF.5	Cedar Farm Ltd.	
G–AYMG	HPR-7 Herald 213	British Island Airways Ltd.	
G–AYMJ	PA-28 Cherokee 140C	C.S.E. (Aircraft Services) Ltd.	
G–AYMK	PA-28 Cherokee 140C	C.S.E. (Aircraft Services) Ltd.	
G–AYML	PA-28 Cherokee 140C	C.S.E. (Aircraft Services) Ltd.	
G–AYMM	Cessna 421B	K. Fletcher	
G–AYMN	PA-28 Cherokee 140C	Skeldor Flying Group	
G–AYMO	PA-23 Aztec 250	Goldstar Publications Ltd.	
G–AYMP	Currie Wot Special	F. H. Gould	
G–AYMR	Lederlin 380L Ladybug	J. S. Brayshaw	
G–AYMT	DR1050 Ambassadeur	Merlin Flying Club Ltd.	
G–AYMU	Jodel D.112	I. R. March	
G–AYMV	Western 20 free balloon	G. F. Turnbull & ptnrs.	
G–AYMW	Bell 206A JetRanger	Wykeham Helicopters Ltd.	
G–AYMX	Bell 206A JetRanger	W. Holmes	
G–AYMY	Bell 47G-5	B.E.A.S. Ltd.	
G–AYMZ	PA-28 Cherokee 140C	C.S.E. (Aircraft Services) Ltd.	
G–AYNA	Currie Wot	R. W. Hart	
G–AYNB	PA-31 Navajo 300	Unigate Ltd.	
G–AYND	Cessna 310Q	Morgan Bentley & ptnrs.	
G–AYNF	PA-28 Cherokee 140C	C.S.E. (Aircraft Services) Ltd.	
G–AYNG	PA-28 Cherokee 140C	C.S.E. (Aircraft Services) Ltd.	
G–AYNJ	PA-28 Cherokee 140C	C.S.E. (Aircraft Services) Ltd.	
G–AYNK	Hughes 369E	Arthur Pitkin Ltd.	
G–AYNM	Beech D.95A Travel Air	Chesterfield Air Towing Group	
G–AYNN	Cessna 185B	Britten-Norman	
G–AYNO	Hughes 269C	Air Gregory Ltd.	
G–AYNR	H.S.125 Srs. 400B	McAlpine Aviation Ltd.	
G–AYNS	Airmaster H2-B1	Airmaster Helicopters Ltd.	
G–AYOD	Cessna 172	K. Cooper	
G–AYOE	Bell 47G	Twyford Moors (Helicopters)	
G–AYOF	Agusta-Bell 47G-2	Twyford Moors (Helicopters) Ltd.	
G–AYOH	Bell 47G-2A	Cropwood Group Ltd.	
G–AYOK	H.S.125 Srs. 400B	Armstrong Equipment Ltd.	
G–AYOL	GY-80 Horizon 180	J. K. Lawson & R. W. Archdale	
G–AYOM	Sikorsky S-61N Mk. 2	BAH	
G–AYOP	BAC One-Eleven 518FG	British Caledonian Isle of Hoy	
G–AYOT	Scheibe SF-27M	P. G. Jeffers	
G–AYOU	Cessna 401B	Bass Charrington Ltd.	
G–AYOV	Cessna FA.150L	Shropshire Aero Club Ltd.	
G–AYOW	Cessna 182N	D. P. H. Lennox	
G–AYOY	Sikorsky S-61N Mk. 2	BAH	
G–AYOZ	Cessna FA.150L	Brymon Aviation Ltd.	
G–AYPA	Beech A-24R Musketeer	J. D. Beaton	
G–AYPB	Beech C-23 Musketeer	Radlet Shooting Centre	
G–AYPC	Beech 70 Queen Air	Vernair Transport Services	
G–AYPD	Beech 95 B.55 Baron	Sir W. S. Dugdale	
G–AYPE	Bo 209 Monsun	P. R. Westacott & A. C. Weedon	
G–AYPF	Cessna F.177RG	Brymon Aviation Ltd.	
G–AYPG	Cessna F.177RG	Overdraught Aviation	
G–AYPH	Cessna F.177RG	S. W. Cooper	
G–AYPI	Cessna F.177RG	Udaset Investments Ltd.	
G–AYPJ	PA-28 Cherokee 180E	S. V. Smith	
G–AYPK	Cessna FA.150L	Leicestershire Aero Club Ltd.	
G–AYPM	PA-18 Super Cub 90	R. Nicholson	
G–AYPO	PA-18 Super Cub 90	A. N. Mavrogordato	
G–AYPP	PA-18 Super Cub 90	Three Counties Aero Club Ltd.	
G–AYPR	PA-18 Super Cub 90	Three Counties Aero Club Ltd.	
G–AYPS	PA-18 Super Cub 90	J. E. L. Goodall	
G–AYPT	PA-18 Super Cub 90	Laarbruch Flying Club	

Registration	Type	Owner or Operator	Where and when seen
G–AYPU	PA-28R Cherokee Arrow 200	Alpine Ltd.	
G–AYPV	PA-28 Cherokee 140D	Meeting Point Ltd.	
G–AYPY	Slingsby T.61D Falke	Vickers Ltd.	
G–AYRA	Campbell Cricket	Campbell Aircraft Ltd.	
G–AYRB	Campbell Cricket	G. L. Clarke	
G–AYRC	Campbell Cricket	G. A. Coventry	
G–AYRE	Campbell Cricket	Campbell Aircraft Ltd.	
G–AYRF	Cessna F.150K	Lowland Aero Service Ltd.	
G–AYRG	Cessna F.172H	Strathspey Aviation Co. Ltd.	
G–AYRH	M.S.892A Rallye Commodore 150	J. D. Watt	
G–AYRI	PA-28R Cherokee Arrow 200	Delta Motor Co. (Windsor) Ltd.	
G–AYRJ	LeVier Cosmic Wind	R. I. McCowen	
G–AYRK	Cessna 150J	K. A. Learmonth	
G–AYRL	Fournier SF.S31 Milan	H. M. Rothwell & ptnrs.	
G–AYRM	PA-28 Cherokee 140D	E. S. Dignam	
G–AYRN	Schleicher ASK-14	D. E. Cadisch & ptnrs.	
G–AYRO	Cessna FA.150L Aerobat	P. & F. & Mrs. J. M. Bramwell	
G–AYRP	Cessna FA.150L Aerobat	Pegasus School of Flying Ltd.	
G–AYRS	D.120 Paris-Nice	J. H. Tetley & G. C. Smith	
G–AYRT	Cessna F.172K	R. L. Orsborn & Son Ltd.	
G–AYRU	BN-2A-6 Islander	Joint Services Parachute Centre	
G–AYRY	H.S.125 Srs. 1B	McAlpine Aviation Ltd.	
G–AYSA	PA-23 Aztec 250C	E. W. Noakes	
G–AYSB	PA-30 Twin Comanche 160C	R. M. English & Son Ltd.	
G–AYSD	Slingsby T.61 Falke	Yorkshire Gliding Club Ltd.	
G–AYSE	PA-31 Navajo 300	Portland Management Ltd.	
G–AYSF	PA-E23 Aztec 250D	Eastlease Ltd.	
G–AYSG	Cessna F.172H	Coventry (Civil) Aviation Ltd.	
G–AYSH	Taylor JT.1 Monoplane	C. J. Lodge	
G–AYSI	Boeing 707-373C	British Caledonian	
G–AYSJ	Dornier-Bücker 133 Jungmeister	James Gilbert	
G–AYSK	Luton L.A.4a Minor	L. Plant	
G–AYSL	Boeing 707-321	Dan-Air Services Ltd.	
G–AYSX	Cessna F.177RG	Nasaire Ltd.	
G–AYSY	Cessna F.177RG	D. W. H. McCowen	
G–AYSZ	Cessna FA.150 Aerobat	Portsmouth Flying School Ltd.	
G–AYTA	M.S.880B Rallye Club	Willoughby Farms Ltd.	
G–AYTB	M.S.880B Rallye Club	H. J. Hartley & H. Swift	
G–AYTC	PA-E23 Aztec 250C	Baylee Air Charter *Bonne Nuit Bay*	
G–AYTD	PA-23 Aztec 250C	Interland Air Services Ltd.	
G–AYTF	Bell 206A JetRanger	Hickstead Ltd.	
G–AYTG	Cessna F.177RG	C. A. J. Hilton	
G–AYTH	Cessna FR.172E	Moore Bros. (Builders) Ltd.	
G–AYTJ	Cessna 207 Super Skywagon	Rhine Army Parachute Association	
G–AYTL	Gray Free Balloon (Hot-Air)	R. F. Gray	
G–AYTM	G.164A Ag-Cat	Miller Aerial Spraying Ltd.	
G–AYTN	Cameron O-65 Hot-air balloon	P. H. Hall & R. F. Jessett	
G–AYTP	PA-23E Aztec 250E	Air Anglia Ltd	
G–AYTR	CP.301A Emeraude	M. Riddin and R. Hannington	
G–AYTT	Phoenix PM-3 Duet	Gp. Capt. A. S. Knowles	
G–AYTV	MJ.2A Tempete	A. Baggallay	
G–AYTY	Bensen Autogyro	J. H. Wood	
G–AYUB	DR.253B Regent	D. M. E. Rawling	
G–AYUC	Cessna F.150L	R. C. Ashford	
G–AYUD	PA-25 Pawnee 235	Farmair Ltd.	
G–AYUG	PA-28 Cherokee 140D	C.S.E. (Aircraft Services) Ltd.	
G–AYUH	PA-28 Cherokee 180F	M. S. Bayliss	
G–AYUI	Evans VP.1 Volksplane	R. F. Selby	
G–AYUL	PA-23 Aztec 250E	Littlewoods Mail Order Stores Ltd.	
G–AYUM	Slingsby T.61 Falke	Doncaster & District Gliding Club	

Registration	Type	Owner or Operator	Where and when seen
G-AYUN	Slingsby T.61 Falke	Dr. D. K. Souper	
G-AYUR	Slingsby T.61 Falke	The Pentland Flying Group	
G-AYUS	Taylor D8 Monoplane	D. G. J. Barker	
G-AYUT	DR.1050 Ambassadeur	R. Norris	
G-AYUV	Cessna F.172H	Executive Air	
G-AYUX	D.H.82A Tiger Moth (PG651)	P. R. Harris	
G-AYUY	Cessna FA.150L Aerobat	K. A. Learmonth	
G-AYVA	Cameron O-84 free balloon	A. Kirk	
G-AYVB	Cessna F.172K	L. G. Raineri	
G-AYVC	PA-23 Aztec 250E	McAlpine Aviation Ltd.	
G-AYVE	Boeing 707-321	British Midland Airways	
G-AYVF	H.S.121 Trident 3B	British Airways	
G-AYVG	Boeing 707-321	British Midland Airways	
G-AYVI	Cessna T.201H	Weatherley Marine (Guernsey) Ltd.	
G-AYVJ	PA-23 Aztec 250D	Drumbard Ltd.	
G-AYVM	PA-31 Navajo 300	Wagley Offshore Ltd.	
G-AYVN	Luton L.A.5a Major	C. T. Gough	
G-AYVO	Wallis WA120 Srs. 1	K. H. Wallis	
G-AYVP	Woody Pusher	J. R. Wright	
G-AYVS	D.H.106 Comet 4C	Dan-Air Services Ltd.	
G-AYVT	Brochet MB.84	Dunelm Flying Group	
G-AYVU	Cameron O-56 free balloon	Shell Mex & B.P. Ltd.	
G-AYVV	ST.10 Diplomate	Covesnon Ltd.	
G-AYVX	M.S.893A Rallye Commodore	London Gliding Club	
G-AYVY	D.H.82A Tiger Moth (PG617)	Hon. R. H. C. Neville	
G-AYWA	Avro 19	Strathallan Collection	
G-AYWD	Cessna 182N	Bardic Films	
G-AYWE	PA-28 Cherokee 140C	Mary J. Kusnlerz	
G-AYWF	PA-23 Aztec 250C	Air West Ltd.	
G-AYWG	PA-E23 Aztec 250C	David Knott (Plant) Ltd.	
G-AYWH	Jodel D.117A	Old Warden Flying Group	
G-AYWI	BN-2A Mk III-1 Trislander	Aurigny Air Services	
G-AYWK	PA-32 Cherokee Six 300D	J. L. Way	
G-AYWL	Taylor Monoplane 2	D. G. Wiggins	
G-AYWM	Glos-Airtourer Super 150	P. A. Dalton	
G-AYWS	Beech Musketeer C23	Transheep Ltd.	
G-AYWT	Stampe SV-4C	R. W. Budge	
G-AYWU	Cessna 150G	C. L. Duke	
G-AYWV	PA-39 Twin Comanche 160 C/R	C.S.E. (Aircraft Services) Ltd.	
G-AYWW	PA-28R Cherokee Arrow 200D	B. Walker & Co. (Dursley) Ltd.	
G-AYWX	D.H.106 Comet 4C	Dan-Air Services Ltd.	
G-AYWY	PA-E23 Aztec 250D	R. Long	
G-AYWZ	PA-39 Twin Comanche 160 C/R	C.S.E. (Aircraft Services) Ltd.	
G-AYXA	PA-39 Twin Comanche 160 C/R	C.S.E. (Aircraft Services) Ltd.	
G-AYXC	BN-2A Islander	Loganair Ltd.	
G-AYXO	Luton L.A.5 Major	C. Drinkwater	
G-AYXP	Jodel D.117A	W. E. Barker & ptnrs.	
G-AYXR	Boeing 707-321	British Midland Airways	
G-AYXS	SIAI-Marchetti S205-18R	W. F. South	
G-AYXU	Champion 7KCAB Citabria	A. K. Brewer	
G-AYXV	Cessna FA.150L	Messenger Aviation Services	
G-AYXW	Evans VP.1 Volksplane	J. S. Penny	
G-AYXX	Cessna F.172H	A. W. Rix & D. V. G. Carey	
G-AYXY	PA-39 Twin Comanche 160 C/R	C.S.E. (Aircraft Services) Ltd.	
G-AYXZ	PA-39 Twin Comanche 160 C/R	C.S.E. (Aircraft Services) Ltd.	

Registration	Type	Owner or Operator	Where and when seen
G–AYYC	Taylor Monoplane	M.A. Ellison-Greene & ptnrs.	
G–AYYD	M.S.894A Rallye Minerva	Udny & Dudwick Estates Ltd.	
G–AYYE	Cessna F.150L	Staverton Flying School	
G–AYYF	Cessna F.150L	Staverton Flying School	
G–AYYG	H.S.748 Srs. 2A	Dakota & South Bend Securities	
G–AYYK	Slingsby T.61A Falke	Polish Flying Club Ltd.	
G–AYYL	Slingsby T.61A Falke	Airways Aero Associations Ltd.	
G–AYYN	PA-28R Cherokee Arrow 200D	Fisher-Karpark Ltd.	
G–AYYT	DR.1050/M1 Sicile Record	R. E. Carpenter	
G–AYYU	Beech C23 Musketeer	European Steel Sales Ltd.	
G–AYYX	M.S.880B Rallye Club	B. E. Knowlson	
G–AYYY	M.S.880B Rallye Club	Soutair Ltd.	
G–AYYZ	M.S.880B Rallye Club	I. M. Kirkwood	
G–AYZC	PA-E23 Aztec 250E	Airgo Ltd.	
G–AYZE	PA-39 Twin Comanche 160 C/R	H. Nordan & ptnrs.	
G–AYZG	Cameron O-86 Hot-air Balloon	P. G. Dunnington	
G–AYZH	Taylor Titch	K. J. Munro	
G–AYZI	Stampe SV-4C	F. M. Barrett	
G–AYZK	DR.1050/M1 Sicile Record	C. G. Gray	
G–AYZN	PA-E23 Aztec D	M. J. L. Batt	
G–AYZO	PA-23 Aztec C	Camera Effect Ltd.	
G–AYZS	D.62B Condor	N. H. Jones	
G–AYZT	D.62B Condor	Wolds Gliding Club	
G–AYZU	Slingsby T.61A Falke	Lasham Gliding Society Ltd.	
G–AYZW	Slingsby T.61A Falke	Portmoak Falke Syndicate	
G–AYZX	Fournier RF-5	R. D. Goodger	
G–AYZY	PA-39 Twin Comanche 160 C/R	Bell Bros. Express Ltd.	
G–AZAB	PA-39 Twin Comanche 160 C/R	T. W. B. Sheffield	
G–AZAC	PA-31 Navajo 300	Cabair Ltd.	
G–AZAD	DR.1051 Sicile	I. C. Young	
G–AZAF	H.S.125 Srs. 400B	Dakota & South Bend Securities Co.	
G–AZAG	A-B 206A JetRanger	Cadogan Formwork & Reinforcing Ltd.	
G–AZAJ	PA-28R Cherokee Arrow 200D	Starline (Sales Ideas) Ltd.	
G–AZAU	Grasshopper Type 02	Cierva Rotocraft Ltd.	
G–AZAV	Cessna 337F	Air Envoy	
G–AZAW	GY-80 Horizon 160	Rogers Autos Ltd.	
G–AZAY	Aeromere F8L Falco	C. Edgecombe	
G–AZAZ	Bensen B-8M	FAA Museum	
G–AZBA	T.66 Nipper 3	Pegasus Aviation Ltd.	
G–AZBB	MBB Bo 209 Monsun	Air Touring Services	
G–AZBC	PA-39 Twin Comanche 160 C/R	Oxford Air Training School	
G–AZBD	PA-39 Twin Comanche 160 C/R	Oxford Air Training School	
G–AZBE	Glos-Airtourer Super 150	T. C. Edwards	
G–AZBF	PA-39 Twin Comanche 160 C/R	Oxford Air Training School	
G–AZBG	PA-31 Navajo 300	Dickenson Services Ltd.	
G–AZBH	Cameron O-84 Hot-air Balloon	Serendipity Balloon Group	
G–AZBI	D.150 Mascaret	M. F. Howe	
G–AZBK	PA-23 Aztec 250D	IDS Aircraft Ltd.	
G–AZBL	Jodel D.9 Bebe	J. H. Underwood	
G–AZBM	Beech C90 King Air	B.I.C.C. Ltd.	
G–AZBN	AT-16 Harvard 2B	Strathallan Collection	
G–AZBP	PA-31 Navajo 300	Sky Petroleum	
G–AZBS	Bell 47G-5	B.E.A.S. Ltd.	
G–AZBT	Western O-65 free balloon	D. J. Harris	

Registration	Type	Owner or Operator	Where and when seen
G–AZBU	Auster Mk. 9	L. C. Mansfield	
G–AZBW	PA–39 Twin Comanche 160 C/R	Rijory Ltd.	
G–AZBX	Western O-65 free balloon	W. R. Midwinter	
G–AZBY	Wessex 60 Srs. I	Bristow Helicopters Ltd.	
G–AZCB	Stampe SV-4C	W. M. Mills	
G–AZCF	Sikorsky S-61N	BAH	
G–AZCH	H.S.125 Srs. 3B/RA	Shell Aircraft Ltd.	
G–AZCI	Cessna 320A Skyknight	Shackleton Aviation Ltd.	
G–AZCJ	B.121 Pup I	P. F. Campkin	
G–AZCK	B.121 Pup I	Cosalt Ltd.	
G–AZCL	B.121 Pup I	Arkle Red	
G–AZCP	B.121 Pup I	Three Counties Aero Club Ltd.	
G–AZCT	B.121 Pup I	D. R. Rolfe	
G–AZCU	B.121 Pup I	Phillimore Western Finance	
G–AZCZ	B.121 Pup I	Aspley Caterers Ltd.	
G–AZDA	B.121 Pup I	D. S. Chandler	
G–AZDB	B.121 Pup I	N. J. Langrick & P. Hirst	
G–AZDC	Sikorsky S-61N	Bristow Helicopters Ltd.	
G–AZDO	MBB Bo 209 Monsun	E. M. Emerson & N. Hughes-Narborough	
G–AZDE	PA-28R Cherokee Arrow 200D	T.B.F. (Aviation) Ltd.	
G–AZDF	Cameron O-84 Hot Air Balloon	M. C. Abram	
G–AZDH	PA-31 Navajo 300	Moseley Group (PSV) Ltd.	
G–AZDJ	PA-32 Cherokee Six 300D	Notable Property Co. Ltd.	
G–AZDK	Beech B55 Baron	Kebbell Holdings Ltd.	
G–AZDW	PA-28 Cherokee 180E	J. Todd	
G–AZDX	PA-28 Cherokee 180E	Anglo-Dansk Marine Engineering Co. Ltd.	
G–AZDY	D.H.82A Tiger Moth	B. A. Mills	
G–AZDZ	Cessna 172K	B. R. Nicholls	
G–AZEA	Cessna 182N	Forth Flying Group Ltd.	
G–AZED	BAC One-Eleven 414	Dan-Air Services Ltd.	
G–AZEE	M.S.880B Rallye Club	P. L. Clements	
G–AZEF	D.120 Paris-Nice	J. A. Milne & J. B. G. Campbell	
G–AZEG	PA-28 Cherokee 140D	W. B. Bateson	
G–AZEI	BN-2A Islander	Airfast Services (Singapore) PTE Ltd.	
G–AZEJ	Hughes 269C	Medminster Ltd.	
G–AZER	Cameron O-42 free balloon	M. P. Dokk-Olsen & P. L. Jaye	
G–AZEU	B.121 Pup 2	S. Richman	
G–AZEV	B.121 Pup 2	M. H. Symes & G. P. Martin	
G–AZEW	B.121 Pup 2	G. D. Robertson	
G–AZFA	B.121 Pup 2	Domestic & Wholesale Applications Ltd.	
G–AZFB	Boeing 720-051B	Monarch Airlines Ltd.	
G–AZFC	PA-28 Cherokee 140D	L. G. Ayling	
G–AZFE	PA-E23 Aztec 250D	Vernair Transport Services Ltd.	
G–AZFF	Jodel D.112	M. K. Field	
G–AZFI	PA-28R Cherokee Arrow 200D	G. Avery & K. Clark	
G–AZFJ	Cessna T.310Q	Svend Munk (Scandinavia) Ltd.	
G–AZFL	Cessna 310P	Lescale Ltd.	
G–AZFM	PA-28R Cherokee Arrow 200D	Marlborough Fine Art	
G–AZFN	Cameron O-56 free balloon	J. R. Gore	
G–AZFO	PA-39 Twin Comanche 160 C/R	Wymondham Developments Co. Ltd.	
G–AZFP	Cessna F.177RG	Basic Metal Co. Ltd.	
G–AZFR	Cessna 401B	Johnson Group Cleaners Ltd.	
G–AZFS	Beech B80 Queen Air	Fairey Surveys Ltd.	
G–AZFZ	Cessna 414	C. H. Taylor & Co. Ltd.	
G–AZGA	D.120 Paris-Nice	G. D. Goss	
G–AZGB	PA-23 Aztec 250D	Willow Vale Electronics Ltd.	
G–AZGC	Stampe SV-4C	The Hon Patrick Lindsay	

Registration	Type	Owner or Operator	Where and when seen
G–AZGD	Stampe SV-4C	F. H. Bateman	
G–AZGE	Stampe SV-4C	M. R. L. Astor	
G–AZGF	B.121 Pup 2	J. A. Macreadie	
G–AZGG	Beech C90 King Air	The Plessey Co. Ltd.	
G–AZGH	M.S.880B Rallye Club	P. F. Zimber	
G–AZGI	M.S.880B Rallye Club	Woolsington Flying Group	
G–AZGJ	M.S.880B Rallye Club	S. C. Howes & T. E. French	
G–AZGK	M.S.880B Rallye Club	H. Tempest	
G–AZGL	M.S.894A Rallye Minerva	The Cambridge Aero Club Ltd.	
G–AZGM	PA-28R Cherokee Arrow 180D	R. Goodwin & Co. Ltd.	
G–AZGY	CP.301B Emeraude	F. A. Ashurst & D. I. Kirkwood	
G–AZGZ	D.H.82A Tiger Moth (NM181)	F. R. Manning	
G–AZHA	PA-E23 Aztec 250E	McDonald Aviation Ltd.	
G–AZHB	Robin HR 100-200	W. H. Everett & Son Ltd.	
G–AZHC	Jodel D.112	Sywell Private Flying Group	
G–AZHD	Slingsby T.61A Falke	West Water Gliding Co. Ltd.	
G–AZHF	Cessna 150L	M. J. Solomans	
G–AZHH	SA 102.5 Cavalier	D. W. Buckle	
G–AZHI	Glos-Airtourer Super 150	Glos-Air Ltd.	
G–AZHJ	S.A. Twin Pioneer Srs. 3	Flight One Ltd.	
G–AZHK	Robin HR 100-200	F. J. Faulkner	
G–AZHL	PA-31 Navajo 300	Comput Air Ltd.	
G–AZHM	Cassutt Racer	M. S. Crossley	
G–AZHN	A.W 650 Argosy 101	Air Bridge Carriers	
G–AZHO	DR.1050 Ambassadeur	G. Weaver	
G–AZHR	Piccard AX6 Hot Air Balloon	J. W. Moss	
G–AZHS	H.S.125 Srs. 600B	Hawker Siddeley Aviation Ltd.	
G–AZHT	Glos-Airtourer T.3	Cadby Engineering Ltd.	
G–AZHU	Luton L.A.4a Minor	A. E. Morris	
G–AZIA	PA-39 Twin Comanche 160 C/R	Heltor Ltd.	
G–AZIB	ST-10 Diplomate	A. M. Fricker & G. S. Goodsie	
G–AZID	Cessna FA.150L	I. Drake	
G–AZIE	PA-25 Pawnee 235	Aerocare Agricultural Services	
G–AZIG	Fournier RF-4D	Sportair Flying Club Ltd.	
G–AZIH	J/IN Alpha	I. R. F. Hammond & L. A. Groves	
G–AZII	Jodel D.117A	J. S. Brayshaw	
G–AZIJ	DR.360 Major	K. H. Tostevin	
G–AZIK	PA-34 Seneca 200	C.S.E. (Aircraft Services) Ltd.	
G–AZIL	Slingsby T.61B Falke	I. Jamieson	
G–AZIM	PA-31 Navajo	Trader Airways Ltd.	
G–AZIN	Canadair CL-44D4	Transmeridian Air Cargo	
G–AZIO	Nord SV-4C	Rollason Aircraft & Engines Ltd.	
G–AZIP	Cameron O-65 Hot-Air Balloon	Dante Balloon Group	
G–AZIR	Stampe SV-4C	Rollason Aircraft & Engines Ltd.	
G–AZIX	AA-1A Yankee	General Aircraft Sales Ltd.	
G–AZJA	BN-2A-I Mk. III Trislander	Aurigny Air Services	
G–AZJB	PA-34 Seneca 200	W. S. Churchill	
G–AZJC	Fournier RF-5	D. W. Sutherland	
G–AZJD	AT-6D Harvard III	Strathallan Collection	
G–AZJE	GY-20 Minicab	J. B. Evans	
G–AZJI	Western O-65 free balloon	The Spire Flying Group	
G–AZJK	Augusta-Bell 47G-2	Twyford Moors (Helicopters) Ltd.	
G–AZJL	Augusta-Bell 47G-2	Twyford Moors (Helicopters) Ltd.	
G–AZJM	Boeing 707-324C	British Caledonian	
G–AZJN	Robin DR.300-125	Seatoller Ltd.	
G–AZJV	Cessna F.172L	T. W. & Mrs. E. E. Howard	
G–AZJW	Cessna F.150L	Gordon King (Aviation) Ltd.	
G–AZJX	Cessna F.150L	Gordon King (Aviation) Ltd.	

Registration	Type	Owner or Operator	Where and when seen
G–AZJZ	PA-23 Aztec 250E	Nosterfield Gravels Ltd.	
G–AZKA	M.S.880B Rallye Club	N. Farley & R. J. Burrough	
G–AZKB	M.S.880B Rallye Club	C. B. Ottaway & A. J. Berry	
G–AZKC	M.S.880B Rallye Club	L. J. Martin	
G–AZKD	M.S.880B Rallye Club	D. G. W. Collett	
G–AZKE	M.S.880B Rallye Club	D. H. Tonkin & B. A. Cook	
G–AZKF	M.S.880B Rallye Club	Cambridge Chemical Co. Ltd.	
G–AZKG	Cessna F.172L	Hurst Aviation Ltd.	
G–AZKH	Cessna F.177RG	Lonmet (Aviation) Ltd.	
G–AZKI	Noorduyn Harvard 2B (FT239)	A. E. Hulton	
G–AZKJ	Canadair CL-44D4	Transmeridian Air Cargo Ltd.	
G–AZKK	Cameron O-56 Hot-Air balloon	Gemini Balloon Group	
G–AZKM	Boeing 720-051B	Monarch Airlines Ltd.	
G–AZKN	Robin HR 100-200	A. H. Carter	
G–AZKO	Cessna F.337	P. & J. A. M. Lee	
G–AZKP	Jodel D.117	C. M. Fitton	
G–AZKR	PA-24 Comanche 180	B. J. Boughton	
G–AZKS	AA-IA Yankee	K. C. Smith	
G–AZKT	Cessna F.177RG	N. R. Kempton & M. C. Turner	
G–AZKU	Cessna F.177RG	Mann Aviation Sales	
G–AZKV	Cessna FRA.150L	Humberstone Engineering Co. Ltd.	
G–AZKW	Cessna F.172L	Banbury Plant Hire Ltd.	
G–AZKZ	Cessna F.172L	Channel Islands Aero Club	
G–AZLA	Taylor Titch	Jeffrey Chappell	
G–AZLB	Western O-65 free balloon	Messrs. R. J. E. Dangerfield & P. A. Lebus	
G–AZLC	Cessna 182P	W. H. & J. Rogers Group	
G–AZLD	Cessna 182P	W. H. & J. Rogers Group	
G–AZLE	Boeing A75 Kaydet	G. A. Harmsworth	
G–AZLF	Jodel D.120	G. J. Bunting	
G–AZLH	Cessna F.150L	Nottingham Aviation Ltd.	
G–AZLJ	BN-2A-I Mk. III Trislander	Aurigny Air Services	
G–AZLK	Cessna F.150L	Mercury Flying Club Ltd.	
G–AZLL	Cessna FRA.150L	Cleveland Flying School	
G–AZLM	Cessna F.172L	Cheshair	
G–AZLN	PA-28 Cherokee 180F	D. H. L. Wigan	
G–AZLO	Cessna F337F	American Airspeed Inc.	
G–AZLP	V.813 Viscount	British Midland Airways	
G–AZLR	V.813 Viscount	British Midland Airways	
G–AZLS	V.813 Viscount	British Midland Airways	
G–AZLT	V.813 Viscount	British Midland Airways	
G–AZLV	Cessna 172K	H. Braithwaite (Aerial Photography) Ltd.	
G–AZLY	Cessna F.150L	Cleveland Flying School	
G–AZLZ	Cessna F.150L	L. Richards	
G–AZMA	Jodel D.140B	W. A. Braim Ltd.	
G–AZMB	Bell 47G-3B	Trent Helicopters Ltd.	
G–AZMC	Slingsby T.61A Falke	Essex Gliding Club Ltd.	
G–AZME	PA-31 Navajo 300	Group Lotus Car Companies	
G–AZMF	BAC One-Eleven 530	British Caledonian Airways	
G–AZMG	PA-23 Aztec C	Cabair Ltd.	
G–AZMH	Morane-Saulnier M.S.500	Hon. P. Lindsay	
G–AZMJ	AA-5 Traveler	A. A. Cansick	
G–AZMK	PA-23 Aztec E	Airde Ltd.	
G–AZML	Canadair CL-44D	Transmeridian Air Cargo	
G–AZMM	ST-10 Diplomate	F. L. Bendelow	
G–AZMN	Glos-Airtourer 150	Staverton Flying School Ltd.	
G–AZMO	PA-23 Cherokee Six 260	Messrs. Hazell & Plaistowe	
G–AZMV	D.62C Condor	N. H. Jones	
G–AZMW	PA-39 Twin Comanche 160 C/R	P. A. Masters	
G–AZMX	PA-28 Cherokee 140	Mooney Aviation Ltd.	
G–AZMY	SIAI-Marchetti SF-260	D. E. Gunner & Miss W. M. Miller	
G–AZMZ	M.S.893A Rallye Commodore 150	M. J. Gartlan	
G–AZNA	V813 Viscount	British Midland Airways	

Registration	Type	Owner or Operator	Where and when seen
G–AZNB	V.813 Viscount	British Midland Airways	
G–AZNC	V.813 Viscount	British Midland Airways	
G–AZNF	Stampe SV-4C	Messrs. Yarnold & Leemhuis	
G–AZNH	V.814 Viscount	Alidair Ltd.	
G–AZNI	S.A.315B Lama	BEAS Ltd.	
G–AZNJ	M.S.880B Rallye Club	Andrewsfield Flying Group	
G–AZNK	Stampe SV-4A	S. Doughi	
G–AZNL	PA-28R Cherokee Arrow 200D	A. R. Hiscox	
G–AZNN	Stampe SV-4A	E. W. Woods	
G–AZNO	Cessna 182P	Strathmarine Flying Group	
G–AZNS	Cameron O-84 free balloon	Cameron Balloons Ltd.	
G–AZNT	Cameron O-84 free balloon	Cameron Balloons Ltd.	
G–AZNX	Boeing 720-051B	Monarch Airlines Ltd.	
G–AZNY	PA-E23 Aztec 250E	Lease Air Ltd.	
G–AZNZ	Boeing 737-222	Britannia Airways	
G–AZOA	MBB-209 Monsun	Dr. G. R. Outwin	
G–AZOB	MBB-209 Monsun	G. N. Richardson	
G–AZOD	PA-23 Aztec 250D	Air West Ltd.	
G–AZOE	Glos-Airtourer 115	Bernell Aviation Ltd.	
G–AZOF	Glos-Airtourer Super150	V. H. Bellamy	
G–AZOG	PA-28R Cherokee Arrow 200D	Winchfield Enterprises Ltd.	
G–AZOH	Beech 65 B.80 Queen Air	Fairey Surveys Ltd.	
G–AZOJ	Beech 56 Baron	Mann Aviation Sales	
G–AZOL	PA-34 Seneca 200	Garnpack Ltd.	
G–AZON	PA-34 Seneca 200	L. G. Payne	
G–AZOO	Western O-65 Hot-Air balloon	Southern Balloon Group	
G–AZOP	Mooney M.20E Chaparral	Avon Electrics (Wholesalers) Ltd.	
G–AZOR	Bolkow Bo 105C	Management Aviation Ltd.	
G–AZOS	Jurca Sirocco	Oliver Smith	
G–AZOT	PA-34 Seneca 200	L. G. Payne	
G–AZOU	Jodel DR 1051 Sicile	R. Emerson & ptnrs.	
G–AZOZ	Cessna FRA.150L	Airwork Services Ltd.	
G–AZPA	PA-25 Pawnee 235	W. P. Miller	
G–AZPB	PA-25 Pawnee 235	W. P. Miller	
G–AZPC	Slingsby T.61C Falke	The Hon. P. R. Smith & Major S. H. C. Marriott	
G–AZPF	Fournier RF-5	Sportair Aviation Ltd.	
G–AZPG	D.H.104 Dove 5	Landsureon (Air Survey) Ltd.	
G–AZPH	Craft-Pitts Special	Aerobatics International Ltd.	
G–AZPV	Luton L.A.4 Minor	J. Scott	
G–AZPX	Western O-31 free balloon	E. R. McCosh	
G–AZRA	MBB-209 Monsun	Phillimore Western Finance	
G–AZRB	Cessna 340	M. K. Dynamics Ltd.	
G–AZRC	Cessna 340	Ryburn Air Ltd.	
G–AZRD	Cessna 401B	John Finlan Ltd.	
G–AZRF	Sikorsky S-61N	Bristow Helicopters	
G–AZRG	PA-23 Aztec 250D	Woodgate Aviation	
G–AZRH	PA-28 Cherokee 140D	E. G. Paterson	
G–AZRI	Payne free balloon	G. F. Payne	
G–AZRK	Fournier RF-5	M. C. Davies	
G–AZRL	PA-18 Super Cub 95	B. A. Dunlop	
G–AZRM	Fournier RF-5	Down Park Estates	
G–AZRN	Cameron O-84 free balloon	T. J. Stafford	
G–AZRO	Boeing 707-340C	British Caledonian Airways County of Lanark	
G–AZRP	Glos-Airtourer 115	Cockburn.Farms Ltd.	
G–AZRR	Cessna 310Q	Ames Company (Transport) Ltd.	
G–AZRS	PA-22 Tri-Pacer 150	E. A. Harrhy	
G–AZRT	Cessna 182P	Anglian Double-Glazing (Kent) Ltd.	
G–AZRU	Agusta AB-206B JetRanger 2	Air Hanson Ltd.	

Registration	Type	Owner or Operator	Where and when seen
G–AZRV	PA-28R Cherokee Arrow 200B	S. G. Daniel	
G–AZRW	Cessna T.337C	A.D.S. (Aerial) Ltd.	
G–AZRX	GY-80 Horizon 160	Eastern Aviation Ltd.	
G–AZRZ	Cessna U-206	Army Parachute Association	
G–AZSA	Stampe SV-4B (MX457)	Pinnacle Market Promotions	
G–AZSC	AT-6 Harvard	Fairoaks Aviation Services	
G–AZSD	Slingsby T29B Motor Tutor	R. G. Boynton	
G–AZSE	PA-28R Cherokee Arrow 200D	A. L. Sergeant	
G–AZSF	PA-28R Cherokee Arrow 200D	P. Blamire	
G–AZSG	PA-28 Cherokee 180E	Scotia Safari	
G–AZSH	PA-28R Cherokee Arrow 180	S. H. Hayward	
G–AZSK	Taylor Monoplane	R. R. Lockwood	
G–AZSL	M.S.890A Rallye Commodore	F. J. Shevill	
G–AZSM	PA-28R Cherokee Arrow 180	Spline Gauges Ltd.	
G–AZSN	PA-28R Cherokee Arrow 200	Burch (Engineering) Ltd.	
G–AZSP	Cameron O-84 free balloon	Esso Petroleum Ltd.	
G–AZSS	Jodel D.9	M. W. Rice	
G–AZSV	Hiller UH-12E	Management Aviation Ltd.	
G–AZSW	Beagle 121 Pup 1	P. Evans & P. J. C. Graves	
G–AZSX	Beagle 121 Pup 1	P. W. Hunter	
G–AZSY	PA-24 Comanche 260	London Sports Car Centre Ltd.	
G–AZSZ	PA-23 Aztec 250	Shuimpex (Services) Ltd.	
G–AZTA	MBB-209 Monsun	Thames Estaury Flying Group	
G–AZTB	MBB-209 Monsun	A. C. Cunliffe	
G–AZTC	MBB-209 Monsun	Inbeing Ltd.	
G–AZTD	PA-32 Cherokee Six 300	BCBM Aviation	
G–AZTE	Cessna FRA.150L	Westcountry Aircraft Servicing Ltd.	
G–AZTF	Cessna F.177RG	M. J. Sparshatt-Worley	
G–AZTG	Boeing 707-321	Dan-Air Services Ltd.	
G–AZTH	Bensen Autogyro	E. Henshaw	
G–AZTI	Bolkow Bo 105C	North Scottish Helicopters Ltd.	
G–AZTK	Cessna F.172F	C. C. Donald	
G–AZTM	Glos-Airtourer 115	A. E. Farr	
G–AZTN	Glos-Airtourer 115	Bernell Aviation Ltd.	
G–AZTO	PA-34 Seneca 200	R. P. Yeoward	
G–AZTR	Stampe SV.4C	M. J. Coburn & T. A. Holding	
G–AZTS	Cessna F.172L	Bennet & Wright Ltd.	
G–AZTT	PA-28R Cherokee Arrow 200	Steepletone Products Ltd	
G–AZTU	Cessna 177	Lonmet (Aviation) Ltd.	
G–AZTV	Stolp Starlet SA 500	S. S. Miles	
G–AZTW	Cessna F.177RG	T. R. Waling	
G–AZUG	AA-5 Traveler	HPM Aviation Ltd.	
G–AZUH	PA-31 Navajo	H.W.B. Knitwear Ltd.	
G–AZUJ	Beech 95-B55 Baron	E. F. Allchin	
G–AZUL	Stampe SV-4B	R. A. Seeley	
G–AZUM	Cessna F.172L	A. M. Thom	
G–AZUN	Cessna F.172L	G. Fraser	
G–AZUO	Cessna F.177RG	Newbury Sand and Gravel Co. Ltd.	
G–AZUP	Cameron O-65 free balloon	C. M. G. Ellis, M. M. James & D. R. Ingle	
G–AZUT	M.S.893A Rallye Commodore 180	Glayvale Ltd.	
G–AZUU	Fournier RF-4D	R. A. Hayne & A. J. Hopson	
G–AZUV	Cameron O-65 free balloon	A. Robins	
G–AZUX	Western O-56 free balloon	R. Hinton	
G–AZUY	Cessna 310L	Channel Islands Aero Engineering Ltd.	

Registration	Type	Owner or Operator	Where and when seen
G–AZUZ	Cessna FRA.150L	D. J. Parker	
G–AZVA	MBB-209 Monsun	K. H. Wallis	
G–AZVB	MBB-209 Monsun	Commercial Go-Karts Ltd.	
G–AZVC	MBB-209 Monsun	Air Touring Services Ltd.	
G–AZVE	AA-5 Traveler	Sherwood Flying Club Ltd.	
G–AZVF	M.S.894A Rallye Minerva	C. Scott	
G–AZVG	AA-5 Traveler	Burlingware Ltd.	
G–AZVH	M.S.894A Rallye Minerva	C. H. T. Trace	
G–AZVI	M.S.893A Rallye Commodore	A. A. Broughton & Son Ltd.	
G–AZVJ	PA-34 Seneca 200	Bernell Aviation Ltd.	
G–AZVK	Cessna F.177RG	The Wergs Garage Ltd.	
G–AZVL	Jodel D.112	A. B. Fisher	
G–AZVM	Hughes 500C	Air Gregory Ltd.	
G–AZVN	Bell 206B JetRanger	A. Smith (Culcheth) Ltd.	
G–AZVP	Cessna F.177RG	R. W. Martin & R. G. Saunders	
G–AZVR	Cessna F.150L	Ann Pascoe	
G–AZVS	H.S.125 Srs. 3B	Beecham Imperial Aviation	
G–AZVT	Cameron O-84 free balloon	Sky Soarer Ltd.	
G–AZVV	PA-28 Cherokee 180G	M. R. Woodgate	
G–AZVW	Bell 47G-5A	Helicopter Hire Ltd.	
G–AZVX	Bell 47G-5A	Helicopter Hire Ltd.	
G–AZVY	Cessna 310Q	Trans Europe Air Charter	
G–AZVZ	PA-28 Cherokee 140	Gordon King (Aviation) Ltd.	
G–AZWA	Boeing 707-321	British Midland Airways	
G–AZWB	PA-28 Cherokee 140	C.S.E. Aviation Ltd.	
G–AZWD	PA-28 Cherokee 140	Airways Aero Associations Ltd.	
G–AZWE	PA-28 Cherokee 140	Airways Aero Associations Ltd.	
G–AZWF	SAN Jodel DR.1050 Ambassadeur	Miss M. M. Truchet	
G–AZWS	PA-28R Cherokee Arrow 200D	Sprengbrook Precision (Brighton) Ltd.	
G–AZWT	Westland Lysander III	Strathallan Collection	
G–AZWU	Cessna F.150L	East Midlands School of Flying Ltd.	
G–AZWV	Cessna U.206 Super Skywagon	Shackleton Aviation Ltd.	
G–AZWW	PA-23 Aztec 250E	Christian Salvesen Ltd.	
G–AZWY	PA-24 Comanche 260	Trago Mills (South Devon) Ltd.	
G–AZXA	Beechcraft 95-C55 Baron	Phillimore Western Finance Ltd.	
G–AZXB	Cameron O-65 free balloon	London Balloon Club Ltd.	
G–AZXC	Cessna F.150L	Brailsford Aviation Ltd.	
G–AZXD	Cessna F.172L	Qualfab Ltd.	
G–AZXE	Jodel D.120A	Kestrel Flying Group	
G–AZXG	PA-23 Aztec 250	Riverside Organ Studios Ltd.	
G–AZXH	PA-34 Seneca 200	Merlin Air Ltd.	
G–AZXI	Hughes 269C	R. W. George	
G–AZXM	H.S.121 Trident 2E	British Airways	
G–AZYA	GY-80 Horizon 160	H. M. Synge, R. H. Richards & R. R. Hall	
G–AZYB	Bell 47H-1	G. Watt	
G–AZYC	Cessna 188C Agwagon	Mindacre Ltd.	
G–AZYD	M.S.893A Rallye Commodore	F. H. Feneley & P. C. H. Clark	
G–AZYE	PA-32 Cherokee Six 260	Lonmet (Aviation) Ltd.	
G–AZYF	PA-28 Cherokee 180	D. H. H. Turner	
G–AZYG	PA-E23 Aztec 250	F. M. Barrett	
G–AZYI	Cessna E-310Q	Fletcher & Stewart Ltd.	
G–AZYJ	PZL-104 Srs. 6 Wilga	Worcestershire Gliding Ltd.	
G–AZYL	Free balloon	R. M. Glover	
G–AZYM	Cessna E-310Q	R. M. Yorke	
G–AZYR	Cessna 340	Davall Gear Co. Ltd.	
G–AZYS	Scintex C.301 CI	K. S. V. Bass	
G–AZYU	PA-E23 Aztec 250	Air Gregory Ltd.	
G–AZYV	Burns free balloon	B. F. G. Ribbans	
G–AZYX	M.S.893A Rallye Commodore	Herefordshire Gliding Club, Ltd.	
G–AZYY	Slingsby T61A	J. A. Towers	

Registration	Type	Owner or Operator	Where and when seen
G-AZYZ	WA.51A Pacific	N. H. Jones	
G-AZZA	PA-E23 Aztec 250	Fairey Britten-Norman Air Services	
G-AZZB	Agusta-Bell AB-206B JetRanger	Ferranti Helicopters Ltd.	
G-AZZC	DC-10 Srs. 10	Laker Airways *Eastern Belle*	
G-AZZD	DC-10 Srs. 10	Laker Airways *Western Belle*	
G-AZZE	Beech A.23-19 Musketeer	The Beech Group	
G-AZZF	M.S.880B Rallye Club	J. Meaden & ptnrs.	
G-AZZG	Cessna 188 Agwagon	Farm Supply Co. (Thirsk) Ltd.	
G-AZZH	Sprite	K. G. Stewart	
G-AZZI	Cessna U.206F	Brymon Aviation Ltd.	
G-AZZK	Cessna 414	Allen Organ Studio (London) Ltd.	
G-AZZL	PA-E23 Aztec 250	Webster Aviation Ltd.	
G-AZZM	BN-2A Mk. III Trislander	Loganair Ltd.	
G-AZZN	PA-28 Cherokee 140	Stapleford Flying Club Ltd.	
G-AZZO	PA-28 Cherokee 140	Stapleford Flying Club Ltd.	
G-AZZP	Cessna F.172H	K. A. Learmonth	
G-AZZR	Cessna F.150L	K. A. Learmonth	
G-AZZS	PA-34 Seneca	J. A. Williams	
G-AZZT	PA-28 Cherokee 180	Stapleford Flying Club Ltd.	
G-AZZU	Glos-Airtourer Super 150	P. R. Selwood	
G-AZZV	Cessna F.172L	Lease Air Ltd.	
G-AZZW	Fournier RF-5	Gloster Aero Group	
G-AZZX	Cessna FRA.150L	J. E. Uprichard, J. N. McClurb & A. D. Keen	
G-AZZZ	D.H.82A Tiger Moth	S. W. McKay	
G-BAAA	L1011-385-1 TriStar	Airlease International	
G-BAAB	L1011-385-1 TriStar	Airlease International	
G-BAAC	Cessna FRA.150L	Lonmet (Aviation) Ltd.	
G-BAAD	Evans Super VP-1	R. W. Husband	
G-BAAF	Manning-Flanders MF I replica	D. E. Bianchi	
G-BAAG	Beechcraft B.55 Baron	Mannin Aviation Ltd.	
G-BAAH	Swalesong SA III	J. R. Coates	
G-BAAI	M.S.893A Rallye Commodore	A. F. Butcher	
G-BAAJ	PA-23 Aztec 250	Graysbrook Leasing Ltd.	
G-BAAK	Cessna 207	Cirrus Aviation Ltd.	
G-BAAL	Cessna 172A	V. H. Bellamy	
G-BAAO	PA-28 Cherokee 180	Shorgard Ltd.	
G-BAAP	PA-28R Cherokee Arrow 200	Syred Aviation Services Ltd.	
G-BAAR	PA-28R Cherokee Arrow 200	Aylesbury Mushrooms Ltd.	
G-BAAS	Cessna FR.172 E	S. E. Clay	
G-BAAT	Cessna 182N	S. J. Martin Ltd.	
G-BAAU	Enstrom F-28A	Spooner Aviation Ltd.	
G-BAAV	Cessna FRA.150L	Cheshire Flying Club	
G-BAAW	Jodel D.112	Glasgow Jodel Group	
G-BAAX	Cameron O-84 free balloon	The New Holker Estate Co. Ltd.	
G-BAAY	Valtion Viima II	P. A. Mann	
G-BAAZ	PA-28R Cherokee Arrow 200D	Eagle Surface Coatings Ltd.	
G-BABA	D.H.82A Tiger Moth	S. W. McKay	
G-BABB	Cessna F.150L	Britten-Norman (Bembridge) Ltd.	
G-BABC	Cessna F.150L	Lonmet (Aviation) Ltd.	
G-BABD	Cessna FRA.150L	Viscount Ednam	
G-BABE	Taylor Titch	P. E. Barker	
G-BABG	PA-28 Cherokee 180	Racing Aviation Holdings	
G-BABH	Cessna F.150L	Ulster Flying Club	
G-BABI	Hughes 269C	Milord Car Service Ltd.	
G-BABK	PA-34 Seneca 200	Group Lotus Car Companies Ltd.	
G-BABW	Beech E90 King Air	Bridon Ltd.	
G-BABX	Beech King Air A100	Eagle Aircraft Services Ltd.	

Registration	Type	Owner or Operator	Where and when seen
G–BABY	Taylor Titch	J. R. D. Bygraves	
G–BABZ	Beech 35-C33 Debonair	Windmill Manor Ltd.	
G–BACA	BAC Petrel	BAC Military Aircraft Division, Apprentice Training Dept.	
G–BACB	PA-34 Seneca 200	IPC Business Press Ltd.	
G–BACC	Cessna FRA.150L	R. F. Development Co. Ltd.	
G–BACD	Cessna FRA.150L	Northair Aviation Ltd.	
G–BACE	Fournier RF-5	S. R. Cannell, J. Barrett & A. B. Gubbay	
G–BACF	Cessna F.337F	Brymon Aviation Ltd.	
G–BACH	Enstrom F.28A	Spooner Aviation Ltd.	
G–BACI	H.S.125 Srs. 400B	BSR Ltd.	
G–BACJ	Jodel D.120	Wearside Flying Association	
G–BACK	D.H.82A Tiger Moth (DF130)	G. R. French, J. D. Watt & J. R. French	
G–BACL	Jodel D.150	G. R. French	
G–BACM	Cessna FRA.150L	Gravesbrook Leasing Ltd.	
G–BACN	Cessna FRA.150L	Gravesbrook Leasing Ltd.	
G–BACO	Cessna FRA.150L	R. Bertorelli & N. Rayner	
G–BACP	Cessna FRA.150L	K. Costello	
G–BADC	Luton Beta	B. E. Smith & S. C. Thompson	
G–BADE	PA-23 Aztec 250	G. Montague (Southern) Ltd.	
G–BADF	PA-34 Seneca 200-2	R. G. Stuart & K. Stuart	
G–BADH	Slingsby T.61A	N. F. W. Eyres & ptnrs.	
G–BADI	PA-E23 Aztec 250	The Earl of Shelbourne	
G–BADJ	PA-E23 Aztec 250	J. G. Hogg	
G–BADK	BN-2A-8 Islander	Byrymon Aviation Ltd.	
G–BADL	PA-34 Seneca 200	Apollo Aviation Ltd.	
G–BADM	D.62B Condor	Rollason Aircraft & Engines Ltd.	
G–BADN	WA.52 Europa	N. H. Jones	
G–BADO	PA-32 Cherokee Six 300	Peter Arundell Ltd.	
G–BADP	Boeing 737-204	Britannia Airways	
G–BADR	Boeing 737-204	Britannia Airways	
G–BADT	Cessna 402B	British Aircraft Corp.	
G–BADU	Cameron O-56 free balloon	J. Phillip & M. Ray	
G–BADV	Brochet MB-50	W. J. Evans	
G–BADW	Pitts S-2A Special	Rothmans International Ltd.	
G–BADX	Pitts S-2A Special	Rothmans International Ltd.	
G–BADY	Pitts S-2A Special	Rothmans International Ltd.	
G–BADZ	Pitts S-2A Special	Rothmans International Ltd.	
G–BAEA	Pitts S-2A Special	Rothmans International Ltd.	
G–BAEB	Robin DR.400/160	Bracknell Refrigeration Services Ltd.	
G–BAEC	Robin HR.100/210	C. MacCartney-Filgate	
G–BAED	PA-E23 Aztec 250	Bon-Air Flights Ltd.	
G–BAEE	DR.1050/M1 Sicile Record	E. J. Clempson	
G–BAEF	Boeing 727-100	Dan-Air Services Ltd.	
G–BAEG	PA-31 Navajo	Chipperfield (Properties) Ltd.	
G–BAEH	Hughes 269C	Medminster Ltd.	
G–BAEI	Cessna 421B	Dovey Holdings South Wales Ltd.	
G–BAEJ	AA-5 Traveler	Campion Aviation Ltd.	
G–BAEL	Boeing 707-321	British Midland Airways	
G–BAEM	Robin DR.400/125 Petit Prince	Sportair Flying Club	
G–BAEN	Robin DR.400/180 Regent	N. C. Jensen	
G–BAEO	Cessna F.172M	W. H. & J. Rogers Group	
G–BAEP	Cessna FRA.150L	Denham Flying Training School Ltd.	
G–BAER	Cosmic Wind	R. S. Voice	
G–BAES	Cessna 337A	R. H. B. Malim & J. R. Thomas	
G–BAET	Piper L-4H Cub	C. M. G. Ellis	
G–BAEU	Cessna F.150L	A. R. Ashley	
G–BAEV	Cessna FRA.150L	Bennett Bros. (Chandlers Ford) Ltd.	
G–BAEW	Cessna F.172M	G. D. Atkinson	
G–BAEX	Cessna F.172M	R. M. English & Son Ltd.	

Registration	Type	Owner or Operator	Where and when seen
G–BAEY	Cessna F.172M	Rentons Garages Ltd	
G–BAEZ	Cessna FRA.150L	F. Butterfield	
G–BAFA	AA-5 Traveler	Lewis Flying Group Ltd.	
G–BAFC	Hughes 269A	P. Desoutter	
G–BAFD	Bölkow Bo 105D	Wimpey Laboratories Ltd.	
G–BAFG	D.H.82A Tiger Moth	C. D. Cyster	
G–BAFH	Evans VP-1 Volksplane	R. C. Wright	
G–BAFI	Cessna F.177RG	J. F. Ayre	
G–BAFL	Cessna 182P	John Roberts Services Ltd.	
G–BAFM	Noorduyn AT-6 Harvard	Hon. P. Lindsay	
G–BAFN	Bell 212	BAH	
G–BAFP	Robin DR.400/16	Trenery & Sons Ltd.	
G–BAFR	Jodel D.120	J. E. Hobbs	
G–BAFS	PA-18 Super Cub 150	Doncaster & District Gliding Club	
G–BAFT	PA-18 Super Cub 150	Cambridge University Gliding Trust Ltd.	
G–BAFU	PA-28 Cherokee 140	R. S. Fenwick	
G–BAFV	PA-18 Super Cub	P. Elliott	
G–BAFW	PA-28 Cherokee 140	B. J. Poulton	
G–BAFX	Robin DR.400/140	Copthorne Precision Products Ltd.	
G–BAFZ	Boeing 727–146	Dan-Air Services Ltd.	
G–BAGA	Cessna 182A	Chinecroft Ltd.	
G–BAGB	SIAI-Marchetti SF.260	Charles Lock Motors Ltd.	
G–BAGC	Robin DR.400/140	Steelfields Ltd.	
G–BAGF	Jodel D.92 Bebe	G. R. French & ptnrs.	
G–BAGG	PA-32 Cherokee Six	J. S. Horne	
G–BAGI	Cameron O-31 free balloon	Cameron Balloons Ltd.	
G–BAGJ	SA.341G Gazelle Srs. I	United Marine (1939) Ltd.	
G–BAGK	SA.341G Gazelle Srs. I	Salvesen Properties Ltd.	
G–BAGL	SA.341G Gazelle Srs. I	Westland Helicopters Ltd.	
G–BAGM	Wassmer WA.41	Alderney Flying Services Ltd.	
G–BAGN	Cessna F.177RG	Manro Products Ltd.	
G–BAGO	Cessna 421B	Brown & Root (U.K.) Ltd.	
G–BAGP	Cessna FT.337P	W. H. & J. Rogers Ltd.	
G–BAGR	Robin DR.400/125 Petit Prince	J. W. T. Burfitt	
G–BAGS	Robin DR.400 2+2	Headcorn Flying School Ltd.	
G–BAGT	Helio H.295 Courier	B. J. C. Woodhall Ltd.	
G–BAGU	Luton L.A.5A Major	J. Gawley	
G–BAGV	Cessna U.206F	G. A. Dommett	
G–BAGW	Cessna F.150J	Sherburn Aero Club Ltd.	
G–BAGX	PA-28 Cherokee 140	B. F. J. Sears & ptnrs.	
G–BAGY	Cameron O-84 free balloon	P. G. Dunnington	
G–BAHC	PA-23 Aztec 250	Berkeley Hotel Ltd.	
G–BAHD	Cessna 182P	Watkiss Group Aviation	
G–BAHE	PA-28 Cherokee 140	Mooney Aviation Ltd.	
G–BAHF	PA-28 Cherokee 140	Mooney Aviation Ltd.	
G–BAHG	PA-24 Comanche 260	J. Marriot & R. Widdowson	
G–BAHH	Wallis WA.121	Wg. Cdr. K. H. Wallis	
G–BAHI	Cessna F.150H	Spooner Aviation Ltd.	
G–BAHJ	PA-24 Comanche 250	Chart Managements & Partners	
G–BAHL	Robin DR.400/160	Norvett Electronics Ltd.	
G–BAHN	Beech 58 Baron	Eagle Aircraft Services Ltd.	
G–BAHO	Beech C.23 Musketeer	Gerrard Properties Ltd.	
G–BAHP	Volmer VJ.22 Sportsman	J. P. Crawford	
G–BAHR	PA-28 Cherokee 140	Rialto Aviation Ltd.	
G–BAHS	PA-28R Cherokee Arrow	Steatite Insulations Ltd.	
G–BAHT	Cessna F.172F	J. E. Malloy	
G–BAHU	Enstrom F-28A	Spooner Aviation Ltd.	
G–BAHW	Cessna 310Q	Air Charter & Travel Ltd.	
G–BAHX	Cessna 182P	S. Cooper & Co. (Fashions)	
G–BAIA	PA-32 Cherokee Six	W. G. Fisher	
G–BAIB	Enstrom F.28A	Contract & Hire (Excavators) Limited	
G–BAIC	Cessna FRA.150L	Aberdeen Aero Club	
G–BAIF	Western O-65 free balloon	B. M. Smith	

G-BALF. (Top) Robin DR.400/125 Petit Prince (125hp Lycoming O-235-F2B)/*Austin J. Brown*

G-BATC. (Centre) Bölkow (MBB) Bo 105C (two 400shp Allison 250–C20)/*John Goring*

G-BAVY. (Above) Piper PA-E23 Aztec 250 (two 250hp Lycoming IO-540-C4B5)/*M. D. West*

Registration	Type	Owner or Operator	Where and when seen
G–BAIG	PA-34 Seneca 200	Airswift Ltd.	
G–BAIH	PA-28R Cherokee Arrow	J. Pemberton	
G–BAII	Cessna FRA.150L	Denham Flying Training School Ltd.	
G–BAIJ	Cessna FRA.150L	Denham Flying Training School Ltd.	
G–BAIK	Cessna F.150L	Park Plant Ltd.	
G–BAIL	Cessna FR.172J	M. N. Dale	
G–BAIM	Cessna 310Q	Anywair Travel (UK) Ltd.	
G–BAIN	Cessna FRA.150L	Airwork Services Ltd.	
G–BAIO	Cessna F.150L	Gordon King Aviation Ltd.	
G–BAIP	Cessna F.150L	J. S. Jones	
G–BAIR	Thunder Balloon 056	P. A. & Mrs. M. L. C. Hutchins	
G–BAIS	Cessna F.177RG	Jones Aviation Services Ltd.	
G–BAIU	Hiller UH-12E	Twyford Moors (Helicopters) Ltd.	
G–BAIW	Cessna F.172M	Phil Read Development Ltd.	
G–BAIX	Cessna F.172M	Rimmer Aviation Ltd.	
G–BAIY	Cameron O-65 Hot-Air balloon	Budget Rent A Car (UK) Ltd.	
G–BAIZ	Slingsby T.61A Falke	Lasham Gliding Society Ltd.	
G–BAJA	Cessna F.177RG	Don Ward Productions Ltd.	
G–BAJB	Cessna F.177RG	Brymon Aviation Ltd.	
G–BAJC	Evans VP-1	J. R. Clements	
G–BAJD	Evans VP-1	J. R. Dunford	
G–BAJE	Cessna 177 Cardinal	L. D. Cloude	
G–BAJN	AA-5 Traveler	Red Lyon Flying Club	
G–BAJO	AA-5 Traveler	Harland of Hull	
G–BAJR	PA-28 Cherokee 180	Millet Shipping Ltd.	
G–BAJT	PA-28R Cherokee Arrow	G. D. Tucker-Everns	
G–BAJU	PA-23 Aztec 250	Peregrine Air Services Ltd.	
G–BAJV	SA.102.5 Cavalier	A. J. Starkey	
G–BAJW	Boeing 727-146	Dan-Air Services Ltd.	
G–BAJX	PA-E23 Aztec 250	A. J. Walgate & Son Ltd.	
G–BAJY	Robin DR.400/180 Regent	J. F. Ingledew	
G–BAJZ	Robin DR.400/125 Petit Prince	G. A. Engineering Services	
G–BAKA	Sikorsky S-61N	Bristow Helicopters Ltd.	
G–BAKB	Sikorsky S-61N	Bristow Helicopters Ltd.	Montrose
G–BAKC	Sikorsky S-61N	Bristow Helicopters Ltd.	
G–BAKD	PA-34 Seneca 200-2	Hockstar Ltd.	
G–BAKE	Cessna T.310Q	Home Counties Cleaning Group Services	
G–BAKF	Bell 206B JetRanger 2	M. J. K. Belmont	
G–BAKG	Hughes 269C	Direct Rentals	
G–BAKH	PA-28 Cherokee 140	M. R. Woodgate	
G–BAKJ	PA-30 Twin Comanche	East Air Travel Ltd.	
G–BAKK	Cessna F.172H	Luton Flying Club Ltd.	
G–BAKL	F.27 Friendship 200	Air Anglia	
G–BAKM	Robin DR.400/140	Hull Aero Club Ltd.	
G–BAKN	SNCAN SV-4C	M. Holloway	
G–BAKO	Cameron O-84 free balloon	D. C. Dokk-Olsen	
G–BAKP	PA-E23 Aztec 250	Vaughan Associates Ltd.	
G–BAKR	Jodel D.117	B. N., P. F. & R. N. Bennison	
G–BAKS	A-B 206B JetRanger 2	Galliford Constructions Ltd.	
G–BAKT	A-B 206B JetRanger 2	Ferranti Helicopters Ltd.	
G–BAKU	A-B 206B JetRanger 2	Horlsey Wood & Co. Ltd.	
G–BAKV	PA-18 Super Cub 150	E. H. S. Warner	
G–BAKW	B.121 Pup 2	J. Trevor-Hicks Ltd.	
G–BAKX	Bell 206B JetRanger 2	Harrison Construction (Midlands) Ltd.	
G–BAKY	Slingsby T.61C Falke	Sir Leonard & Lady Joan Redshaw	
G–BAKZ	BN-2A-3 Islander	Helicopter Hire Ltd.	
G–BALB	Air & Space Model 18A	Interflight Ltd.	
G–BALC	Bell 206B JetRanger 2	E. A. Savory & Associates	
G–BALD	Cameron O-84 free balloon	M. Norton-Griffiths	
G–BALE	Enstrom F.28A	C.S.E. Aviation Ltd.	

Registration	Type	Owner or Operator	Where and when seen
G-BALF	Robin DR.400/125 Petit Prince	Headcorn Flying School Ltd.	
G-BALH	Robin DR.400/140	Tarevale Ltd.	
G-BALI	Robin DR.400 2+2	Avions Robin (UK) Ltd.	
G-BALJ	Robin DR.400/180 Regent	E. F. Bowe	
G-BALK	SNCAN SV-4C	J. C. Brierley	
G-BALL	Bede BD-5	Capt. G. A. Ball, USAF	
G-BALM	Cessna 340	Patgrove Ltd.	
G-BALN	Cessna T.310Q	Swanport Aviation Ltd.	
G-BALP	PA-39 Twin Comanche 160 C/R	J. Rutherford	
G-BALR	Wittman W.8 Tailwind	R. L. Hughes	
G-BALT	Enstrom F.28A	Franklin Aviation Ltd.	
G-BALU	PA-E23 Aztec 250C	Baylee Air Charter Ltd.	
G-BALV	BN-2A-8 Islander	Britten-Norman (Bembridge) Ltd.	
G-BALW	PA-28R Cherokee Arrow 200 Mk. II	H. A. W. Pilkington	
G-BALX	D.H.82A Tiger Noth (N6848)	J. Burningham	
G-BALY	Practavia Pilot Sprite 150	A. L. Young	
G-BALZ	Bell 212	British Executive Air Services Ltd.	
G-BAMA	Cameron O-77 hot-air balloon	Cameron Balloons Ltd.	
G-BAMB	Slingsby T.61C	Universities of Glasgow & Strathclyde Gliding Club	
G-BAMC	Cessna F.150L	Leicestershire Aero Club Ltd.	
G-BAMD	Beech 95-A55 Baron	Porte Aviation Ltd.	
G-BAME	Volmer Jensen	V. H. Bellamy	
G-BAMF	Bölkow Bo 105D	Management Aviation Ltd.	
G-BAMG	Avions Lobet Ganagobie	J. D. Brompton	
G-BAMI	Beech 95-B55 Baron	Ace Belmont International Ltd.	
G-BAMJ	Cessna 182P	M. B. Mavroleon	
G-BAMK	Cameron D-96 hot-air airship	Cameron Balloons Ltd.	
G-BAML	Bell 206A JetRanger	Somerton-Rayner Helicopters Ltd.	
G-BAMM	PA-28 Cherokee 235	E. R. Walters	
G-BAMN	Cessna U.206C Super Skywagon	Grindale Parachuting Ltd.	
G-BAMR	PA-16 Clipper	C. C. Lovell	
G-BAMS	Robin DR.400 Knight 160	Bostock Aviation Ltd.	
G-BAMT	Robin DR.400 Knight 160	R. W. Gaskell	
G-BAMU	Robin DR.400 Knight 160	W. J. C. Scrope, J. R. Carwithen & C. J. Stephenson	
G-BAMV	Robin DR.400 Knight 160	J. H. Fenton	
G-BAMW	SAN DR.1050 Ambassadeur	D. H. Wilson-Spratt	
G-BAMY	PA-28R Cherokee Arrow 200D Mk. II	Western Leasings	
G-BAMZ	PA-34 Seneca 200-2	Dublilier Ltd.	
G-BANA	Robin DR.221 Dauphin	Jason Flying Services Ltd.	
G-BANB	Robin DR.400/180 Regent	Time Electronics Ltd.	
G-BANC	Gardan GY-201 Minicab	C. D. B. Trollope	
G-BAND	Cameron O-84 hot-air balloon	Mid-Bucks Farmers Balloon Group	
G-BANE	Cessna FRA.150L	Denham Flying Training School Ltd.	
G-BANF	Luton L.A.4a Minor	D. W. Bosworth	
G-BANG	Cameron O-84 hot-air balloon	I. J. NcDonnell & C. T. L. Radcliffe	
G-BANI	Cessna 188A Agwagon	Mindacre Ltd.	
G-BANK	PA-34 Seneca 200-2	Mann Aviation Sales Ltd.	
G-BANL	BN-2A-8 Islander	Loganair Ltd.	
G-BANP	Douglas DC-4	British Air Ferries Ltd.	
G-BANS	PA-34 Seneca 200-2	Air Swift Ltd.	
G-BANT	Cameron O-65 hot-air balloon	M. D. Tweedie, I. P. D. Carter & R. I'Anson	

Registration	Type	Owner or Operator	Where and when seen
G–BANU	Wassmer Jodel D.120 Paris-Nice	C. E. NcKinney	
G–BANV	Phoenix Currie Wot	C. Turner	
G–BANW	CP.1330 Super Emeraude	J. Toulmin & ptnrs.	
G–BANX	Cessna F.172M	A. J. Keen & ptnrs.	
G–BANY	Glos-AESL Airtourer 115	Bernell Aviation Ltd.	
G–BAOB	Cessna F.172N	Gordon King Aviation Ltd.	
G–BAOC	M.S.894E Rallye Minerva	C. F. & Mrs. P. J. Dance	
G–BAOD	M.S.880B Rallye Club	Delta-Flying	
G–BAOE	M.S.880B Rallye Club	Westward Aviation Co. Ltd.	
G–BAOF	M.S.880B Rallye Club	G.B. Instrument Panel Co. Ltd.	
G–BAOG	M.S.880B Rallye Club	Valentine Aviation Ltd.	
G–BAOH	M.S.880B Rallye Club	J. D. Jackson & N. Stephenson	
G–BAOJ	M.S.880B Rallye Club	John Finlay Concrete Pipes Ltd.	
G–BAOK	M.S.880B Rallye Club	Air Touring Services Ltd.	
G–BAOM	M.S.880B Rallye Club	A. W. Braybrooke	
G–BAOO	Cessna 421B Golden Eagle	Christian Salvesen Ltd.	
G–BAOP	Cessna FRA.150L	Lease-Air	
G–BAOR	Cessna F.177RG	Brymon Aviation Ltd.	
G–BAOS	Cessna F.172M	D. Sherloff & W. E. Cattle	
G–BAOT	M.S.880B Rallye Club	W. Johnstone	
G–BAOU	AA-5 Traveler	H. Ingram	
G–BAOV	AA-5 Traveler	Longcroft Smith & Co.	
G–BAOW	Cameron O-65 hot-air balloon	P. A. White	
G–BAOX	Cessna 310Q	J. M. E. Byng	
G–BAOY	Cameron S-31 hot-air balloon	Shell-Mex & BP Ltd.	
G–BAOZ	Cessna 414	Cowick Hall Aviation Ltd.	
G–BAPA	RF-5B Sperber	R. Pasold & D. Stuynor	
G–BAPB	DHC-1 Chipmunk 22	J. Garston	
G–BAPC	L.A.4a Minor	Midland Preservation Society	
G–BAPE	V.814 Viscount	British Midland Airways Ltd.	
G–BAPG	V.814 Viscount	British Midland Airways Ltd.	
G–BAPH	Cessna FRA.150L	Luton Flying Club	
G–BAPI	Cessna FRA.150L	Record Aviation Ltd.	
G–BAPJ	Cessna FRA.150L	Business Air Travel Ltd.	
G–BAPK	Cessna F.150L	Ulster Flying Club (1961) Ltd.	
G–BAPL	PA-23 Aztec 250E	Scottish Malt Distillers Ltd.	
G–BAPM	Fuji FA.200–160	A. D. Smith & J. L. Williams	
G–BAPN	PA-28 Cherokee 180 Challenger	John Willmott Plant Ltd.	
G–BAPP	Evans VP-1	M. J. Drybankski & N. Crow	
G–BAPR	Jodel D.11	Crantech Flying Group	
G–BAPS	Campbell Cougar	A. M. W. Curzon-Howe-Herrick	
G–BAPT	Fuji FA.200-180	Hornsea Metal Co. Ltd.	
G–BAPV	Robin DR.400/160 Knight	J. D. Millne & ptnrs.	
G–BAPW	PA-28R Cherokee Arrow	N. Stanbury & B. Foley	
G–BAPX	Robin DR.400/160	G. E. H. Terry	
G–BAPY	Robin HR.100/210	Engineering Appliances Ltd.	
G–BARB	PA-34 Seneca 200-2	L. G. Ayling	
G–BARC	Cessna FR.172J	M. C. Aviation Ltd.	
G–BARD	Cessna 337C Super Skymaster	Europa Aviation Ltd.	
G–BARF	Jodel D.112 Club	Brunton Flying Group	
G–BARG	Cessna 310Q	G. E. Platt	
G–BARH	Beech C.23 Sundowner	Malcolm (Enamellers) Ltd.	
G–BARJ	Bell 212	BEAS Ltd.	
G–BARN	Taylor Titch	R. G. W. Newton	
G–BARO	Bell 206B JetRanger	A. Streeter & Co. Ltd.	
G–BARP	Bell 206B JetRanger	Patgrove Ltd.	
G–BARR	H.S.125 Srs. 600B	Rolls-Royce (1971) Ltd.	
G–BARS	D.H.C.I. Chipmunk 22	T. I. Sutton	
G–BART	H.S.125 Srs. 600B	Green Shield Trading Stamp Co. Ltd.	
G–BARV	Cessna 310Q	Old England Watches	
G–BARW	Cessna 402B	Comber Group Ltd.	

Registration	Type	Owner or Operator	Where and when seen
G–BARX	Bell 206B JetRanger	Sutton & Son (St. Helens) Ltd.	
G–BARY	CP.301A Emeraude	A. E. P. Dobson	
G–BARZ	Scheibe SF28A	G. H. Daniels	
G–BASB	Enstrom F-28A	Travel Centre (Norwich) Ltd.	
G–BASC	Bell 47G-5A	North-Scottish Helicopters Ltd.	
G–BASD	B.121 Pup 2	G. W. Archer	
G–BASE	Bell 206B JetRanger	Endeavour Aviation Ltd.	
G–BASF	PA-28 Cherokee 180 Challenger	Cranleigh Travel Centre	
G–BASG	AA-5 Traveler	General Aviation Sales Ltd.	
G–BASI	PA-28 Cherokee 140	R. A. Sutton	
G–BASJ	PA-28 Cherokee 180	Merseyside Trailer Sales & Service Ltd.	
G–BASK	PA-E23 Aztec 250	C. E. Edwards (Engineers) Ltd.	
G–BASL	PA-28 Cherokee 140	Air Navigation & Trading Ltd.	
G–BASM	PA-34 Seneca 200-2	Gill Aviation Ltd.	
G–BASN	Beech C.23 Sundowner	Galleon Aviation Ltd.	
G–BASO	Lake LA-4 Buccaneer	Sutton & Son (St. Helens) Ltd.	
G–BASP	B.121 Pup 1	T. L. Darby Ltd. & L. R. Fogg	
G–BASR	PA-25 Pawnee 235C	H. J. Shuttleworth & Son Ltd.	
G–BASS	Cessna 421B	Bass Charrington Ltd.	
G–BAST	Cameron O-84 hot-air balloon	P. A. Salmons & D. A. Tinley	
G–BASU	PA-31 Navajo Chieftain	Yewlands Engineering Co. Ltd.	
G–BASV	Enstrom F.28A	Quantel Ltd.	
G–BASY	Jodel D.9 Bebe	R. L. Sambell	
G–BATA	H.S.125 Srs. 400B	De Beers International Air Services	
G–BATB	Bolkow Bo 105C	Rolls-Royce (1971) Ltd.	
G–BATC	Bolkow Bo 105C	Management Aviation Ltd.	
G–BATD	Cessna U206F	R. Slarke	
G–BATH	Cessna F.337G	S. White & L. H. Bedden	
G–BATI	Cessna FR.172J	A. A. Wild, C. C. D. Clark & R. Leitch	
G–BATJ	Jodel D.119	P. G. Barrow & ptnrs.	
G–BATM	PA-32 Cherokee Six 300	Patgrove Ltd.	
G–BATN	PA-E23 Aztec 250	Daleview Investments Ltd.	
G–BATR	PA-34 Seneca 200	Cega Aviation Ltd.	
G–BATS	Taylor Monoplane	J. Jennings	
G–BATT	Hughes 269C	United Marine (1939) Ltd.	
G–BATU	Enstrom F.28	Dick Hampton (Earth Moving) Ltd.	
G–BATV	PA-28 Cherokee 180	Mooney Aviation Ltd.	
G–BATW	PA-28 Cherokee 140	Mooney Aviation Ltd.	
G–BATX	PA-23 Aztec 250E	Melton Securities Ltd.	
G–BATY	Bell 206A JetRanger	Alan Mann Helicopters Ltd.	
G–BAUA	PA-E23 Aztec 250	Florin Enterprises Ltd.	
G–BAUB	Bell 206B JetRanger	Ben Turner & Sons (Helicopters) Ltd.	
G–BAUC	PA-25 Pawnee 235C	Airfarmers	
G–BAUD	Robin DR.400/160	Light Aircraft Sales (Northern) Ltd.	
G–BAUE	Cessna 310Q	A. J. Dyer	
G–BAUF	Hughes 269C	Point to Point Helicopters Ltd.	
G–BAUH	Jodel D.112	Walhouse Flying Group	
G–BAUI	PA-E23 Aztec 250	Measurex International Systems Ltd.	
G–BAUJ	PA-E23 Aztec 250	T. Brady & Sons Ltd.	
G–BAUK	Hughes 269C	Troy-Air Ltd.	
G–BAUL	Schweizer Teal TSC-1A1	Spencer Aviation	
G–BAUM	Bell 206B JetRanger	S. G. Blair & Co. Ltd.	
G–BAUN	Bell 206A JetRanger	Ben Turner & Sons (Helicopters) Ltd.	
G–BAUO	PA-E23 Aztec 250	Petalian Enterprises	
G–BAUP	Spitfire XVI (SL721)	Fairoaks Air Taxis Ltd.	
G–BAUR	F.27 Friendship Mk. 200	Air Anglia Ltd.	
G–BAUV	Cessna F.150L	Bell Associates	
G–BAUW	PA-E23 Aztec 250	Myson Group Ltd.	
G–BAUX	Limba Lapwing	B. J. Jacobson; R. M. Fisher	
G–BAUY	Cessna FRA.150L	Rogers Aviation Ltd.	
G–BAUZ	Nord NC.854S	M. P. Hallam	

Registration	Type	Owner or Operator	Where and when seen
G–BAVA	PA-18 Super Cub	G. M. Hill & G. Mackie	
G–BAVB	Cessna F.172M	C. H. Slaughter & Co. Ltd.	
G–BAVC	Cessna F.150L	Biggin Hill Aviation	
G–BAVE	Beech A.100 King Air	J. C. Bamford Excavators Ltd.	
G–BAVF	Beech 58 Baron	R. W. S. & Co. (Engineers) Ltd.	
G–BAVG	Beech E.90 King Air	Moseley Group (PSV) Ltd.	
G–BAVH	D.H.C.I. Chipmunk 22	J. A. Simms	
G–BAVI	Bell 206B JetRanger	Oldway Ltd.	
G–BAVJ	PA-31 Navajo Chieftain 350	Vickers Ltd.	
G–BAVK	Schweizer Teal TSC-IAI	J. N. Eccott	
G–BAVL	PA-E23 Aztec 250	Otter Controls Ltd.	
G–BAVM	PA-31 Navajo Chieftain	Vickers Ltd.	
G–BAVN	Boeing Stearman PT-17	R.T.A. Smith	
G–BAVO	Boeing Stearman PT-17	Keenair Services Ltd.	
G–BAVP	Beech A.23-24 Musketeer	Foyle Aviation Ltd.	
G–BAVR	AA-5 Traveler	J. E. Fazackerly	
G–BAVS	AA-5 Traveler	Crystal Heart Salad Co. Ltd.	
G–BAVT	BN-2A-6 Islander	Intra Airways Ltd.	
G–BAVU	Cameron A-105 hot-air balloon	J. D. Michaelis	
G–BAVW	PA-E23 Aztec 250	Edinburgh Flying Services Ltd.	
G–BAVX	HPR-7 Herald 214	British Midland Airways Ltd.	
G–BAVY	PA-E23 Aztec 250	British Car Auctions Ltd.	
G–BAVZ	PA-E23 Aztec 250	Southampton Airport Ltd.	
G–BAWA	PA-28R Cherokee Arrow 200-2	Lynwood Upholstery & Furnishing	
G–BAWB	PA-E23 Aztec 250	Robinames Holdings Ltd.	
G–BAWG	PA-28R Cherokee Arrow 200-2	Richard Flint & Co. Ltd.	
G–BAWI	Enstrom F.28A	G. S. Rose	
G–BAWK	PA-28 Cherokee 140	Woodgate Aviation Ltd.	
G–BAWL	Airborne Industries gas airship	A. J. F. Smith	
G–BAWM	Jodel D.112	Wearside Flying Association	
G–BAWN	PA-30C Twin Comanche	J. W. Chafer Ltd.	
G–BAWR	Robin HR.100/210	Clevestones Trans Ltd.	
G–BAWS	PA-25 Pawnee 235C	Farm Aviation Services Ltd.	
G–BAWT	M.S.894E Rallye Minerva	M. J. J. Paterson	
G–BAWU	PA-30 Twin Comanche 160	E. Brooksbank	
G–BAWV	PA-E23 Aztec 250	K. I. Andrew Ltd.	
G–BAWW	Thunder AX-7 0-77 hot-air balloon	Miss Marjory L. C. Hutchins	
G–BAWX	PA-28 Cherokee 180	Plasticisers Ltd.	
G–BAWY	PA-E23 Aztec 250	Moseley Group (PSU) Ltd.	
G–BAWZ	Cessna 402	Kina Holdings Ltd.	
G–BAXC	BN-2A-8 Islander	Britten-Norman (Bembridge) Ltd.	
G–BAXD	BN-2A Mk. III Trislander	Loganair Ltd.	
G–BAXE	Hughes 269A	Walter Downs Ltd.	
G–BAXF	Cameron O-77 hot-air balloon	I. R. Williams, G. Smith & R. G. Bickerdike	
G–BAXG	H.S.125 Srs. IB	Merlot International Aviation Ltd.	
G–BAXH	Cessna 310Q	Force One Ltd.	
G–BAXI	PA-39 Twin Comanche	C.S.E. (Aircraft Services) Ltd.	
G–BAXJ	PA-32 Cherokee Six 300	G. S. Savage & W. D. Vale	
G–BAXK	Thunder Balloon AX-7/77	R. Wilson, J. Woodhead & A. R. Snook	
G–BAXL	H.S.125 Srs. 3B	McAlpine Aviation Ltd.	
G–BAXM	Beech B.24R Sierra	Strangford Flying Group	
G–BAXN	PA-34 Seneca 200-2	Brentercost Ltd.	
G–BAXO	Cessna 414	Charles Spreckley & Co. Ltd.	
G–BAXP	PA-E23 Aztec 250	Air West Ltd.	
G–BAXR	Beech B.55 Baron	Palacelli Aviation Ltd.	
G–BAXS	Bell 47G-5	T. C. Barton	
G–BAXT	PA-28R Cherokee Arrow 180	Williams & Griffin Ltd.	
G–BAXU	Cessna F.172M	West Lancs Aero Club	
G–BAXV	Cessna F.150L	Lease Air Ltd.	

Registration	Type	Owner or Operator	Where and when seen
G–BAXW	Cessna F.150L	Wycombe Air Centre Ltd.	
G–BAXX	Cessna F.150L	Rogers Aviation Ltd.	
G–BAXY	Cessna F.172M	Airgo Ltd.	
G–BAXZ	PA-28 Cherokee 140	A. J. Smith & ptnrs.	
G–BAYA	Bell 206B JetRanger	Goldington Investments Ltd.	
G–BAYC	Cameron O-65 hot-air balloon	Cameron Balloons Ltd.	
G–BAYE	BN-2A-6 Islander	Britten-Norman (Bembridge) Ltd.	
G–BAYH	BN-2A-6 Islander	Britten-Norman (Bembridge) Ltd.	
G–BAYK	Cessna 340	W. H. & J. Rogers Ltd.	
G–BAYL	Nord 1203/111 Norecrin	D. M. Fincham	
G–BAYO	Cessna 150L	Cheshire Air Training School Ltd.	
G–BAYP	Cessna 150L	Bell Associates	
G–BAYR	Robin HR.100/210	Thorney Machinery Co. Ltd.	
G–BAYT	H.S.125 Srs. 600B	Management Agency and Music Ltd.	
G–BAYU	Cessna 310Q	A-One Transport (Leeds) Ltd.	
G–BAYW	Bell 47G-2	Alan Mann Helicopters Ltd.	
G–BAYX	Bell 47G-5	Ben Turner & Sons (Helicopters) Ltd.	
G–BAYY	Cessna 310C	Medburn Air Services Ltd.	
G–BAYZ	Bellanca 7GC BC Citabria	Cambridge University Gliding Trust Ltd.	
G–BAZA	H.S.125 Srs 400B	Armitage Industrial Holdings Ltd.	
G–BAZB	H.S.125 Srs 400B	Dakota & South Bend Securities	
G–BAZC	Robin DR.400/160	Scot-Stock Ltd.	
G–BAZD	PA-31 Navajo	Tolvade Ltd.	
G–BAZG	Boeing 737-204	Britannia Airways Ltd.	
G–BAZH	Boeing 737-204	Britannia Airways Ltd.	
G–BAZI	Boeing 737-204	Britannia Airways Ltd.	
G–BAZJ	HPR-7 Herald 209	British Island Airways	
G–BAZK	Cessna 340	Janet Hunt Ltd.	
G–BAZL	SA.341G Gazelle Srs 1	House of Fraser Ltd.	
G–BAZM	Jodel D.11	Bingley Flying Group	
G–BAZN	Bell 206 JetRanger	Somerton-Rayner Helicopters Ltd.	
G–BAZO	Bell 47G-2	John Pierce (Aviation) Ltd.	
G–BAZP	Cessna F.150L	Biggin Hill Aviation	
G–BAZR	Cessna F.150L	Lonmet (Aviation) Ltd.	
G–BAZS	Cessna F.150L	Channel Islands Aero Services Ltd.	
G–BAZT	Cessna F.172M	Pinhoe Flying Club Ltd.	
G–BAZU	PA-28R Cherokee Arrow 200	R. Bolsover	
G–BAZV	PA-E23 Aztec 250	Skycab (Europe) Northampton Ltd.	
G–BBAB	M.S.894A Minerva	Bluffrye Ltd.	
G–BBAC	Cameron O-77 hot-air balloon	P. G. Dunnington	
G–BBAE	L.1011 TriStar	British Airways	
G–BBAF	L.1011 TriStar	British Airways	
G–BBAG	L.1011 TriStar	British Airways	
G–BBAH	L.1011 TriStar	British Airways	
G–BBAI	L.1011 TriStar	British Airways	
G–BBAJ	L.1011 TriStar	British Airways	
G–BBAK	M.S.894A Rallye Minerva	H. M. Bonquierre	
G–BBAR	Jodel D.117	J. F. Wright	
G–BBAT	Beech C.23 Sundowner	Midland Development Group & Co. (Bristol)	
G–BBAU	Enstrom F.28	Spooner Aviation Ltd.	
G–BBAV	PA-E23 Aztec 250	Baylee Air Charter *St. Owens Bay*	
G–BBAW	Robin HR.100/210	A. Tundisi	
G–BBAX	Robin DR.400/140	S. R. Young	
G–BBAY	Robin DR.400/140	G. A. Pentelow & D. B. Roadnight	
G–BBAZ	Hiller UH-12E	Management Aviation Ltd.	

Registration	Type	Owner or Operator	Where and when seen
G–BBBA	Hiller UH-12E	Management Aviation Ltd.	
G–BBBB	Taylor JT.1 Monoplane	S. A. MacConnacher	
G–BBBC	Cessna F.150L	East Midland School of Flying	
G–BBBD	PA-E23 Aztec 250	Moseley Group (PSV) Ltd.	
G–BBBE	AA-5 Traveler	C. W. Willis	
G–BBBI	AA-5 Traveler	Rosefair Ltd.	
G–BBBJ	PA-E23 Aztec 250	Dateline Aviation Ltd.	
G–BBBK	PA-28 Cherokee 140	D. J. & Mrs. S. E. Merritt	
G–BBBL	Cessna 337	Alderney Air Charter Ltd.	
G–BBBM	Bell 206B JetRanger	Aircraft Transmain Ltd.	
G–BBBN	PA-28 Cherokee 180	Stannair Services Ltd.	
G–BBBO	SIPA 903	R.E. & Mrs. B. A. Ogden	
G–BBBP	Bell 212	Bristow Helicopters Ltd.	
G–BBBR	Enstrom F.28A	Twyford Moors (Helicopters) Ltd.	
G–BBBS	Cessna 182P	Shiftrealm	
G–BBBT	Cameron O-56 hot-air balloon	N. A. Robertson	
G–BBBU	Pitts Special Model 51D	K. Harness	
G–BBBW	FRED Series 2	D. L. Webster	
G–BBBX	Cessna E310L	General Aviation Services Ltd.	
G–BBBY	PA-28 Cherokee 140	Channel Aviation Ltd.	
G–BBBZ	Enstrom F-28	Spooner Aviation Ltd.	
G–BBCA	Bell 206A JetRanger	Hambros Bank Ltd.	
G–BBCB	Western O-65 hot-air balloon	M. Westwood	
G–BBCC	PA-E23 Aztec 250	Peter Clifford Aviation Ltd.	
G–BBCD	Beech 95 B.55 Baron	Turner Engineering Co.	
G–BBCF	Cessna FRA.150L	Lonmet (Aviation) Ltd.	
G–BBCG	Robin DR.400/2+2	Headcorn Flying School Ltd.	
G–BBCH	Robin DR.400/2+2	Headcorn Flying School Ltd.	
G–BBCI	Cessna 150H	Eastern Aviation Ltd.	
G–BBCJ	Cessna 150J	Jack Braithwaite (Aerial Photography) Ltd.	
G–BBCK	Cameron O-77 balloon	R. J. Leathart	
G–BBCM	PA-E23 Aztec 250	Site Aviation Ltd.	
G–BBCN	Robin HR.100/210	Trenery & Sons Ltd.	
G–BBCO	Cessna F.177RG	Lonmet (Aviation) Ltd.	
G–BBCP	Thunder Balloon AX-6/56	Albert J. Parsons & Sons Ltd.	
G–BBCR	Z.326 Trener Master	M. J. S. Jones & Rosamond M. Jones	
G–BBCS	Robin DR.400/140	Avions Robin (UK) Ltd.	
G–BBCT	PA-31 Navajo Chieftain 350	Whitbread & Co. Ltd.	
G–BBCU	PA-E23 Aztec 250	Eastern-Air Executive Ltd.	
G–BBCV	A.188B Agtruck	Mindacre Ltd.	
G–BBCW	PA-E23 Aztec 250	Airgo Ltd.	
G–BBCX	Airship (hot-air) radio-controlled	E. A. Willis & G. W. Moger	
G–BBCY	Luton L.A.4a Minor	C. H. Difford	
G–BBCZ	AA-5 Traveler	V. Bernard	
G–BBDA	AA-5 Traveler	Heron Plastics Ltd.	
G–BBDB	PA-28 Cherokee 180	G. O. McMeekin & K. Newby	
G–BBDC	PA-28 Cherokee 140	Apache Aircraft Services Ltd.	
G–BBDD	PA-28 Cherokee 140	Channel Aviation Ltd.	
G–BBDF	PA-28R Cherokee Arrow 200-2	Lawrence Goodwin Machine Tools Ltd.	
G–BBDG	Concorde 202	BAC Ltd. (Commercial Aircraft Division)	
G–BBDH	Cessna F.172M	Leicestershire Aero Club Ltd.	
G–BBDI	PA-18 Super Cub 150	Scottish Gliding Union Ltd.	
G–BBDJ	Thunder balloon AX6-56	S. W. D. Ashby & H. B. Ashby	
G–BBDK	V.808 Viscount	Air Bridge Carriers Ltd.	
G–BBDL	AA-5 Traveler	A. Howard	
G–BBDM	AA-5 Traveler	T. Kilroe & Sons Ltd.	
G–BBDN	Taylor Monoplane	D. A. Nice	
G–BBDO	PA-E23 Aztec 250	Sealed Motor Construction Co. Ltd.	
G–BBDP	Robin DR.400/160	Braddon & Sons (Haulage) Ltd.	
G–BBDR	PA-31 Navajo	I. D. S. Aircraft Ltd.	

Registration	Type	Owner or Operator	Where and when seen
G–BBDS	PA-31 Navajo	Broad Oak Air Services	
G–BBDT	Cessna 150H	Sherburn Aero Club	
G–BBDU	PA-31 Navajo	Erie Electronics Ltd.	
G–BBDV	SIPA S.903	B. Price	
G–BBEA	Luton L.A.4a Minor	G. J. Hewitt & J. B. Stocks	
G–BBEB	PA-28R Cherokee Arrow 200-2	Everest Aviation Ltd.	
G–BBEC	PA-28 Cherokee 180	Kearns-Barker Associates	
G–BBED	M.S.894B Rallye Minerva	Trago Mills Ltd.	
G–BBEE	Learjet 25B	Pendleton Aviation Ltd.	
G–BBEF	PA-28 Cherokee 140	Air Navigation & Trading Co. Ltd.	
G–BBEG	Bell 206A JetRanger	Shirelade Ltd.	
G–BBEI	PA-31 Navajo	G. Montague (Southern) Ltd.	
G–BBEJ	PA-31 Navajo Chieftain 350	Bejam Group Ltd.	
G–BBEL	PA-28R Cherokee Arrow 180	Ratlin Ltd.	
G–BBEM	Beech B.55 Baron	M. J. Coburn & L. C. G. Hughes	
G–BBEN	Bellanca 7GC-BC Citabria	Airways Aero Association Ltd.	
G–BBEO	Cessna FRA.150L	Pegasus Aviation Ltd.	
G–BBEP	H.S.125 Srs. 600B	De Beers International Air Services Ltd.	
G–BBER	Bell 47G-5A	Hewitts Investment Co. Ltd.	
G–BBEU	Bell 206B JetRanger	Alan Mann Helicopters Ltd.	
G–BBEV	PA-28 Cherokee 140	Bernell Aviation Ltd.	
G–BBEW	PA-E23 Aztec 250	Armstrong Autoparts Ltd.	
G–BBEX	Cessna 185A	Shackleton Aviation Ltd.	
G–BBEY	PA-E23 Aztec 250	Donington Aviation Ltd.	
G–BBFB	Bell 206B JetRanger	Anthony Hutley Ptnrs. Ltd.	
G–BBFC	AA-1B Trainer	V. Bernard	
G–BBFD	PA-28R Cherokee Arrow 200-2	Hambrair Ltd.	
G–BBFE	Bell 206 JetRanger	W. Holmes	
G–BBFF	PA-34 Seneca 200	Airgo Ltd.	
G–BBFK	BN-2A-6 Islander	Britten-Norman (Bembridge) Ltd.	
G–BBFL	GY-201 Minicab	J. K. Davies	
G–BBFM	BN-2A-6 Islander	Britten-Norman (Bembridge) Ltd.	
G–BBFN	BN-2A-6 Islander	Britten-Norman (Bembridge) Ltd.	
G–BBFO	BN-2A-6 Islander	Britten-Norman (Bembridge) Ltd.	
G–BBFS	Van Den Bemden free balloon (Gas)	A. J. F. Smith	
G–BBFT	Cessna A.188B Agtruck	Mindacre Ltd.	
G–BBFU	PA-E23 Aztec 250	Robertson Foods Ltd.	
G–BBFV	PA-32 Cherokee Six 260	G. N. Cassir	
G–BBFW	PA-E23 Aztec 250B	Spooner Aviation Ltd.	
G–BBFX	PA-34 Seneca 200	C. D. Welswall	
G–BBFY	PA-31P Navajo	Armstrong Equipment Ltd.	
G–BBFZ	PA-28R Cherokee Arrow 200-2	Larkfield Garage (Chepstow) Ltd.	
G–BBGA	Scheibe SF-28A	Coventry Gliding Club Ltd.	
G–BBGB	PA-E23 Aztec 250	New Equipment Ltd.	
G–BBGC	M.S.893E Rallye Commodore 180	Channel Island Mortgage Brokers	
G–BBGD	Cessna F.337G	D. Grepne & Co. Ltd.	
G–BBGE	PA-E23 Aztec 250	Casair Aviation Services Ltd.	
G–BBGF	Cessna 340	W. Bridgford Machine Co. Ltd.	
G–BBGG	AA-5 Traveler	Lindsay Motors (Bournemouth) Ltd.	
G–BBGH	AA-5 Traveler	Lindsay Motors (Bournemouth) Ltd.	
G–BBGI	Fuji FA.200-160	Sureway Security Ltd.	
G–BBGJ	Cessna 180	E. J. Parker	
G–BBGK	Lake LA-4-200	Lindrom Racing Service Ltd.	
G–BBGL	Baby Great Lakes	B. C. Cooper	
G–BBGN	Cameron A-150 hot-air balloon	J. P. R. Nott	

Registration	Type	Owner or Operator	Where and when seen
G–BBGO	Robin HR.100/210	Bomford & Evershed	
G–BBGR	Cameron O-65 hot-air balloon	J. N. Burrow & I. J. McDonnell	
G–BBGS	Sikorsky S-61N	Bristow Helicopters Ltd.	
G–BBGU	H.S.125 Srs. 400B	McAlpine Aviation Ltd.	
G–BBGW	Fuji FA.200-180	Shotteswell Flying Group	
G–BBGX	Cessna 182P	Lockwoods Technical Services (Liverpool) Ltd.	
G–BBGZ	(CHABA 42) free balloon	R. A. & G. Laslett, J. Haigh & J. L. Hinton	
G–BBHB	PA-31 Turbo-Navajo	Meridian Airmaps Ltd.	
G–BBHC	Enstrom F-28A	Wm. Shyvers Ltd.	
G–BBHD	Enstrom F-28A	Spooner Aviation Ltd.	
G–BBHE	Enstrom F-28A	T. W. Walker Ltd.	
G–BBHF	PA-23 Aztec 250E	Warner Holidays Ltd.	
G–BBHG	Cessna E-310Q	B. H. Owen & Leaquest Ltd.	
G–BBHI	Cessna 177RG	Hi-Lines Ltd.	
G–BBHJ	Piper J3C-65 Cub	R. V. Miller & R. H. Heath	
G–BBHK	AT-16 Harvard IIB	R. Lamplough	
G–BBHL	Sikorsky S-61N Mk II	Bristow Helicopters Ltd.	
G–BBHM	Sikorsky S-61N Mk II	Bristow Helicopters Ltd.	
G–BBHN	Sikorsky S-61N Mk II	Bristow Helicopters Ltd.	
G–BBHU	SA.341G Gazelle I	Bouley Investments Ltd.	
G–BBHV	SA.341G Gazelle I	A. Smith (Culcheth) Ltd.	
G–BBHW	SA.341G Gazelle I	McAlpine Aviation Ltd.	
G–BBHX	M.S.893E Rallye Commodore	Ankh Enterprises Ltd.	
G–BBHY	PA-28 Cherokee 180	P. J. Whelan	
G–BBHZ	PA-31P Navajo	Berrico Publicity Co. Ltd.	
G–BBIA	PA-28R Cherokee Arrow	Essex Aviation Ltd.	
G–BBIB	B.121 Pup 2	C. A. Lock	
G–BBIC	Cessna 310Q	ATA Grinding Processes	
G–BBID	PA-28 Cherokee 140	CSE Aviation Ltd.	
G–BBIE	PA-28 Cherokee 140	Gold Star Publications Ltd.	
G–BBIF	PA-E23 Aztec 250	Northern Executive Aviation Ltd.	
G–BBIH	Enstrom F-28A	K. D. Gomm	
G–BBII	Fiat G-46-3B	The Hon. Patrick Lindsay	
G–BBIJ	Cessna 421B	Measure International Systems Ltd.	
G–BBIK	Bell 47G-5A	Cedar Farm Ltd.	
G–BBIL	PA-28 Cherokee 140	P. Wimbourne	
G–BBIM	Cessna E-310Q	Arthur Woolacott Ltd.	
G–BBIO	Robin HR.100/210	H. A. Rapp	
G–BBIP	Hughes 269	Point to Point Helicopters Ltd.	
G–BBIR	Hughes 269	Diagnostic Reagents Ltd.	
G–BBIS	Hughes 269	W. P. Brierley-Jones	
G–BBIT	Hughes 269B	W. R. Finance Ltd.	
G–BBIU	Hughes 269C	W. R. Finance Ltd.	
G–BBIV	Hughes 269C	W. R. Finance Ltd.	
G–BBIW	Hughes 269C	W. R. Finance Ltd.	
G–BBIX	PA-28 Cherokee 140	J. E. Fricker	
G–BBIY	Taylor Monoplane	D. S. Bateman	
G–BBJB	Thunder balloon AX7/77	Anglia Balloon School Ltd.	
G–BBJD	Cessna 172M	Cheshire Scaffold Co. Ltd.	
G–BBJE	SA.318C Alouette	Medminster Ltd.	
G–BBJF	Beech 58 Baron	Allied Breweries (UK) Ltd.	
G–BBJG	PA-31 Navajo Chieftain 350	McAlpine Aviation Ltd.	
G–BBJH	Cessna A-188B Agtruck	Bowker Air Services Ltd.	
G–BBJI	Isaacs Spitfire	J. O. Isaacs	
G–BBJT	Robin HR.200/100	Avions Robin (UK) Ltd.	
G–BBJU	Robin DR.400/140	Highford Transport Ltd.	
G–BBJV	Cessna F.177RG	Warner Holidays Ltd.	
G–BBJW	Cessna FRA.150L	Gordon King (Aviation) Ltd.	
G–BBJX	Cessna F.150L	Westair Flying Services Ltd.	
G–BBJY	Cessna F.172M	J. Lucketti	
G–BBJZ	Cessna F.172M	Westair Flying Services Ltd.	
G–BBKA	Cessna F.150 Commuter	Executive Air	

Registration	Type	Owner or Operator	Where and when seen
G–BBKB	Cessna F.150L	Earl of Ronaldshay	
G–BBKC	Cessna F.172M	Stoa Trading Ltd.	
G–BBKE	Cessna F.150 Commuter	Park Plant Ltd.	
G–BBKF	Cessna FRA.150L	J. H. Heath Ltd.	
G–BBKG	Cessna FR.172J	Lawrence Wilson & Son Ltd.	
G–BBKH	Cessna F.172M	B. D. & Mrs. W. Phillips	
G–BBKI	Cessna F.172M	G. Crawford	
G–BBKJ	Cessna FT.337G	Carters Gold Medal Soft Drinks Ltd.	
G–BBKK	Cessna E310	The Balby Cinema Ltd.	
G–BBKL	Piel CP.310A Emeraude	W. J. Walker	
G–BBKM	Beech King Air E90	Brismo Finance Ltd.	
G–BBKN	Beech King Air C90	St. Mary's (Plant Hire) Ltd.	
G–BBKO	Thunder AX7/77	British Bacon Curers Federation	
G–BBKR	Scheibe Motorspatz	D. W. Bridson	
G–BBKU	Cessna FRA.150L	Lonmet (Aviation) Ltd.	
G–BBKV	Cessna FRA.150L	Lonmet (Aviation) Ltd.	
G–BBKW	Bell 47G-2	Alan Mann Helicopters Ltd.	
G–BBKX	PA-28 Cherokee Challenger 180	D. W. Houlston (Farms) Ltd.	
G–BBKY	Cessna F.150L	Leicestershire Aero Club Ltd.	
G–BBKZ	Cessna F.172M	West Country Aircraft Servicing Ltd.	
G–BBLA	PA-28 Cherokee 140	D. C. Annis	
G–BBLB	Hiller UH-12E	Central Helicopters Services Ltd.	
G–BBLC	Hiller UH-12E	Central Helicopters Services Ltd.	
G–BBLD	Hiller UH-12E	Central Helicopters Services Ltd.	
G–BBLE	Hiller UH-12E	Central Helicopters Services Ltd.	
G–BBLG	Hiller UH-12E	Sloane Aviation Ltd.	
G–BBLH	Piper O-59A Grasshopper	R. S. Ball & Miss S. C. Brooks	
G–BBLI	Aero Commander 500S	Dennis Vanguard Intnl (Switchgear) Ltd.	
G–BBLJ	Cessna 402B	Lewis Trusts	
G–BBLL	Cameron O-84 hot-air balloon	University of East Anglia Hot-Air Ballooning Club	
G–BBLM	Rallye 100 Sport	E. F. G. Flying Services Ltd.	
G–BBLP	PA-E23 Aztec	Lonmet (Aviation) Ltd.	
G–BBLS	AA-5 Traveler	General Aviation Sales Ltd.	
G–BBLT	AA-5 Traveler	R. H. Neale	
G–BBLU	PA-34 Seneca	Pauling (Middle East) Ltd.	
G–BBLX	BN-2A-8 Islander	George Wimpey & Co. Ltd.	
G–BBMB	Robin DR.400/180	R. B. Tyler	
G–BBME	BAC One-Eleven 401	British Airways	
G–BBMF	BAC One-Eleven 401	British Airways	
G–BBMG	BAC One-Eleven 408	British Airways	
G–BBMH	E.A.A. Sport Biplane Model P.1	K. Dawson	
G–BBMI	Dewoitine D.26 (282)	R. J. Willies	
G–BBMJ	PA-E23 Aztec 250	Webster Aviation Ltd.	
G–BBMK	PA-31 Navajo	Bovis Ltd.	
G–BBML	PA-31 Navajo	Norwich Union Fire Insurance Society Ltd.	
G–BBMN	D.H.C.1 Chipmunk 22	R. Steiner	
G–BBMO	D.H.C.1 Chipmunk 22	Chiltern Valley Aviation	
G–BBMP	D.H.C.1 Chipmunk 22	M. J. Harvey & J. R. Rochester	
G–BBMS	D.H.C.1 Chipmunk 22	Colton Aviation Services Ltd.	
G–BBMT	D.H.C.1 Chipmunk 22	A. T. Letts & ptnrs.	
G–BBMU	D.H.C.1 Chipmunk 22	A. G. Horsley	
G–BBMV	D.H.C.1 Chipmunk 22	Wilrow Products Co. Ltd.	
G–BBMW	D.H.C.1 Chipmunk 22	S. J. Leonard	
G–BBMX	D.H.C.1 Chipmunk 22	B. R. C. Wild	
G–BBMY	D.H.C.1 Chipmunk 22	A. C. B. Chapman	
G–BBMZ	D.H.C.1 Chipmunk 22	A. G. Horsley	
G–BBNA	D.H.C.1 Chipmunk 22	RAFGSA Bicester	
G–BBNB	D.H.C.1 Chipmunk 22	A. J. Hurst	

Registration	Type	Owner or Operator	Where and when seen
G–BBND	D.H.C.I Chipmunk 22	West Johnson Property Holdings	
G–BBNE	*D.H.C.I Chipmunk T.10 (WZ873)	Aeroplane Collection Ltd.	
G–BBNF	D.H.C.I Chipmunk 22	A. G. Horsley	
G–BBNG	Bell 206A JetRanger	Bristow Helicopters Ltd.	
G–BBNH	PA-34 Seneca	Ackrill Johnson-Homes Ltd.	
G–BBNI	PA-34 Seneca	H. A. Stradling & Sons Ltd.	
G–BBNJ	Cessna F.150L	Channel Islands Aero Services Ltd.	
G–BBNK	PA-23 Aztec 250E	George House Holdings Ltd.	
G–BBNL	BN-2A-Mk III Trislander	Loganair Ltd.	
G–BBNM	PA-E23 Aztec 250E	Mann Aviation Sales Ltd.	
G–BBNN	PA-E23 Aztec 250D	J. W. B. Wimble	
G–BBNO	PA-E23 Aztec 250E	Caring Securities Ltd.	
G–BBNR	Cessna 340	J. Lipton	
G–BBNS	Cessna 310Q	Birchwood Boat Co. Ltd.	
G–BBNT	PA-31-350 Navajo Chieftain	Simpson Ready Foods Ltd.	
G–BBNV	Fuji FA.200-160	C.S.E. (Aircraft Services) Ltd.	
G–BBNW	Cessna F.177RG	Fairoaks Aviation Services Ltd.	
G–BBNX	Cessna FRA.150L	Three Counties Aero Club Ltd.	
G–BBNY	Cessna FRA.150L	Air Tows Ltd.	
G–BBNZ	Cessna F.172M	Clark Masts Ltd.	
G–BBOA	Cessna F.172M	George House Holdings Ltd.	
G–BBOB	Cessna 421B	Barclays Export & Finances Co. Ltd.	
G–BBOC	Cameron O-77 hot-air balloon	A. G. Hopkins, B. J. Campbell, M. A. Campbell, K. Chapman, J. R. Joiner & A. C. Maclaurin-Jones	
G–BBOD	Thunder A-6 0-56A balloon	Thunder Balloons Ltd.	
G–BBOE	Robin HR.200/100	Goodwood Terrena Ltd.	
G–BBOH	Pitts S-IS Special	P. Meeson	
G–BBOI	Bede BD-5B	Heather V. B. Wheeler	
G–BBOJ	PA-E23 Aztec 250	Bernell Aviation Ltd.	
G–BBOK	PA-E23 Aztec 250E	Clyde Foster Ltd.	
G–BBOL	PA-18 Super Cub 150	Sir Leonard & Lady Joan M. Redshaw	
G–BBOM	PA-E23 Aztec 250E	Bristol Air Taxis Ltd.	
G–BBOO	Thunder A-6 0-56 Balloon	K. Meehan	
G–BBOP	PA-28R Cherokee Arrow 200 Mk. II	Plasterstrip Ltd.	
G–BBOR	Bell 206B JetRanger	Bowater Packaging Ltd.	
G–BBOS	Bell 206B JetRanger	British Executive Air Services Ltd.	
G–BBOX	Thunder Ax-7 0-77 balloon	Quixote Balloon Group	
G–BBOY	Thunder Ax-6 0-56A balloon	Thunder Balloons Ltd.	
G–BBPC	PA-31 Navajo Commuter	Robertson Foods Ltd.	
G–BBPJ	Cessna F.172M	Anderson Flying School Ltd.	
G–BBPK	Evans VP-I	P. D. Kelsey	
G–BBPM	Enstrom F-28A	Graysbrook Leasing Ltd.	
G–BBPN	Enstrom F-28A	Compton-Sager Ltd.	
G–BBPO	Enstrom F-28A	Spooner Aviation Ltd.	
G–BBPP	PA-28 Cherokee 180	J. D. B. Hamilton	
G–BBPS	Jodel D.117	P. T. Nelson	
G–BBPU	Boeing 747-136	British Airways	
G–BBPW	Robin HR.100/210	Parlway Ltd.	
G–BBPX	PA-34 Seneca 200-2	L. Hinchcliffe & E. Appleyard Ltd.	
G–BBPY	PA-28 Cherokee 180 Challenger	J. R. Lees	
G–BBPZ	PA-E23 Aztec 250D	Casair Aviation Services Ltd.	
G–BBRA	PA-E23 Aztec 250E	Bristol Air Taxis Ltd.	

* Historic aircraft, preserved in non-flying condition.

Registration	Type	Owner or Operator	Where and when seen
G–BBRB	D.H.82A Tiger Moth (DF198)	R. Barham	
G–BBRC	Fuji FA.200-180	Zachary (Fencing) Ltd.	
G–BBRD	PA-E23 Aztec 250	Omega Consultants	
G–BBRE	Fuji FA.200-160	Baitstrand of Kirton Ltd.	
G–BBRG	Bell 47G-5A	N. H. Andrew	
G–BBRH	Bell 47G-5A	Webster Aviation Ltd.	
G–BBRI	Bell 47G-5A	Camlet Helicopters Ltd.	
G–BBRJ	PA-E23 Aztec 250E	P. E. Cadbury	
G–BBRK	D.H.C. Ia Chipmunk 22	B. R. Kay	
G–BBRL	PA-31P Pressurised Navajo	Rialto Aviation Ltd.	
G–BBRM	BN-2A-3 Islander	Britten-Norman (Bembridge) Ltd.	
G–BBRN	Procter Kittiwake	RN Gliding & Soaring Assoc.	
G–BBRO	H.S.125 Srs. 600B	McAlpine Aviation Ltd.	
G–BBRP	BN-2A-9 Islander	George Wimpey & Co. Ltd.	
G–BBRS	Enstrom F-28A	Helicopter Hire Ltd.	
G–BBRV	D.H.C.I Chipmunk 22	HSA (Chester) Sports & Social Club	
G–BBRW	PA-28 Cherokee 140	J. Martin	
G–BBRX	SIAI-Marchetti S.205-18F	R. G. Lowerson	
G–BBRY	Cessna 210	Mrs. S. E. Warrilow	
G–BBRZ	AA-5 Traveler	Galaxy Publications Ltd.	
G–BBSA	AA-5 Traveler	G. W. Hind	
G–BBSB	Beech C23 Sundowner	Hitchin (Hatfield) Ltd.	
G–BBSC	Beech B24R Sierra	Universal Film Laboratory	
G–BBSD	Beech 58 Baron	A.B.I. Caravans Ltd.	
G–BBSE	D.H.C.I Chipmunk 22	R. Goodwin & Co. Ltd.	
G–BBSF	Cessna 310Q	Offenview Construction Co. Ltd.	
G–BBSG	Cessna 182P	Westair Flying Services Ltd.	
G–BBSH	SA.341G Gazelle I	Rogers Aviation Ltd.	
G–BBSI	SA.341G Gazelle I	McAlpine Aviation Ltd.	
G–BBSL	PA-E23 Aztec 250E	Brooklands Aviation Ltd.	
G–BBSM	PA-32 Cherokee Six 300	All Seasons Aviation Co. Ltd.	
G–BBSN	PA-E23 Aztec 250	Burnthills	
G–BBSO	PA-28 Cherokee 140	CSE Aviation Ltd.	
G–BBSR	PA-E23 Aztec 250D	LDL Enterprises	
G–BBSS	D.H.C. Ia Chipmunk	Northumbria Gliding Club	
G–BBST	PA-E23 Aztec 250	Luton Flying Club	
G–BBSU	Cessna 421B	P. E. Cadbury	
G–BBSV	Cessna 421B	Ernest George Aviation Ltd.	
G–BBSW	Pietenpol Air Camper	J. K. S. Wills	
G–BBSX	Cessna 310Q	Ambrian Aviation Ltd.	
G–BBSZ	DC-10 Srs. 10	Laker Airways (International) Ltd.	
G–BBTB	Cessna FRA.150L	Fairey Britten-Norman Air Services Ltd.	
G–BBTC	Cessna FRA.150L	Fairoaks Aviation Services Ltd.	
G–BBTG	Cessna F.172M	Light Planes (Lancashire) Ltd.	
G–BBTH	Cessna F.172M	N. J. Orr	
G–BBTJ	PA-E23 Aztec 250E	Moseley Group (PSV) Ltd.	
G–BBTK	Cessna FRA.150L	Airwork Services Ltd.	
G–BBTL	PA-E23 Aztec 250C	Northern Executive Aviation Ltd.	
G–BBTM	D.H.C.I Chipmunk T.10	M. D. N. Fisher	
G–BBTS	Beech V35B Bonanza	Golden Sands Estates Ltd.	
G–BBTT	Cessna F.150L	Ulster Aviation Ltd.	
G–BBTU	Socata ST-10 Diplomate	F. T. Arnold	
G–BBTV	Bell 206B JetRanger	Trident Management	
G–BBTW	PA-31P Pressurised Navajo	Siwel Charter Ltd.	
G–BBTX	Beech C23 Sundowner	T.C.F.W. Ltd.	
G–BBTY	Beech C23 Sundowner	M. R. Joyce	
G–BBTZ	Cessna F.150L	Ulster Aviation Ltd.	
G–BBUD	Sikorsky S-61N Mk. II	British Airways Helicopters Ltd.	
G–BBUE	AA-5 Traveler	Jobar Properties Ltd.	
G–BBUF	AA-5 Traveler	Bernell Aviation Ltd.	
G–BBUG	PA-16 Clipper	C. M. L. Edwards	

Registration	Type	Owner or Operator	Where and when seen
G–BBUH	AA-1B Trainer	Flight-Line Ltd.	
G–BBUI	AA-5 Traveler	Barfax Distributing Co. Ltd.	
G–BBUJ	Cessna 421B Golden Eagle	The Automobile Association	
G–BBUK	Bell 47G-2	Bristow Helicopters Ltd.	
G–BBUL	Mitchell-Procter Kittiwake I	R. Bull	
G–BBUN	Cessna 182P	Brymon Aviation Ltd.	
G–BBUO	Cessna 150L	West Country Aircraft Servicing Ltd.	
G–BBUP	B.121 Pup I	C. C. Brown	
G–BBUT	Western O-65 Hot Air Balloon	Wg. Cdr. G. F. Turnbull & Mrs. K. Turnbull	
G–BBUU	Piper L-4B Cub	McAully Flying Group	
G–BBUV	D.H.106 Comet 4B	Dan-Air Services Ltd.	
G–BBUW	K. & S. SA.102.5 Cavalier	A. D. Mills & K. Gwilliam	
G–BBUX	Bell 206B JetRanger 2	Alan Mann Helicopters Ltd.	
G–BBUY	Bell 206B JetRanger 2	O. G. Lywood Ltd.	
G–BBVA	Sikorsky S-61N Mk. II	Bristow Helicopters Ltd.	
G–BBVB	Sikorsky S-61N Mk. II	Bristow Helicopters Ltd.	
G–BBVC	Slingsby T-59D Kestrel	Vickers Ltd.	
G–BBVE	Cessna 340	Planet Gloves (Industrial) Ltd.	
G–BBVF	Scottish Aviation Twin Pioneer III	Flight One Ltd.	
G–BBVG	PA-E23 Aztec 250D	Keenair Services Ltd.	
G–BBVH	V.807 Viscount	Gibraltar Airways Ltd.	
G–BBVI	Enstrom F.28A	CSE Aviation Ltd.	
G–BBVJ	Beech B24R Sierra	Moto Baldet (Northampton) Ltd.	
G–BBVK	Beech C.90 King Air	Eagle Aircraft Services Ltd.	
G–BBVM	Beech A.100 King Air	Dowty Group Services	
G–BBVO	Isaacs Fury II	D. B. Wilson	
G–BBVP	Westland-Bell 47G-3B1	Freemans of Bewdley (Aviation) Ltd.	
G–BBVR	PA-31-350 Navajo Chieftain	Comput Air Ltd.	
G–BBWI	D.H.C.1 Chipmunk T.10	Hendry and Hawkins Ltd.	
G–BBWK	D.H.C.1 Chipmunk T.10	Sky Trade (Components) Ltd.	
G–BBWL	D.H.C.1 Chipmunk T.10	Sky Trade (Components) Ltd	
G–BBWM	PA-E23 Aztec 250E	Sun Valley Poultry	
G–BBWN	D.H.C.1 Chipmunk T.10	Colton Aviation Services	
G–BBWZ	AA-1B Trainer	Freemans of Bewdly (Aviation) Ltd.	
G–BBXA	Beech B.55 Baron	Culley Transport (Luton) Ltd.	
G–BBXB	Cessna FRA.150L	Lonmet (Aviation) Ltd.	
G–BBXD	Bensen B.8M-VW	J. Remington	
G–BBXE	PA-E23 Aztec 250	Sovereign Chemical Industries Ltd.	
G–BBXF	Hughes 369HS	Gerry Hill (VW) Ltd.	
G–BBXG	PA-34-200 Seneca	Milford Car Services Ltd.	
G–BBXH	Cessna FR.172H	Vale Hire & Contracting Co., Ltd.	
G–BBXI	HPR-7 Herald 203	British Island Airways Ltd.	
G–BBXJ	HPR-7 Herald 203	British Island Airways Ltd.	
G–BBXK	PA-34-200 Seneca	Channel Aviation Ltd.	
G–BBXL	Cessna 310	Kearns-Barker Associates Ltd.	
G–BBXO	Enstrom F.28A	CSE Aviation Ltd.	
G–BBXP	PA-34-200 Seneca	Northern Executive Aviation Ltd.	
G–BBXR	PA-31-350 Navajo Chieftain	Rolls-Royce (1971) Ltd.	
G–BBXS	Piper J3C-65 Cub	J. Connolly	
G–BBXT	Cessna F 172M	McLarnon Aviation	
G–BBXU	Beech B24R Sierra	Eagle Aircraft Services Ltd.	
G–BBXV	PA-28 Cherokee Warrior	Marshall Langston Ltd.	
G–BBXW	PA-28 Cherokee Warrior	K. S. F. Clark & G. Avery	
G–BBXX	PA-31-350 Navajo Chieftain	Rolls-Royce (1971) Ltd.	
G–BBXY	Bellanca 7GC BC Scout	Wallis and Sons Ltd.	

Registration	Type	Owner or Operator	Where and when seen
G–BBXZ	Evans VP-I	G. D. M. Price	
G–BBYA	D.H.104 Dove 6	IMI Aviation Ltd.	
G–BBYB	PA-18 Super Cub	Hornet Aviation Ltd.	
G–BBYE	Cessna 195	Wilrow Products Ltd.	
G–BBYH	Cessna 182P	Sanderson (Forklifts) Ltd.	
G–BBYK	PA-E23 Aztec 250	Bristol Air Taxis Ltd.	
G–BBYL	Cameron O-77 Hot-air Balloon	Cameron Balloons Ltd.	
G–BBYM	H.P.137 Jetstream 200	The Morgan Crucible Co. Ltd.	
G–BBYO	BN-2A Mk. III Trislander	Aurigny Airlines	
G–BBYP	PA-28 Cherokee 140	Channel Aviation Ltd.	
G–BBYR	Cameron O-65 Hot-Air Balloon	D. M. Winder	
G–BBYS	Cessna 182P	Forth Engineering Ltd.	
G–BBYT	Cessna 414	K. W. Hawes Electrical Co. Ltd.	
G–BBYU	Cameron O-56 Hot-Air Balloon	C. J. T. Davey	
G–BBYW	PA-28 Cherokee 140	C.S.E. (Aircraft Services) Ltd.	
G–BBZB	PA-31 Navajo Chieftain 350	Hit Record Productions Ltd.	
G–BBZE	PA-28 Cherokee 140	C.S.E. (Aircraft Services) Ltd.	
G–BBZF	PA-28 Cherokee 140	C.S.E. (Aircraft Services) Ltd.	
G–BBZG	Boeing 720-051B	Monarch Airlines Ltd.	
G–BBZH	PA-28R Cherokee Arrow 200	TFC Foods Ltd.	
G–BBZI	PA-31 Navajo 310	Reckitt & Colman Products Ltd.	
G–BBZJ	PA-34 Seneca 200	C.S.E. (Aircraft Services) Ltd.	
G–BBZK	Westland-Bell 47G-3B1	Trent Helicopters Ltd.	
G–BBZL	Westland-Bell 47G-3B1	St. Lawrence H. Webb	
G–BBZN	Fuji FA.200-180	Drillfield Engineering Co. Ltd.	
G–BBZO	Fuji FA.200-160	A. W. Faulkener	
G–BBZP	PA-31 Navajo Chieftain 360	Fairflight Charters Ltd.	
G–BBZR	Enstrom F-28A	CSE Aviation Ltd.	
G–BBZS	Enstrom F-28A	Spooner Aviation Ltd.	
G–BBZU	BN-2A-6 Islander	Britten-Norman (Bembridge) Ltd.	
G–BBZV	PA-28R Cherokee Arrow 200 Mk. II	Unicol Engineering	
G–BBZW	BN-2A-6 Islander	Britten-Norman (Bembridge) Ltd.	
G–BCAB	M.S.894A Rallye Minerva 220	P. V. & Mrs. E. M. Gillian	
G–BCAC	M.S.894A Rallye Minerva 220	Judd Studios Ltd.	
G–BCAD	M.S.894A Rallye Minerva 220	R. & Mrs. M. Allan t/a RMA Aviation	
G–BCAH	D.H.C.I Chipmunk 10	D. E. Hughes & J. Powell	
G–BCAJ	PA-25 Pawnee 235	Farmair Ltd.	
G–BCAL	Boeing 707-338C	British Caledonian Airways Ltd.	
G–BCAN	Thunder Ax-7-77 Hot-Air Balloon	R. B. Williamson & ptnrs.	
G–BCAP	Cameron O-56 Hot-Air Balloon	P. A. Salmons	
G–BCAR	Thunder Ax-7-77 Hot-Air Balloon	T. J. Woodbridge	
G–BCAS	Thunder Ax-7-77 Hot-Air Balloon	Lasham Ballooning Society	
G–BCAT	PA-31 Turbo Navajo 310	—	
G–BCAY	Rockwell Commander 685	Anglian Double Glazing (Kent) Ltd.	
G–BCAZ	PA-12 Super Cruiser	Dr. C. J. Pennycuick	
G–BCBA	Boeing 720-023B	Invicta International	
G–BCBD	Bede BD-5	Brockmore-Bede Aircraft Ltd.	
G–BCBG	PA-E23 Aztec 250	D. R. Burrell	
G–BCBH	Fairchild 24R-46A	Aeromac Ltd.	
G–BCBI	Cessna 402B	Fairoaks Aviation Services Ltd.	
G–BCBJ	PA-25 Pawnee 235	Westwick Distributors Ltd.	
G–BCBK	Cessna 421B Golden Eagle	Lloyds & Scottish Development Ltd.	

G-BBAE. (Top) Lockheed L.1011-1 TriStar (three 42,000lb st Rolls-Royce RB.211-22B)/*Peter J. Bish*

G-BBEP. (Centre) Hawker Siddeley H.S.125 Srs. 600B (two 3,750lb st Rolls-Royce Bristol Viper 601-22)/
Austin J. Brown

G-BBNL. (Above) Britten-Norman BN-2A-Mk III Trislander (three 260hp Lycoming O-540-E4C5)/
Peter J. Bish

G-BCEB.   (Top)   Sikorsky S-61N Mk II (two 1,500shp General Electric CT58-140-2)/*John Goring*

G-BCHX.   (Centre)   Scheibe SF.23A Sperling (95hp Continental C90-12F)/*Air Portraits*

G-BCWE.   (Above)   Handley Page HPR-7 Herald 206 (two 1,910shp Rolls-Royce Dart Mk 527)/*John Goring*

Registration	Type	Owner or Operator	Where and when seen
G–BCBL	Fairchild 24R-46A Argus III	A. V. Horsey	
G–BCBM	PA-E23 Aztec 250	Southend Light Aviation Centre Ltd.	
G–BCBN	Scheibe SF-27	D. B. James	
G–BCBO	PA-31P Pressurised Navajo	C.S.E. Aviation Ltd.	
G–BCBP	M.S.880B Rallye 100S Sport	B. W. J. Pring	
G–BCBR	AJEP/Wittman Tailwind	V. G. & D. V. Orme	
G–BCBT	PA-28R Cherokee Arrow 180	Spooner Aviation Ltd.	
G–BCBU	PA-25 Pawnee 235	Miller Aerial Spraying Ltd.	
G–BCBV	PA-25 Pawnee 235	Miller Aerial Spraying Ltd.	
G–BCBW	Cessna 182P	Brailsford Aviation Ltd.	
G–BCBX	Cessna F.150L	Ulster Aviation Ltd.	
G–BCBZ	Cessna 337C Super Skymaster	B. W. G. Bower	
G–BCCA	Cessna A.188B Agwagon	Yellow Bird Air Services	
G–BCCB	Robin HR.200/100 Club	Goodwood Terrena Ltd.	
G–BCCC	Cessna F.150L	Airgo Ltd.	
G–BCCD	Cessna F.172M	Airgo Ltd.	
G–BCCE	PA-E23 Aztec 250	J. & Y. Plastics (Aviation) Ltd.	
G–BCCF	PA-28 Cherokee 180 Challenger	J. T. Friskney Ltd.	
G–BCCG	Thunder Ax-7-65 Hot-Air Balloon	Ascentive Promotions	
G–BCCH	Thunder Ax-6-56A Hot-Air Balloon	Wrangler, Bluebell Apparel Ltd.	
G–BCCK	AA-5 Traveler	M. Rahman	
G–BCCL	HS.125 Srs. 600B	McAlpine Aviation Ltd.	
G–BCCN	Robin HR.200/100 Club	Brooklands Aviation Ltd.	
G–BCCO	Robin HR.200/100 Club	Brooklands Aviation Ltd.	
G–BCCP	Robin HR.200/100 Club	Brooklands Aviation Ltd.	
G–BCCR	Piel CP.301A Emeraude	A. B. Fisher	
G–BCCW	Bell 47D-1	Twyford Moors (Helicopters) Ltd.	
G–BCCX	DHC.1 Chipmunk 22	RAFGSA	
G–BCCY	Robin HR.200/100 Club	Goodwood Terrena Ltd.	
G–BCDA	Boeing 727-46	Dan-Air Services Ltd.	
G–BCDB	PA-34 Seneca 200	C.S.E. (Aircraft Services) Ltd.	
G–BCDC	PA-18 Super Cub 95	J. Braithwaite (Aerial Photography)	
G–BCDE	Sikorsky S-58-ET	Bristow Helicopters Ltd.	
G–BCDF	Sikorsky S-58-ET	Bristow Helicopters Ltd.	
G–BCDG	Sikorsky S-58-ET	Bristow Helicopters Ltd.	
G–BCDH	MBB BO.105D	North-Scottish Helicopters Ltd.	
G–BCDI	Cessna T.310Q-11	Anglo African Machinery	
G–BCDJ	PA-28 Cherokee 140	Andrewsfield Flying Club	
G–BCDK	Partenavia P.68B Victor	DK Aviation Ltd.	
G–BCDL	Cameron O-42 Hot-Air Balloon	D. P. & Mrs. B. O. Turner	
G–BCDN	F.27 Friendship Mk. 200	Air Anglia	
G–BCDO	F.27 Friendship Mk. 200	Air Anglia	
G–BCDP	Cessna 182P	Anderson Flying School Ltd.	
G–BCDR	Thunder Ax7-77 Hot-Air Balloon	Edinburgh University Hot-Air Ballooning Club	
G–BCDS	PA-E23 Aztec 250	Exir (Aviation) Ltd.	
G–BCDU	Cessna 414	Kasugo Ltd.	
G–BCDV	Western O-65 Hot-Air Balloon	M. Westwood	
G–BCDW	Hughes 269C	Point-to-Point Helicopters Ltd.	
G–BCDY	Cessna FRA.150L	Westair Flying Services Ltd.	
G–BCDZ	H.S.748 Srs. 2A	Hawker Siddeley Aviation Ltd.	
G–BCEA	Sikorsky S-61N Mk. II	British Airways Helicopters Ltd.	
G–BCEB	Sikorsky S-61N Mk. II	British Airways Helicopters Ltd.	
G–BCEC	Cessna F.172M	East Midlands School of Flying Ltd.	
G–BCED	Cessna 421B	J. L. Shaw (HFX) Ltd.	

Registration	Type	Owner or Operator	Where and when seen
G–BCEE	AA-5 Traveler	K. Dando	
G–BCEF	AA-5 Traveler	Channel Motors Ltd.	
G–BCEO	AA-5 Traveler	Peter Scott Aviation	
G–BCEP	AA-5 Traveler	Nottingham Industrial Cleaners Ltd.	
G–BCER	GY-201 Minicab	R. C. Duggleby	
G–BCES	PA-31 Navajo Chieftain 350	Peter Clifford Aviation Ltd.	
G–BCEU	Cameron O-42 Hot-Air Balloon	Entertainment Services Ltd.	
G–BCEX	PA-E23 Aztec 250	Weekes Bros. (Welling) Ltd.	
G–BCEY	D.H.C.I Chipmunk T.10	D. O. Wallis	
G–BCEZ	Cameron O-84 Hot-Air Balloon	Anglia Aeronauts Ascension Association	
G–BCFB	Cameron O-77 Hot-Air Balloon	J. J. Harris & P. Pryce-Jones	
G–BCFC	Cameron O-65 Hot-Air Balloon	R. J. B. Horton	
G–BCFD	West Hot-Air Balloon	E. D. & J. N. West	
G–BCFE	Odyssey 4000 Hot-Air Balloon	R. M. Glover	
G–BCFF	Fuji FA-200-160	C.S.E. (Aircraft Services)	
G–BCFN	Cameron O-65 Hot-Air Balloon	T. Aston & Partners	
G–BCFO	PA-18 Super Cub	Bristol & Gloucestershire Gliding Club (Pty) Ltd.	
G–BCFP	Enstrom F.28A	Northfield Carpets Ltd.	
G–BCFR	Cessna FRA.150L	W. H. & J. Rogers Group Ltd.	
G–BCFS	Saab 91D Safir	A. J. Walter (Aviation) Ltd.	
G–BCFV	Saab 91D Safir	A. J. Walter (Aviation) Ltd.	
G–BCFW	Saab 91D Safir	A. J. Walter (Aviation) Ltd.	
G–BCFY	Luton L.A.4a Minor	G. F. M. Garner	
G–BCFZ	Cameron A.500 Hot-Air Balloon	Heineken Ltd.	
G–BCGA	PA-34 Seneca 200	Graham How Holdings Ltd.	
G–BCGB	Bensen B8	P. C. Lovegrove	
G–BCGC	D.H.C.I Chipmunk 22	Culdrose Gliding Club	
G–BCGD	PA-28R Cherokee Arrow 200	Thistle Metalics Ltd.	
G–BCGE	Bell 212	British Executive Air Services Ltd.	
G–BCGG	AJEP/Wittman Tailwind	C. G. Gray	
G–BCGH	Nord NC.854S	M. P. Hallam	
G–BCGI	PA-28 Cherokee 140	C.S.E. (Aircraft Services) Ltd.	
G–BCGJ	PA-28 Cherokee 140	C.S.E. (Aircraft Services) Ltd.	
G–BCGK	PA-28 Cherokee 140	C.S.E. (Aircraft Services) Ltd.	
G–BCGL	Jodel D.112	J. R. Webster	
G–BCGM	Jodel D.120	I. E. Fisher	
G–BCGN	PA-28 Cherokee 140	C.S.E. (Aircraft Services) Ltd.	
G–BCGO	PA-25 Pawnee 260	Harvest Air Ltd.	
G–BCGS	PA-28R Cherokee Arrow 200	Spooner Aviation Ltd.	
G–BCGT	PA-28 Cherokee 140	A. J. Wilkinson & A. W. Prior	
G–BCGU	HP.137 Jetstream 200	A. Guinness Son & Co.	
G–BCGW	Jodel D.11	G. H. & M. D. Chittenden	
G–BCGX	Bede BD-5A/B	R. Hodgson	
G–BCGZ	BN-2A-6 Islander	Britten-Norman (Bembridge) Ltd.	
G–BCHF	BN-2A-6 Islander	Britten-Norman (Bembridge) Ltd.	
G–BCHI	Hughes 269C	Autair International Ltd.	
G–BCHJ	Cessna F.172H	Martleair Ltd.	
G–BCHK	Cessna F.172H	Cunliffe Engineering Ltd.	
G–BCHL	D.H.C.I Chipmunk 22A	I. Paul & R. Rutherford	
G–BCHM	SA.341G Gazelle	Westland Helicopters Ltd.	
G–BCHN	SA.341G Gazelle	Westland Helicopters Ltd.	
G–BCHO	BN-2A-6 Islander	Britten-Norman (Bembridge) Ltd.	
G–BCHP	CP.1310-C3 Super Emeraude	B. V. Mayo	
G–BCHR	PA-23 Aztec 250	J. D. Read	

Registration	Type	Owner or Operator	Where and when seen
G–BCHT	Schleicher ASK.16	K. M. Barton & partners	
G–BCHU	Dawes VP-2	G. Dawes	
G–BCHV	D.H.C.I. Chipmunk 22	N. F. Charles	
G–BCHW	D.H.C.I Chipmunk 22	N. F. Charles	
G–BCHX	SF.23A Sperling	Doncaster Sailplane Services	
G–BCIC	PZL-104 Wilga	Daltrade Ltd.	
G–BCID	PA-34 Seneca 200	K. C. Aviation Ltd.	
G–BCIE	PA-28 Cherokee Warrior	IDS Fanjets Ltd.	
G–BCIF	PA-28 Cherokee 140	Cotgrave Service Station Ltd.	
G–BCIH	D.H.C.I Chipmunk T.10	J. M. Hosey & R. A. Schofield	
G–BCII	Cessna 500 Citation	Burmah Oil Trading Ltd.	
G–BCIJ	AA-5 Traveler	Marlow Chemical Co. Ltd.	
G–BCIK	AA-5 Traveler	W. Nutt & Son Ltd.	
G–BCIL	AA-1B Trainer	West Lancashire Aero Club	
G–BCIM	AA-1B Trainer	Bernell Aviation Ltd.	
G–BCIN	Thunder Ax7/77 Hot-Air balloon	Isambard Kingdom Brunel Balloon Group	
G–BCIO	PA-39 Twin Comanche	C.S.E. (Aircraft Services) Ltd.	
G–BCIP	PA-39 Twin Comanche	C.S.E. (Aircraft Services) Ltd.	
G–BCIR	PA-28 Cherokee Warrior	Start Communications Ltd.	
G–BCIS	Beagle B.206 Srs. I	D. F. Smith	
G–BCIT	CIT/A1 Srs. I	Cranfield Institute of Technology	
G–BCIU	Beagle B.206 Srs. I	CSL Electronics (Swansea) Ltd.	
G–BCIV	Beagle B.206 Srs. I	Denair (GB) Ltd.	
G–BCIW	D.H.C.Ia Chipmunk T.10	Gordon King (Aviation) Ltd.	
G–BCIY	Beagle B.206 Srs. I	Scottish Aviation Ltd.	
G–BCJD	Beagle B.206 Srs. I	Northern Air Taxis Ltd.	
G–BCJF	Beagle B.206 Srs. I	A. A. Mattacks	
G–BCJG	Beagle B.206 Srs. I	M. Flynn	
G–BCJH	Mooney M.20F	V. J. Cousin	
G–BCJI	PA-31 Navajo Chieftain 350	Owledge Ltd.	
G–BCJK	PA-28 Cherokee 180	Warwick Engineering Investments Ltd.	
G–BCJL	PA-28 Cherokee 140	C.S.E. (Aircraft Services) Ltd.	
G–BCJM	PA-28 Cherokee 140	TBF (Aviation) Ltd.	
G–BCJN	PA-28 Cherokee 140	Mann Aviation Sales Ltd.	
G–BCJO	PA-28 Cherokee 140	B. C. Harding	
G–BCJP	PA-28 Cherokee 140	C. C. Smith	
G–BCJR	PA-E23 Aztec 250	Baltic Union Shipbrokers Ltd.	
G–BCJS	PA-E23 Aztec 250	Woodgate Aviation Ltd.	
G–BCJU	HS.125 Srs. 600B	Short Bros & Harland Ltd.	
G–BCKA	Rockwell Thrush Commander 600	ADS (Aerial) Ltd.	
G–BCKB	Rockwell Thrush Commander 600	ADS (Aerial) Ltd.	
G–BCKC	Rockwell Thrush Commander 600	ADS (Aerial) Ltd.	
G–BCKD	PA-28R Cherokee Arrow	K. W. Ford	
G–BCKF	SA.102.5 Cavalier	K. Fairness	
G–BCKH	Hawker Sea Fury T.20	Fairoaks Aviation Services Ltd.	
G–BCKJ	PA-23 Aztec 250	E.T.S. Ltd.	
G–BCKL	Cessna 310O	Airwork Services Ltd.	
G–BCKM	Cessna 500 Citation	IDS Fanjets Ltd.	
G–BCKN	D.H.C. Ia Chipmunk 22	RAF Gliding & Soaring Assn.	
G–BCKO	PA-E23 Aztec 250	Donington Aviation Ltd.	
G–BCKP	Luton L.A.5 Major	J. R. Callow	
G–BCKR	PA-28R Cherokee Arrow	Houston Management Services Ltd.	
G–BCKS	Fuji FA.200-180	Air Associates Ltd.	
G–BCKT	Fuji FA.200-180	Littlewick Green Service Station Ltd.	
G–BCKU	Cessna FRA.150L	Airwork Services Ltd.	
G–BCKV	Cessna FRA.150L	Airwork Services Ltd.	
G–BCLA	Sikorsky S-61N	Bristow Helicopters Ltd.	
G–BCLB	Sikorsky S-61N	Bristow Helicopters Ltd.	
G–BCLC	Sikorsky S-61N	Bristow Helicopters Ltd.	
G–BCLD	Sikorsky S-61N	Bristow Helicopters Ltd.	
G–BCLI	AA-5 Traveler	Scotia Safari Ltd.	
G–BCLJ	AA-5 Traveler	KK Aviation	

Registration	Type	Owner or Operator	Where and when seen
G–BCLK	Rockwell 500S Shrike Commander	Glos-Air Ltd.	
G–BCLL	PA-28 Cherokee 180	DMJ Travel	
G–BCLM	GY-201 Minicab	Lima Mike Flying Group	
G–BCLN	Sikorsky S-58ET	British Airways Helicopters Ltd.	
G–BCLO	Sikorsky S-58ET	British Airways Helicopters Ltd.	
G–BCLP	J-3C-65 Cub	J. S. Sproule	
G–BCLS	Cessna 170B	C. W. Proffitt-White	
G–BCLT	M.S.894A Rallye Minerva 220	Guy Morton & Sons Ltd.	
G–BCLU	Jodel D.117	G. W. Bisshopp	
G–BCLV	Bede BD-5A	R. A. Gardiner	
G–BCLW	AA-1B Trainer	Scotia Safari Ltd.	
G–BCLY	Cessna 182P	Jacquair Ltd.	
G–BCMA	Beech B.55 Baron	Eagle Aircraft Services Ltd.	
G–BCMB	Partenavia P-68B Oscar	D.K. Aviation Ltd.	
G–BCMD	PA-18 Super Cub	R. J. Durrant	
G–BCMF	Levi Go-Plane RL-6 Srs. 1	R. Levi	
G–BCMG	D.H.C.1 Chipmunk T.10	F & H (Aircraft) Ltd.	
G–BCMJ	SA.102.5 Cavalier	M. Johnson	
G–BCML	Sipa S.903	M. Emery	
G–BCMR	Robin HR.100/285 Tiara	Deville & Lear	
G–BCMT	Isaacs Fury II	M. H. Turner	
G–BCMU	BN-2A-21 Islander	Britten-Norman (Bembridge) Ltd.	
G–BCMV	BN-2A-21 Islander	Britten-Norman (Bembridge) Ltd.	
G–BCMY	BN-2A-21 Islander	Britten-Norman (Bembridge) Ltd.	
G–BCMZ	BN-2A-6 Islander	Britten-Norman (Bembridge) Ltd.	
G–BCNB	BN-2A-6 Islander	Britten-Norman (Bembridge) Ltd.	
G–BCNC	GY.201 Minicab	N. J. Cole	
G–BCND	BN-2A-6 Islander	Britten-Norman (Bembridge) Ltd.	
G–BCNE	BN-2A-6 Islander	Britten-Norman (Bembridge) Ltd.	
G–BCNF	BN-2A-6 Islander	Britten-Norman (Bembridge) Ltd.	
G–BCNG	BN-2A-6 Islander	Britten-Norman (Bembridge) Ltd.	
G–BCNH	BN-2A-6 Islander	Britten-Norman (Bembridge) Ltd.	
G–BCNJ	BN-2A-6 Islander	Britten-Norman (Bembridge) Ltd.	
G–BCNO	BN-2A Mk. III-1 Trislander	Zeekoegat Ltd.	
G–BCNP	Cameron O-77 Hot-Air Balloon	A. W. Murray	
G–BCNR	Thunder Ax7-77A Hot-Air Balloon	S. J. Milliken, D. Gibbons & R. Riddell	
G–BCNS	Cameron O-84 Hot-Air Balloon	J. G. Green	
G–BCNT	Partenavia P.68B Oscar	D.K. Aviation Ltd.	
G–BCNX	J-3C-65 Cub	N. J. R. Empson & ptnrs.	
G–BCNZ	Fuji FA.200-160	Dismore Aviation Ltd.	
G–BCOA	Cameron O-65 Hot-Air Balloon	E. E. J. & Mrs. E. Sutton	
G–BCOB	J-3C-65 Cub	R. W. & Mrs. J. W. Marjoram	
G–BCOD	PA-31 Navajo Chieftain 350	Group Lotus Car Companies Ltd.	
G–BCOE	HS.748 Srs. 2A	British Airways	
G–BCOF	HS.748 Srs. 2A	British Airways	
G–BCOG	Jodel D.112	B. A. Bower, M. A. Jones & A. Everex	
G–BCOH	Avro 683 Lancaster 10	Strathallan Collection	
G–BCOI	D.H.C.1 Chipmunk T.10	D. S. McGregor & A. T. Letham	

Registration	Type	Owner or Operator	Where and when seen
G-BCOJ	Cameron O-56 Hot-Air Balloon	Anglian Industrial Gases Ltd.	
G-BCOL	Cessna F.172M	Park Plant Ltd.	
G-BCOM	J-3C-65 Cub	W. L. Grose	
G-BCON	Cessna E.310R	Northair Aviation Ltd.	
G-BCOO	D.H.C.I Chipmunk T.10	T. G. Gielding & M. S. Morton	
G-BCOP	PA-28R Cherokee Arrow 200	Firmin Coates & Sons Ltd.	
G-BCOR	M.S.880B Rallye 100ST	Air Touring Services	
G-BCOS	D.H.C.I Chipmunk T.10	Bristol & Wessex Aeroplane Club Ltd.	
G-BCOT	Enstrom F-28A	Wm. Shyvers Ltd.	
G-BCOU	D.H.C.Ia Chipmunk T.10	P. J. Loweth	
G-BCOV	Hawker Sea Fury TT.20	War Birds of Great Britain Ltd.	
G-BCOW	Hawker Sea Fury TT.20	War Birds of Great Britain Ltd.	
G-BCOX	Bede BD-5A	H. J. Cox	
G-BCOY	D.H.C.I Chipmunk T.10	Coventry Gliding Club Ltd.	
G-BCPA	SA.315B Alouette II	British Executive Air Services Ltd.	
G-BCPB	Howes Radio-Controlled Model Free Balloon	R. B. & Mrs. C. Howes	
G-BCPC	PA-31-350 Navajo Chieftain	George Wimpey & Co. Ltd.	
G-BCPD	G.Y.201 Minicab	A. H. K. Denniss	
G-BCPE	Cessna F.150M	Channel Islands Aero Services Ltd.	
G-BCPF	PA-23 Aztec 250	Spooner Aviation Ltd.	
G-BCPG	PA-28R Cherokee Arrow 200	D. Pollard	
G-BCPH	J-3C-65 Cub	J. A. Chandler	
G-BCPI	PA-18 Super Cub 135	Kent Gliding Club Ltd.	
G-BCPJ	J-3C-65 Cub	M. C. Barraclough & T. M. Storey	
G-BCPK	Cessna F.172M	Skegness Air Taxi Service Ltd.	
G-BCPL	AA-5 Traveler	Flight-Line Ltd.	
G-BCPM	AA-5 Traveler	Waste Lubricating Oils Ltd.	
G-BCPN	AA-5 Traveler	Pioneer Works & Fabricators	
G-BCPO	Partenavia P.68B Victor	D.K. Aviation Ltd.	
G-BCPP	Partenavia P.68B Victor	D. K. Aviation Ltd.	
G-BCPU	D.H.C.I Chipmunk T.10	P. Waller	
G-BCPV	PA-28 Cherokee 140	R. A. Schofield	
G-BCPX	HFC.125	A. Szep	
G-BCPZ	Rockwell 500S Shrike Commander	Greenline Refrigerated Transport Ltd.	
G-BCRA	Cessna F.150M	Three Counties Aero Club	
G-BCRB	Cessna F.172M	F. D. Forbes & Co.	
G-BCRC	D.31 Turbulent	R. A. G. Chapman	
G-BCRD	D.H.82A Tiger Moth	R. G. A. Dent	
G-BCRE	Cameron O-77 Hot-Air Balloon	J. P. Bertie & ptnrs.	
G-BCRF	PA-23 Aztec 250	Pauling (Middle East) Ltd.	
G-BCRG	Bolkow BO 105D	GKN Group Services Ltd.	
G-BCRH	Alaparma Baldo B.75	A. L. Scadding	
G-BCRI	Cameron O-65 Hot-Air Balloon	V. J. Thorne	
G-BCRJ	Taylor Monoplane JT.I	E. Willis	
G-BCRK	SA.102.5 Cavalier	R. Y. Kendal	
G-BCRL	PA-28 Cherokee Warrior 151	Norden (Builders) Ltd.	
G-BCRM	Cessna 500C Citation	Marshalls of Cambridge (Engineering) Ltd.	
G-BCRN	Cessna FRA.150L	Airwork Services Ltd.	
G-BCRP	PA-E23 Aztec 250	American Airspeed Inc. Ltd.	
G-BCRR	AA-5B Tiger	Flight-Line Ltd.	
G-BCRT	Cessna F. 150M	P. J. Webb	
G-BCRU	Sikorsky S-58ET	Bristow Helicopters Ltd.	
G-BCRV	Sikorsky S-58ET	Bristow Helicopters Ltd.	
G-BCRW	Sikorsky S-58ET	Bristow Helicopters Ltd.	
G-BCRX	D.H.C.I Chipmunk 22	J. P. V. Hunt & P. G. H. Tony	
G-BCSA	D.H.C.I Chipmunk 22	A. W. Gough	
G-BCSB	D.H.C.I Chipmunk 22	A. W. Gough	

Registration	Type	Owner or Operator	Where and when seen
G–BCSL	D.H.C. I Chipmunk 22	Banbury Plant Hire Ltd.	
G–BCSM	Bellanca 8GC BC	Hendon Air Services Ltd.	
G–BCSR	Bellanca 7ECA	Hendon Air Services Ltd.	
G–BCSS	M.S.892A Rallye Commodore 150	F. H. Feneley & P.C.H. Clarke	
G–BCST	M.S.893A Rallye Commodore 180	P. J. Wilcox	
G–BCSV	Cessna 421B	Northair Aviation Ltd.	
G–BCSW	PA-23 Aztec 250	Oldham Tyre Cord Co. Ltd.	
G–BCSX	Thunder AX7/77 balloon	A. T. Wood & C. Wolstenholme	
G–BCSZ	PA-28R Cherokee Arrow 200	Peter Clifford Aviation Ltd.	
G–BCTA	PA-28 Cherokee Warrior 151	Landis Engineers Ltd.	
G–BCTB	Cameron O-65 balloon	G. W. Reader	
G–BCTC	Cessna F.337G	J. S. Freedman	
G–BCTD	Scheibe SF.25B	E. R. Boyle	
G–BCTE	Bolkow BO 105D	Ferranti Helicopters Ltd.	
G–BCTF	PA-28 Cherokee Warrior 151	Martini and Rossi Ltd.	
G–BCTH	PA-28 Cherokee 140	John V. White Ltd.	
G–BCTI	Schleicher ASK.16	R. J. Steward	
G–BCTJ	Cessna 310Q	Airwòrk Services Ltd.	
G–BCTK	Cessna FR.172J	R. C. Wilkinson Farms	
G–BCTR	Taylor J.T.2 Titch	T. Reagan	
G–BCTT	Evans VP-2	B. J. Boughton	
G–BCTU	Cessna FRA.150M	W. H. & J. Rogers Group Ltd.	
G–BCTV	Cessna F.150M	Fairoaks Aviation Services Ltd.	
G–BCTW	Cessna F.150M	Ulster Aviation Ltd.	
G–BCTX	Sikorsky S-58ET	Bristow Helicopters Ltd.	
G–BCTZ	BN-2A-26 Islander	Britten-Norman (Bembridge) Ltd.	
G–BCUB	J3C-65 Cub	D. S. Morgan	
G–BCUC	J3C-65 Cub	Sajan Ltd.	
G–BCUD	BN-2A-26 Islander	The Anglo-Thai Corporation Ltd.	
G–BCUF	Cessna F.172N	G. H. C. B. Kirke	
G–BCUG	Cessna F.150N	Aberdeen Aero Club	
G–BCUH	Cessna F.150M	Gordon King (Aviation) Ltd.	
G–BCUI	Cessna F.172N	Hillhouse Estates Ltd.	
G–BCUJ	Cessna F.150M	Hillhouse Estates Ltd.	
G–BCUK	Cessna F.172M	Q. Quitmann Ltd.	
G–BCUL	M.S.8808 Rallye 100ST	W. O. Williams	
G–BCUM	Stinson HW-75	B. M. O'Brien	
G–BCUW	Cessna F.177RG Cardinal	B. Beer	
G–BCUY	Cessna FRA. 150M	Vectair Aviation Ltd.	
G–BCUZ	Beechcraft Super 200	United Biscuits Ltd.	
G–BCVA	Cameron O-65	J. T. & L. S. Whicher, D. Barefore, Anne Featherstone, G. D. Henley & C. V. Morse	
G–BCVB	Piper PA-17 Vagabond	B. C. & Mrs. J. I. Cooper	
G–BCVC	M.S.880B Rallye 100ST	Air Touring Services Ltd.	
G–BCVE	Evans VP-2	G. A. Bentley	
G–BCVF	Practavia Pilot Sprite	G. B. Castle	
G–BCVG	Cessna FRA.150L	Light Planes (Lancs.) Ltd.	
G–BCVH	Cessna FRA.150L	Blundell Holiday Group Ltd.	
G–BCVI	Cessna FR.172J Rocket	Kenco Engineering Co. Ltd.	
G–BCVJ	Cessna F.172M	Westair Flying Services	
G–BCVK	BN-2A-6 Islander	The Anglo-Thai Corporation	
G–BCVN	BN-2A-6 Islander	Britten-Norman (Bembridge) Ltd.	
G–BCVP	BN-2A-6 Islander	Britten-Norman (Bembridge) Ltd.	
G–BCVR	BN-2A-21 Islander	Britten-Norman (Bembridge) Ltd.	
G–BCVS	BN-2A-6 Islander	Britten-Norman (Bembridge) Ltd.	
G–BCVT	BN-2A-6 Islander	The Anglo-Thai Corporation	
G–BCVU	BN-2A-27 Islander	Britten-Norman (Bembridge) Ltd.	

Registration	Type	Owner or Operator	Where and when seen
G–BCVV	PA-28-151 Cherokee Warrior	Channel Islands Aero Services Ltd.	
G–BCVW	GY-80 Horizon 180	Horizon Flyers Ltd.	
G–BCVX	DR.1050 Ambassador	K. D. Gomm	
G–BCVY	PA-34 Seneca 200T	Cega Aviation Ltd.	
G–BCVZ	A-B 206B JetRanger 2	Alan Mann Helicopters	
G–BCWA	BAC One-Eleven 518	Dan-Air Services Ltd.	
G–BCWB	Cessna 182P	Northair Aviation Ltd.	
G–BCWD	Sikorsky S-58T	Management Aviation Ltd.	
G–BCWE	HPR-7 Herald 206	Trans-World Leasing Ltd.	
G–BCWF	Scottish Aviation Twin Pioneer	Flight One Ltd.	
G–BCWG	BAC One-Eleven 518	Monarch Airlines Ltd.	
G–BCWH	Practavia Pilot Sprite	K. B. Parkinson & R. Tasker	
G–BCWI	Bensen B.8M	W. H. Beevers	
G–BCWJ	Canadair CL-44D6	Tradewinds Airways Ltd.	
G–BCWK	Alpavia Fournier RF-3	D. I. Nickolls, T. Hartwell & D. Wilkinson	
G–BCWL	Westland Lysander III	P. A. Mann	
G–BCWM	A-B 206B JetRanger 2	Alan Mann Helicopters Ltd.	
G–BCWN	A-B 206B JetRanger 2	Alan Mann Helicopters Ltd.	
G–BCWU	BN-2A-21 Islander	Marchwiel Plant & Engineering Co. Ltd.	
G–BCWW	HP.137 Jetstream 200	The Distillers Co. Ltd.	
G–BCXA	M.S.880B Rallye 100ST	Air Touring Services Ltd.	
G–BCXB	M.S.880B Rallye 100ST	Air Touring Services Ltd.	
G–BCXC	M.S.880B Rallye 100ST	Air Touring Services Ltd.	
G–BCXD	Pitts S-2A	Kelly Aeroplane Ltd.	
G–BCXE	Robin DR.400 "2+2"	Headcorn Flying School Ltd.	
G–BCXF	HS.125 Srs. 600B	The Marconi Co. Ltd.	
G–BCXH	PA-28 Cherokee 140F	Mann Aviation Sales Ltd.	
G–BCXI	G–164A Ag-Cat	W. P. Miller	
G–BCXJ	J-3C-65 Cub	K. J. Pyle	
G–BCXM	Cameron O-77 Balloon	C. R. Kirby, N. I. Kennedy, A. J. Moore & Mary E. U. Baker	
G–BCXN	D.H.C.I Chipmunk 22	P. G. D. Bell	
G–BCXO	MBB BO.105D	Helicopter Marketing Ltd.	
G–BCXP	PA-E23 Aztec 250E	Universal Film Laboratory Ltd.	
G–BCXR	BAC One-Eleven 517	Monarch Airlines Ltd.	
G–BCXS	Rockwell Commander 690A	Ferranti Ltd.	
G–BCXT	Cessna F.150M	Gordon King (Aviation) Ltd.	
G–BCXU	BN-2A Mk. III-2 Trislander	The Anglo-Thai Corporation Ltd.	
G–BCXV	BN-2A Mk. III-1 Trislander	Zeekoegat Ltd.	
G–BCXW	BN-2A Mk. III-2 Trislander	Britten-Norman (Bembridge) Ltd.	
G–BCXX	BN-2A Mk. III-2 Trislander	Britten-Norman (Bembridge) Ltd.	
G–BCXY	BN-2A Mk. III-2 Trislander	Britten-Norman (Bembridge) Ltd.	
G–BCXZ	Cameron O-56 Balloon	Olives from Spain Ltd.	
G–BCYB	Cessna F.177G	Anderson Flying School Ltd.	
G–BCYC	BN-2A Mk. III-2 Trislander	Britten-Norman (Bembridge) Ltd.	
G–BCYE	D.H.C.I Chipmunk 22	L. T. Mersh	
G–BCYF	Dassault Mystère 20	Falcon Jet Centre Ltd.	
G–BCYH	Privateer Mk. 2 Motor Glider	D. C. Pattison & D. A. Wilson	
G–BCYI	Schleicher AKS-16	D. J. Pearce, J. Fox & W. Maidment	
G–BCYJ	D.H.C.I Chipmunk 22	O. A. Haydon-Baillie	
G–BCYK	Avro CF.100 Mk. 4 Canuck	O. A. Haydon-Baillie	
G–BCYL	D.H.C.I Chipmunk 22	P. C. Henry	
G–BCYM	D.H.C.I Chipmunk 22	C. R. R. Eagleton	
G–BCYP	A-B 206B JetRanger	Alan Mann Helicopters Ltd.	
G–BCYR	Cessna F.172M	Channel Islands Aero Engineering Ltd.	
G–BCYS	J-3C-65 Cub	R. P. M. Dawson	

Registration	Type	Owner or Operator	Where and when seen
G–BCYT	BN-2A Islander	Britten-Norman (Bembridge) Ltd.	
G–BCYW	BA-2A Islander	The Anglo-Thai Corporation Ltd.	
G–BCYY	Westland-Bell 47G-3B1	Freemans of Bewdley (Aviation)	
G–BCYZ	Westland-Bell 47G-3B1	Freemans of Bewdley (Aviation)	
G–BCZA	BN-2A Islander	Britten-Norman (Bembridge) Ltd.	
G–BCZB	BN-2A Islander	Britten-Norman (Bembridge) Ltd.	
G–BCZC	BN-2A Islander	Britten-Norman (Bembridge) Ltd.	
G–BCZD	BN-2A Islander	Britten-Norman (Bembridge) Ltd.	
G–BCZE	BN-2A Islander	Britten-Norman (Bembridge) Ltd.	
G–BCZF	PA-28 Cherokee 180 Challenger	C.S.E. Aviation Ltd.	
G–BCZG	HPR-7 Dart Herald 202	Trans-World Leasing Ltd.	
G–BCZH	D.H.C.1 Chipmunk 22	R. B. Stratton t/a RAFGSA	
G–BCZI	Thunder Ax7-77 Balloon	Motor Tyres & Accessories	
G–BCZK	Westland-Bell 47G-3B1	British Executive Air Services Ltd.	
G–BCZL	Westland-Bell 47G-3B1	British Executive Air Services Ltd.	
G–BCZM	Cessna F.172M	Channel Islands Aero Engineering Ltd.	
G–BCZN	Cessna F.150M	T. M. G. Hanley	
G–BCZO	Cameron O-77 Balloon	W. O. T. Holmes	
G–BCZP	Cessna T.210L	K. & F. L. Equipment & Aircraft Hiring Ltd.	
G–BCZR	V.838 Viscount	Field Aircraft Services Ltd.	
G–BCZS	BN-2A-21 Islander	Britten-Norman (Bembridge) Ltd.	
G–BDAB	SA.102.5 Cavalier	A. H. Brown	
G–BDAC	Cameron O.77 Balloon	Cameron Balloons Ltd.	
G–BDAD	Taylor JT1 Monoplane	J. F. Bakewell	
G–BDAE	BAC One-Eleven 518	Dan-Air Services Ltd.	
G–BDAG	Taylor JT1 Monoplane	R. S. Basinger	
G–BDAH	Evans VP-1	R. W. Lowe	
G–BDAI	Cessna FRA.150M	Corance Ltd.	
G–BDAJ	Rockwell Commander 112A	T. A. Bowring	
G–BDAK	Rockwell Commander 112A	W. M. P. Miller	
G–BDAL	Shrike Commander 500S	Corance Ltd.	
G–BDAM	AT-6 Harvard IIB	D. G. Jones	
G–BDAN	Boeing 727-146	Dan-Air Services Ltd.	
G–BDAO	SIPA 91	R. Bowler	
G–BDAP	Wittman W8 Tailwind	J. Whiting	
G–BDAR	Evans VP-1	S. C. Foggin & M. T. Dugmore	
G–BDAS	BAC One-Eleven 518	Dan-Air Services Ltd.	
G–BDAT	BAC One-Eleven 518	Dan-Air Services Ltd.	
G–BDAU	Cessna FRA.150M	Airwork Services Ltd.	
G–BDAV	PA-23 Aztec 250	Woodward Air Services	
G–BDAW	Enstrom F-28A	A. W. Alloys Ltd.	
G–BDAX	PA-E23 Aztec 250	Fairflight Charters Ltd.	
G–BDAY	Thunder Ax5-42A Hot-Air Balloon	Thunder Balloons Ltd.	
G–BDAZ	Thunder Ax7-77A Hot-Air Balloon	Thunder Balloons Ltd.	
G–BDBA	Thunder Ax7-77 Hot-Air Balloon	Thunder Balloons Ltd.	
G–BDBB	Cessna F.150M	Anderson Flying School Ltd.	
G–BDBD	Wittman W.8 Tailwind	H. Best-Devereux	
G–BDBE	Thunder Ax7-77A Balloon	Thunder Balloons Ltd.	
G–BDBF	Clutton-Tabenor FRED Srs. 2	W. T. Morrell	
G–BDBH	Bellanca 7GCBC	B. A. Jesty	

Registration	Type	Owner or Operator	Where and when seen
G—BDBI	Cameron O-77 Hot-Air Balloon	Royston Cooper Design Consultants	
G—BDBJ	Cessna 182P	Cosworth Engineering Ltd.	
G—BDBK	Cameron O-56	J. G. Green	
G—BDBL	D.H.C.I Chipmunk 22	Sq. Ldr J. E. M. McDonald t/a Wycombe Gliding School Syndicate	
G—BDBM	Cameron O-56 Hot-Air Balloon	A. H. K. Olpin	
G—BDBN	D.H.C.I Chipmunk 22	A. R. & Mrs. D. A. Coulson	
G—BDBP	D.H.C.I Chipmunk 22	E. C. Geary & G. S. F. Tatum	
G—BDBR	A-B 206B JetRanger 2	William Monks (BM) Ltd.	
G—BDBS	Short SD3-30	Short Bros. & Harland Ltd.	
G—BDBU	Cessna F.150M	Channel Islands Aero Services Ltd.	
G—BDBV	Jodel D.11A	Monika Sieboldt	
G—BDBW	Heintz Zenith 100 AI8	D. B. Winstanley	
G—BDBX	Evans VP-I	Montgomeryshire Ultra-Light Flying Club	
G—BDBZ	W-S.55 Whirlwind Srs. 2	Autair Ltd.	
G—BDCA	M.S.880B Rallye 100ST	B. W. J. Pring, R. H. P. Foote & A. J. Wickenden	
G—BDCB	D.H.C.I Chipmunk 22	D. R. Hodgson	
G—BDCC	D.H.C.I Chipmunk 22	Coventry Gliding Club Ltd.	
G—BDCD	J-3C-65 Cub	B. A. Dunlop	
G—BDCE	Cessna F.172H	H. A. Baillie	
G—BDCF	Boeing Stearman A75-NI	Keenair Services Ltd.	
G—BDCI	Piel CP.301A Emeraude	J. R. Ramshaw	
G—BDCK	AA-5 Traveler	Flight-Line (Aviation) Ltd.	
G—BDCL	AA-5 Traveler	Bernell Aviation Ltd.	
G—BDCM	Cessna F.177RG	Oldham Aviation	
G—BDCN	Boeing 707-349C	British Caledonian Airways	
G—BDCO	Beagle B.121 Pup I	Eastern Aviation Ltd.	
G—BDCP	A-B 206B JetRanger	Ben Turner & Sons (Helicopters) Ltd.	
G—BDCS	Cessna 421B Golden Eagle	Marchwiel Plant & Engineering Co. Ltd.	
G—BDCT	Piper PA-25 Pawnee 235C	Bowker Air Services Ltd.	
G—BDCU	Cameron O-77 Hot-Air Balloon	Swan Flight	
G—BDCV	A.W.660 Argosy I	Field Aircraft Services Ltd.	
G—BDDA	Sikorsky S-61N Mk. II	British Airways Helicopters	
G—BDDB	Practavia Pilot Sprite	H. P. Burrill	
G—BDDC	D.H.C.I Chipmunk 22	J. F. Young	
G—BDDD	D.H.C.I Chipmunk 22	J. T. Thornes	
G—BDDE	Douglas DC-8 Srs. 54F	International Aviation Services	
G—BDDF	Jodel D.120 Paris-Nice	C. G. Shaw	
G—BDDG	Jodel D.112	A. C. Watt & I. C. Greig	
G—BDDH	F.27 Friendship Mk. 200	Air Anglia Ltd.	
G—BDDI	Lake LA.4-200 Buccaneer	Medburn Air Services Ltd.	
G—BDDJ	Luton L.A.4A Minor	D. D. Johnson	
G—BDDK	BN-2A-9 Islander	Britten-Norman (Bembridge) Ltd.	
G—BDDM	BN-2A-21 Islander	Britten-Norman (Bembridge) Ltd.	
G—BDDS	PA-25 Pawnee 260	Farmair Ltd.	
G—BDDT	PA-25 Pawnee 260	Colton Aviation Services Ltd.	
G—BDDV	BN-2A-8 Islander	Loganair Ltd.	
G—BDDW	BN-2A-21 Islander	Britten-Norman (Bembridge) Ltd.	
G—BDDX	Whittaker MW.28	Charles Robertson (Developments) Ltd.	
G—BDDY	Stinson 108-3	C. R. & Mrs. M. M. Heaton	
G—BDDZ	Piel CP.301A Emeraude	N. J. Cole	
G—BDEA	Boeing 707-338C	British Caledonian Airways Ltd.	
G—BDEB	M.S.880B Rallye 100ST	Air Touring Services Ltd.	
G—BDEC	M.S.880B Rallye 100ST	Air Touring Services Ltd.	
G—BDED	M.S.880B Rallye 100ST	Air Touring Services Ltd.	
G—BDEE	Westland-Bell 47G-3B1	Trent Helicopters Ltd.	

Registration	Type	Owner or Operator	Where and when seen
G–BDEF	PA-34 Seneca 200T	Barratt Developments Ltd.	
G–BDEG	M.S.880B Rallye 100ST	Air Touring Services Ltd.	
G–BDEH	Jodel D.120A Paris-Nice	P. G. Phelps	
G–BDEI	Jodel D.9 Bebe	L. T. Dix	
G–BDEJ	Rockwell Commander 112	W. P. J. Davison	
G–BDEN	SIAI-Marchetti SF.260	Micro Consultants Ltd.	
G–BDEO	Cessna F.150M	Ulster Flying Club (1961) Ltd.	
G–BDEP	Cessna F.172M	Ulster Flying Club (1961) Ltd.	
G–BDER	Auster AOP.9	F. & H. (Aircraft) Ltd.	
G–BDES	Sikorsky S-61N Mk. II	British Airways Helicopters	
G–BDET	D.H.C.I Chipmunk 22	P. M. Graham	
G–BDEU	D.H.C.I Chipmunk 22	R. E. Dagless	
G–BDEV	Taylor JT.I Monoplane	P. J. Houston	
G–BDEW	Cessna FRA.150M	George House (Holdings) Ltd.	
G–BDEX	Cessna FRA.150M	George House (Holdings) Ltd.	
G–BDEY	J-3C-65 Cub	B. A. Dunlop	
G–BDEZ	J-3C-65 Cub	B. A. Dunlop	
G–BDFB	Currie Wot	D. F. Faulkner-Bryant	
G–BDFC	Rockwell Commander 112A	Glos-Air Ltd.	
G–BDFE	HPR-7 Dart Herald 206	Trans-World Leasing Ltd.	
G–BDFF	Supermarine S.5 Replica	Leisure Sport Ltd.	
G–BDFG	Cameron O-65 Hot-Air Balloon	N. A. Robertson	
G–BDFH	Auster AOP.9	F. & H. (Aircraft) Ltd.	
G–BDFI	Cessna F.150M	Lonmet (Aviation) Ltd.	
G–BDFJ	Cessna F.150M	Lonmet (Aviation) Ltd.	
G–BDFK	Cessna 414	Brush Electrical Machines Ltd.	
G–BDFL	PA-28R Cherokee Arrow Mk. II	F. B. Gibbons & Sons Ltd.	
G–BDFM	Caudron C.270 Luciole	G. V. Gower	
G–BDFN	PA-31 Navajo Chieftain 350	Fairflight Charters Ltd.	
G–BDFO	Hiller UH-12E	C. & K. Helicopters (Engineering) Ltd.	
G–BDFP	Hughes 369HS	Hughes of Beaconsfield Ltd.	
G–BDFR	Fuji FA.200-160	Air Associates Ltd.	
G–BDFS	Fuji FA.200-160	Air Associates Ltd.	
G–BDFT	V.668 Varsity T.I	D. W. Mickleburgh	
G–BDFU	Dragonfly MPA Mk. I	R. J. A. Hardy & R. Churcher	
G–BDFV	AA-5 Traveler	P. & Mrs. M. E. Biggins	
G–BDFW	Rockwell Commander 112A	Universal Aviation Supply Co. Ltd.	
G–BDFX	Auster 5	I. A. Haddon & M. J. Kirk	
G–BDFY	AA-5 Traveler	E. O. Liebert	
G–BDFZ	Cessna F.150M	A. R. Ashley	
G–BDGA	Bushby-Long Midget Mustang	J. R. Owen	
G–BDGB	GY-20 Minicab	D. G. Burden	
G–BDGC	BN-2A Mk. III-2 Trislander	Britten-Norman (Bembridge) Ltd.	
G–BDGD	BN-2A Mk. III-2 Trislander	Britten-Norman (Bembridge) Ltd.	
G–BDGE	BN-2A Mk. III-2 Trislander	Britten-Norman (Bembridge) Ltd.	
G–BDGF	BN-2A Mk. III-2 Trislander	Britten-Norman (Bembridge) Ltd.	
G–BDGG	BN-2A Mk. III-2 Trislander	Britten-Norman (Bembridge) Ltd.	
G–BDGH	Thunder Ax6-56 Hot-Air Balloon	Thunder Balloons Ltd.	
G–BDGI	Thunder Ax6-56A Hot-Air Balloon	Thunder Balloons Ltd.	
G–BDGJ	Cameron O-56 Hot-Air Balloon	N. J. Dunsford	
G–BDGK	Beechcraft D.17S	Customline Ltd.	
G–BDGL	Cessna U.206 Super Skywagon	C. Wren	
G–BDGM	PA-28-151 Cherokee Warrior	Channel Islands Aero Services Ltd.	

Registration	Type	Owner or Operator	Where and when seen
G–BDGN	AA-5B Tiger	Hamblin & Glover Oil Field (Services) Ltd.	
G–BDGO	Thunder Ax7-77 Hot-Air Balloon	Thunder Balloons Ltd.	
G–BDGP	—	—	
G–BDGR	D.H C.I Chipmunk 22	J. K. Avis	
G–BDGX	SF.25E Super Falke	British Gliding Association Ltd.	
G–BDGY	PA-28 Cherokee 40	R. E. Wooldridge	
G–BDGZ	AA-5B Tiger	Flight-Line (Aviation) Ltd.	
G–BDHA	—	—	
G–BDHB	Isaacs Fury II	D. H. Berry	
G–BDHC	D.H.C.6 Twin Otter 300	Brymon Aviation Ltd.	
G–BDHD	Riley Dove 2	Fairlight Charters Ltd.	
G–BDHG	BN-2A-21 Islander	Britten-Norman (Bembridge) Ltd.	
G–BDHH	BN-2A-21 Islander	Britten-Norman (Bembridge) Ltd.	
G–BDHJ	Pazmany PL.I	H. James	
G–BDHK	J-3C-65 Cub	H. Knight	
G–BDHL	PA-E23 Aztec 250E	Granpack Ltd.	
G–BDHM	SA.102.5 Cavalier	D. H. Mitchell	
G–BDHN	BN-2A Islander	Britten-Norman (Bembridge) Ltd.	
G–BDHO	BN-2A Islander	Britten-Norman (Bembridge) Ltd.	
G–BDHP	BN-2A Islander	Britten-Norman (Bembridge) Ltd.	
G–BDHR	BN-2A Islander	Britten-Norman (Bembridge) Ltd.	
G–BDHS	BN-2A Islander	Britten-Norman (Bembridge) Ltd.	
G–BDHT	BN-2A Islander	Britten-Norman (Bembridge) Ltd.	
G–BDHU	BN-2A Islander	Britten-Norman (Bembridge) Ltd.	
G–BDHV	BN-2A islander	Britten-Norman (Bembridge) Ltd.	
G–BDHW	BN-2A Islander	Britten-Norman (Bembridge) Ltd.	
G–BDHX	BN-2A Islander	Britten-Norman (Bembridge) Ltd.	
G–BDHY	Westland-Bell 47G-3B1	Trent Helicopters Ltd.	
G–BDHZ	Westland-Bell 47G-3B1	Trent Helicopters Ltd.	
G–BDIA	Westland-Bell 47G-3B1	Autair Ltd.	
G–BDIB	Enstrom Shark 280	Penarth Commercial Properties Ltd.	
G–BDIC	D.H.C.I Chipmunk 22	Air Navigation & Trading Co. Ltd.	
G–BDID	D.H.C.I Chipmunk 22	Coventry Gliding Club Ltd.	
G–BDIE	Rockwell Commander 112A	Industrial Fuels Transportation Ltd.	
G–BDIF	D.H.106 Comet 4C	Dan-Air Services Ltd.	
G–BDIG	Cessna 182P	Roger Clarke (Air Transport) Ltd.	
G–BDIH	Jodel D.117	P. Meeson & J. Chisholm	
G–BDII	—	—	
G–BDIJ	Sikorsky S-61N Mk. II	Bristow Helicopters Ltd.	
G–BDIK	V.708 Viscount	Alidair Ltd.	
G–BDIL	Bell 212	British Executive Air Services Ltd.	
G–BDIM	D.H.C.I Chipmunk 22	John Barwell Motors	
G–BDIT	D.H.106 Comet 4C	Dan-Air Services Ltd.	
G–BDIU	D.H.106 Comet 4C	Dan-Air Services Ltd.	
G–BDIV	D.H.106 Comet 4C	Dan-Air Services Ltd.	
G–BDIW	D.H.106 Comet 4C	Dan-Air Services Ltd.	
G–BDIX	D.H.106 Comet 4C	Dan-Air Services Ltd.	
G–BDIY	Luton L.A.4a Minor	M. A. Musslewhite	
G–BDIZ	BN-2A-21 Islander	Britten-Norman (Bembridge) Ltd.	
G–BDJA	BN-2A-21 Islander	Britten-Norman (Bembridge) Ltd.	

Registration	Type	Owner or Operator	Where and when seen
G–BDJB	Taylor Monoplane Srs. 2	J. T. Barber	
G–BDJC	Wittman W.8 Tailwind	A. Whiting	
G–BDJD	Jodel D.112	J. V. Derrick	
G–BDJE	H.S.125 Srs. 600B	Hawker Siddeley Aviation Ltd.	
G–BDJF	—	—	
G–BDJG	Luton L.A.4a Minor	D. J. Gaskin	
G–BDJH	—	—	
G–BDJI	—	—	
G–BDJJ	—	—	
G–BDJN	Robin HR200/100	Avions Robin (UK) Ltd.	
G–BDJO	D.H.C.1 Chipmunk T.10	F. & H. (Aircraft) Ltd.	
G–BDJP	J-3C-75 Cub	J. M. Pothecary	
G–BDJR	Nord NC.858	H. J. W. Ellison	
G–BDJS	BN-2A Islander	Britten-Norman (Bembridge) Ltd.	
G–BDJT	BN-2A-21 Islander	Britten-Norman (Bembridge) Ltd.	
G–BDJU	BN-2A Islander	Britten-Norman (Bembridge) Ltd.	
G–BDJV	BN-2A Islander	Britten-Norman (Bembridge) Ltd.	
G–BDJW	BN-2A Islander	Britten-Norman (Bembridge) Ltd.	
G–BDJX	BN-2A-27 Islander	Britten-Norman (Bembridge) Ltd.	
G–BDJY	BN-2A Islander	Britten-Norman (Bembridge) Ltd.	
G–BDJZ	BN-2A Islander	Britten-Norman (Bembridge) Ltd.	
G–BDKA	M.S.892A Rallye 150ST	Air Touring Services Ltd.	
G–BDKB	M.S.892A Rallye 150ST	Air Touring Services Ltd.	
G–BDKC	Cessna A185F	Bridge of Tilt Co. Ltd.	
G–BDKD	Enstrom F-28A	Helicopter Hire Ltd.	
G–BDKE	Boeing 707-338C	British Caledonian Airways	
G–BDKF	HS.125 Srs. 400B	Hawker Siddeley Aviation Ltd.	
G–BDKG	Beech 65 Queen Air A80	Vernair Transport Services	
G–BDKH	Piel CP.301A Emeraude	K. Horrocks	
G–BDKI	—	—	
G–BDKJ	SA.102.5 Cavalier	H. B. Yardley	
G–BDKK	Bede BD-5B	A. W. Odell	
G–BDKL	Hughes 369HM	A & B Cars (Distributors) Ltd.	
G–BDKM	SIPA 903	S. W. Markham	
G–BDKN	BN-2A Mk. III-2 Trislander	Britten-Norman (Bembridge) Ltd.	
G–BDKO	BN-2A Mk. III-2 Trislander	Britten-Norman (Bembridge) Ltd.	
G–BDKP	BN-2A Mk. III-2 Trislander	Britten-Norman (Bembridge) Ltd.	
G–BDKR	BN-2A Mk. III-2 Trislander	Britten-Norman (Bembridge) Ltd.	
G–BDKS	Pitts S-2A Special	Kelly Aeroplane Ltd.	
G–BDKT	Cameron O-84 Hot-Air Balloon	A.R.M. Fraser & R. Fermor-Hesketh	
G–BDKU	Taylor JT.1	N. F. Whistler, M. A. Knapp & D. Kynaston	
G–BDKV	PA-28R Cherokee Arrow 200 Mk. II	T. Lennon	
G–BDKW	Rockwell Commander 112A	Glos-Air Ltd.	
G–BDKX	BN-2A Islander	Britten-Norman (Bembridge) Ltd.	
G–BDKY	BN-2A Islander	Britten-Norman (Bembridge) Ltd.	
G–BDKZ	V.838 Viscount	Field Aircraft Services Ltd.	
G–BDLF	BN-2A Islander	Britten-Norman (Bembridge) Ltd.	
G–BDLG	BN-2A Islander	Britten-Norman (Bembridge) Ltd.	
G–BDLH	BN-2A Islander	Britten-Norman (Bembridge) Ltd.	

Registration	Type	Owner or Operator	Where and when seen
G–BDLI	BN-2A Islander	Britten-Norman (Bembridge) Ltd.	
G–BDLJ	BN-2A Islander	Britten-Norman (Bembridge) Ltd.	
G–BDLK	BN-2A Islander	Britten-Norman (Bembridge) Ltd.	
G–BDLL	BN-2A Islander	Britten-Norman (Bembridge) Ltd.	
G–BDLM	Boeing 707-338C	British Caledonian Airways	
G–BDLN	BN-2A Islander	Britten-Norman (Bembridge) Ltd.	
G–BDLO	AA-5A Cheetah	Flight-Line (Aviation) Ltd.	
G–BDLP	Thunder Ax-8-105 Hot-Air Balloon	Thunder Balloons Ltd.	
G–BDLR	AA-5B Tiger	Flight-Line (Aviation) Ltd.	
G–BDLS	AA-1B Trainer	Flight-Line (Aviation) Ltd.	
G–BDLT	Rockwell Commander 112A	Glos-Air Ltd.	
G–BDLU	Thunder Ax-7-77A Hot-Air Balloon	Thunder Balloons Ltd.	
G–BDLV	Chilton DW.1A	R. E. Nevoce	
G–BDLW	G-164A Ag-Cat	Miller Aerial Spraying Ltd.	
G–BDLX	SA. Twin Pioneer 3	Transportation Ltd.	
G–BDLY	SA.102.5 Cavalier	B. S. Reeve	
G–BDLZ	B.175 Britannia 253	Air Faisel	
G–BDMA	Shorts SD3-30	Short Bros & Harland Ltd.	
G–BDMB	HR100 Royal	A. G. J. Baldet	
G–BDMC	Bolkow Bo 105D	Management Aviation Ltd.	
G–BDMD	PA-31 Navajo Chieftain 350	Air Anglia	
G–BDME	DR400 Earl 140B	Headcorn Flying School	
G–BDMF	G.1159 Gulfstream II	Rolls-Royce (1971) Ltd.	
G–BDMM	Jodel D.11	D. M. Metcalf	
G–BDMN	Cessna 337	R. E. Husband & A. D. Widdows	
G–BDMO	Thunder Ax-7-77A Hot-Air Balloon	Thunder Balloons Ltd.	
G–BDMP	—		
G–BDMR	BN-2A Islander	Britten-Norman (Bembridge) Ltd.	
G–BDMS	J-3C-65 Cub	D. M. Squires	
G–BDMT	BN-2A Islander	Britten-Norman (Bembridge) Ltd.	
G–BDMU	BN-2A Islander	Britten-Norman (Bembridge) Ltd.	
G–BDMV	BN-2A Islander	Britten-Norman (Bembridge) Ltd.	
G–BDMW	Jodel DR.100	J. T. Nixon	
G–BDMX	BN-2A Islander	Britten-Norman (Bembridge) Ltd.	
G–BDMY	BN-2A Islander	Britten-Norman (Bembridge) Ltd.	
G–BDMZ	BN-2A Islander	Britten-Norman (Bembridge) Ltd.	
G–BDNA	BN-2A Islander	Britten-Norman (Bembridge) Ltd.	
G–BDNB	BN-2A Islander	Britten-Norman (Bembridge) Ltd.	
G–BDNC	Taylor JT.1	N. J. Cole	
G–BDND	BN-2A Islander	Britten-Norman (Bembridge) Ltd.	
G–BDNE	Harker Hawk	D. Harker	
G–BDNF	Bensen Gyroplane	W. F. O'Brien	
G–BDNG	Taylor Monoplane	D. J. Phillips	
G–BDNM	BN-2A Islander	Britten-Norman (Bembridge) Ltd.	
G–BDNN	BN-2A Islander	Britten-Norman (Bembridge) Ltd.	
G–BDNO	Taylor Monoplane	A. J. Gray	
G–BDNP	BN-2A Islander	Britten-Norman (Bembridge) Ltd.	

Registration	Type	Owner or Operator	Where and when seen
G-BDNR	Cessna FRA.150M	Northair Aviation Ltd.	
G-BDNS	Saro Skeeter 12	M. Eastman & M. Ridley	
	(XM529)		
G-BDNT	Jodel D.92	J. S. Barker & A. Tringham	
G-BDNU	Cessna F.172M	Rogers Aviation Ltd.	
G-BEAK	L-1011 TriStar	British Airways	
G-BJCB	HS.125 Srs. 600B	J. C. Bamford Ltd. *Exporter V*	
G-BOAA	Concorde 204	British Airways	
G-BOAB	Concorde 206	British Airways	
G-BOAC	Concorde 208	British Airways	
G-BOAD	Concorde 210	British Aircraft Corporation	
G-BOAE	Concorde 212	British Aircraft Corporation	
G-BSBH	Short SD3-30	Short Bros & Harland Ltd.	
G-BSST	Concorde 002	British Aircraft Corporation	
G-HAWK	HS.1182 Hawk	Hawker Siddeley Aviation	
G-OAHB	T-33 Mk. 3 Silver Star	O. A. Haydon-Baillie	
G-VTOL	H.S. Harrier T.52A	Hawker Siddeley Aviation Ltd.	
G-WGHB	T-33 Mk. 3 Silver Star	O. A. Haydon-Baillie	

Overseas Airline Fleet Lists

(TRANSPORT AIRCRAFT USED ON SCHEDULED SERVICES
TO THE U.K., AND THOSE SEEN FREQUENTLY ON
NON-SCHEDULED FLIGHTS TO THE U.K.)

A40 (Oman)

Registration	Type	Owner or Operator	Where and when seen
A40–TW	L-1011 TriStar	Gulf Air	
A40–TX	L-1011 TriStar	Gulf Air	
A40–TY	L-1011 TriStar	Gulf Air	
A40–TZ	L-1011 TriStar	Gulf Air	
A40–VC	V.1101 VC10	Gulf Air	
A40–VG	V.1101 VC10	Gulf Air	
A40–VI	V.1101 VC10	Gulf Air	
A40–VK	V.1101 VC10	Gulf Air	
A40–VL	V.1101 VC10	Gulf Air	

AP (Pakistan)

AP–AMG	Boeing 720-040B	Air Malta (leased from PIA)
AP–AMJ	Boeing 720-040B	Air Malta (leased from PIA)
AP–ATQ	Boeing 720-051B	Pakistan International Airlines
AP–AUN	Boeing 707-340C	Pakistan International Airlines (leased to JAT, Yugoslavia as YU–AGE)
AP–AUO	Boeing 707-340C	Pakistan International Airlines (leased to JAT, Yugoslavia as YU–AGG)
AP–AWU	Boeing 707-373C	Pakistan International Airlines (leased from World Airways)
AP–AWV	Boeing 707-373C	Pakistan International Airlines (leased from World Airways)
AP–AWY	Boeing 707-340C	Pakistan International Airlines
AP–AWZ	Boeing 707-340C	Pakistan International Airlines
AP–AXA	Boeing 707-340C	Pakistan International Airlines
AP–AXC	Douglas DC-10 Srs. 30	Pakistan International Airlines
AP–AXD	Douglas DC-10 Srs. 30	Pakistan International Airlines
AP–AXE	Douglas DC-10 Srs. 30	Pakistan International Airlines
AP–	Douglas DC-10 Srs. 30	Pakistan International Airlines
AP–AXG	Boeing 707-340C	Pakistan International Airlines
AP–AXK	Boeing 720-047B	Pakistan International Airlines
AP–AXL	Boeing 720-047B	Pakistan International Airlines
AP–AXM	Boeing 720-047B	Pakistan International Airlines

CCCP (Russia)

Aeroflot have operated mainly Tu-104, Tu-134, Il-18 and Il-62 aircraft on scheduled and charter services to the U.K. Tu-104 registrations observed have been in the range CCCP-42330 to CCCP-42509. Tu-134 registrations logged have been in the range CCCP-65610 to CCCP-65663 inclusive; and Tu-134As in the CCCP-65801 to 65964 series. Il-18 registrations logged have been in the range CCCP-74250 to -75890 inclusive. Il-62 registrations logged have been in the range CCCP-86605 to -86704 inclusive.

CF and C (Canada)

Registration	Type	Owner or Operator	Where and when seen
C–FCRA	Boeing 747-217B	Canadian Pacific Air *Empress of Japan*	
C–FCRB	Boeing 747-217B	Canadian Pacific Air *Empress of Canada*	
C–FCRD	Boeing 747-217B	Canadian Pacific Air *Empress of Australia*	
C–FCRE	Boeing 747-217B	Canadian Pacific Air *Empress of Italy*	
C–FFUN	Boeing 747-124	Wardair Canada Ltd. *Romeo Vachon*	
C–FTOE	Boeing 747-133	Air Canada	
C–GAGA	Boeing 747-233B	Air Canada	
CF–CPF	Douglas DC-8 Srs. 43	Canadian Pacific Air *Empress of Rome*	
CF–CPG	Douglas DC-8 Srs. 43	Canadian Pacific Air *Empress of Buenos Aires*	
CF–CPH	Douglas DC-8 Srs. 43	Canadian Pacific Air *Empress of Lima*	
CF–CPI	Douglas DC-8 Srs. 43	Canadian Pacific Air *Empress of Amsterdam*	
CF–CPJ	Douglas DC-8 Srs. 43	Canadian Pacific Air *Empress of Mexico City*	
CF–CPL	Douglas DC-8 Srs. 63	Canadian Pacific Air *Empress of Athens*	
CF–CPM	Douglas DC-8 Srs. 53	Canadian Pacific Air *Empress of Lisbon*	
CF–CPO	Douglas DC-8 Srs. 63	Canadian Pacific Air *Empress of Tokyo*	
CF–CPP	Douglas DC-8 Srs. 63	Canadian Pacific Air *Empress of Honolulu*	
CF–CPQ	Douglas DC-8 Srs. 63	Canadian Pacific Air *Empress of Hong Kong*	
CF–CPS	Douglas DC-8 Srs. 63	Canadian Pacific Air *Empress of Madrid*	
CF–CPT	Douglas DC-8 Srs. 55F	Canadian Pacific Air *Empress of Santiago*	
CF–DJC	Boeing 747-1D1	Wardair Canada Ltd. *Phil Garratt*	
CF–FAN	Boeing 707-311C	Wardair Canada Ltd. *C. H. Punch Dickins*	
CF–PWJ	Boeing 707-351C	Pacific Western	
CF–PWK	L-100-20 Hercules	Pacific Western	
CF–PWN	L-100-20 Hercules	Pacific Western	
CF–PWR	L-100-20 Hercules	Pacific Western	
CF–PWV	Boeing 707-138B	Pacific Western	
CF–PWX	L-100-20 Hercules	Pacific Western	
CF–TIH	Douglas DC-8 Srs. 53	Air Canada	
CF–TII	Douglas DC-8 Srs. 53	Air Canada	
CF–TIK	Douglas DC-8 Srs. 63	Air Canada	
CF–TIL	Douglas DC-8 Srs. 63	Air Canada	
CF–TIM	Douglas DC-8 Srs. 63	Air Canada	
CF–TIN	Douglas DC-8 Srs. 63	Air Canada	
CF–TIO	Douglas DC-8 Srs. 63	Air Canada	
CF–TIP	Douglas DC-8 Srs. 63	Air Canada	
CF–TIQ	Douglas DC-8 Srs. 63	Air Canada	
CF–TIR	Douglas DC-8 Srs. 63	Air Canada	
CF–TIS	Douglas DC-8 Srs. 63	Air Canada	
CF–TIU	Douglas DC-8 Srs. 63	Air Canada	
CF–TIV	Douglas DC-8 Srs. 63	Air Canada	
CF–TIX	Douglas DC-8 Srs. 63	Air Canada	
CF–TJA	Douglas DC-8 Srs. 41	Air Canada	

Registration	Type	Owner or Operator	Where and when seen
CF–TJB	Douglas DC-8 Srs. 41	Air Canada	
CF–TJC	Douglas DC-8 Srs. 41	Air Canada	
CF–TJD	Douglas DC-8 Srs. 41	Air Canada	
CF–TJF	Douglas DC-8 Srs. 43	Air Canada	
CF–TJG	Douglas DC-8 Srs. 43	Air Canada	
CF–TJH	Douglas DC-8 Srs. 43	Air Canada	
CF–TJI	Douglas DC-8 Srs. 43	Air Canada	
CF–TJJ	Douglas DC-8 Srs. 43	Air Canada	
CF–TJK	Douglas DC-8 Srs. 43	Air Canada	
CF–TJL	Douglas DC-8F Jet Trader	Air Canada	
CF–TJO	Douglas DC-8F Jet Trader	Air Canada	
CF–TJP	Douglas DC-8F Jet Trader	Air Canada	
CF–TJQ	Douglas DC-8 Srs. 54	Air Canada	
CF–TJR	Douglas DC-8 Srs. 54	Air Canada	
CF–TJS	Douglas DC-8 Srs. 54	Air Canada	
CF–TJT	Douglas DC-8 Srs. 61	Air Canada	
CF–TJU	Douglas DC-8 Srs. 61	Air Canada	
CF–TJV	Douglas DC-8 Srs. 61	Air Canada	
CF–TJW	Douglas DC-8 Srs. 61	Air Canada	
CF–TJX	Douglas DC-8 Srs. 61	Air Canada	
CF–TJY	Douglas DC-8 Srs. 61	Air Canada	
CF–TJZ	Douglas DC-8 Srs. 61	Air Canada	
CF–TOA	Boeing 747-133	Air Canada	
CF–TOB	Boeing 747-133	Air Canada	
CF–TOC	Boeing 747-133	Air Canada	
CF–TOD	Boeing 747-133	Air Canada	
CF–ZYP	Boeing 707-396C	Wardair Canada Ltd. W. R. Wop May	

CN (Morocco)

CN–CCF	Boeing 727-2B6	Royal Air Maroc Fes	
CN–CCG	Boeing 727-2B6	Royal Air Maroc l'Oiseau de la Providence	
CN–CCH	Boeing 727-2B6	Royal Air Maroc Marrakesh	
CN–CCI	Boeing 727-2B6	Royal Air Maroc	
CN–	Boeing 707-3B6C	Royal Air Maroc	
CN–CCT	S.E.210 Caravelle III	Royal Air Maroc Tafraout	
CN–CCW	Boeing 727-2B6	Royal Air Maroc Agadir	
CN–CCX	S.E.210 Caravelle III	Royal Air Maroc Nador	
CN–CCY	S.E.210 Caravelle III	Royal Air Maroc Ifrane	
CN–CCZ	S.E.210 Caravelle III	Royal Air Maroc Zagora	
CN–RMA	Boeing 707-328	Royal Air Maroc	

CS (Portugal)

CS–TBA	Boeing 707-382B	Transportes Aereos Portugueses Santa Cruz	
CS–TBB	Boeing 707-382B	Transportes Aereos Portugueses Santa Maria	
CS–TBC	Boeing 707-382B	Transportes Aereos Portugueses Cidade de Luanda	
CS–TBD	Boeing 707-382B	Transportes Aereos Portugueses Cidade de Lourenço Marques	
CS–TBE	Boeing 707-382B	Transportes Aereos Portugueses Pedro Alvares Cabral	

Registration	Type	Owner or Operator	Where and when seen
CS–TBF	Boeing 707-382B	Transportes Aereos Portugueses *Vasco da Gama*	
CS–TBG	Boeing 707-382B	Transportes Aereos Portugueses *Fernao de Magalhaes*	
CS–TBH	Boeing 707-399C	Transportes Aereos Portugueses *Pedro Nunes*	
CS–TBI	Boeing 707-399C	Transportes Aereos Portugueses *D. João de Castro*	
CS–TBJ	Boeing 707-373C	Transportes Aereos Portugueses *Lisboa*	
CS–TBK	Boeing 727-82	Transportes Aereos Portugueses *Açores*	
CS–TBL	Boeing 727-82	Transportes Aereos Portugueses *Madeira*	
CS–TBM	Boeing 727-82	Transportes Aereos Portugueses *Algarve*	
CS–TBN	Boeing 727-82QC	Transportes Aereos Portugueses *Cidade do Porto*	
CS–TBO	Boeing 727-82QC	Transportes Aereos Portugueses *Costa do Sol*	
CS–TBP	Boeing 727-82	Transportes Aereos Portugueses *Cabo Verde*	
CS–TBQ	Boeing 727-172C	Transportes Aereos Portugueses *Bissau*	
CS–TBR	Boeing 727-282	Transportes Aereos Portugueses *Sacadura Cabral*	
CS–TBS	Boeing 727-282	Transportes Aereos Portugueses *Gago Coutinho*	
CS–TCA	S.E.210 Caravelle VI-R	Transportes Aereos Portugueses *Goa*	
CS–TCB	S.E.210 Caravelle VI-R	Transportes Aereos Portugueses *Damao*	
CS–TCC	S.E.210 Caravelle VI-R	Transportes Aereos Portugueses *Diu*	
CS–TJA	Boeing 747-282B	Transportes Aereos Portugueses *Portugal*	
CS–TJB	Boeing 747-282B	Transportes Aereos Portugueses *Brasil*	
CS–TJC	Boeing 747-282B	Transportes Aereos Portugueses *Luis de Camões*	
CS–TJD	Boeing 747-282B	Transportes Aereos Portugueses	

D (Germany)

Hapag-Lloyd

Condor
Flugdienst

Lufthansa

Bavaria
Fluggesellschaft

D–ABAF	S.E.210 Caravelle 10-R	LTU	
D–ABAP	S.E.210 Caravelle 10-R	LTU	
D–ABAV	S.E.210 Caravelle 10-R	LTU	
D–ABAW	S.E.210 Caravelle 10-R	LTU	
D–ABBE	Boeing 737-230C	Lufthansa *City Jet Remscheid*	
D–ABBI	Boeing 727-30QC	Lufthansa *Mainz*	
D–ABCE	Boeing 737-230C	Lufthansa *City Jet Landshut*	
D–ABCI	Boeing 727-230	Lufthansa *Karlsruhe*	
D–ABDE	Boeing 737-230C	Lufthansa *City Jet Bamberg*	

Registration	Type	Owner or Operator	Where and when seen
D–ABDI	Boeing 727-230	Lufthansa *Lübeck*	
D–ABEA	Boeing 737-130	Lufthansa *City Jet Coburg*	
D–ABEB	Boeing 737-130	Lufthansa *City Jet Regensburg*	
D–ABEC	Boeing 737-130	Lufthansa *City of Osnabrück*	
D–ABED	Boeing 737-130	Lufthansa *City Jet Flensburg*	
D–ABEF	Boeing 737-130	Lufthansa *City Jet Kempten*	
D–ABEG	Boeing 737-130	Lufthansa *City Jet Offenbach*	
D–ABEH	Boeing 737-130	Lufthansa *City Jet Solingen*	
D–ABEI	Boeing 737-130	Lufthansa *City Jet Oldenburg*	
D–ABEK	Boeing 737-130	Lufthansa *City Jet Konstanz*	
D–ABEL	Boeing 737-130	Lufthansa *City Jet Mülheim a.d.R.*	
D–ABEM	Boeing 737-130	Lufthansa *City Jet Wolfsburg*	
D–ABEN	Boeing 737-130	Lufthansa *City Jet Tübingen*	
D–ABEO	Boeing 737-130	Lufthansa *City Jet Göttingen*	
D–ABEP	Boeing 737-130	Lufthansa *City Jet Wilhelmshaven*	
D–ABEQ	Boeing 737-130	Lufthansa *City Jet Koblenz*	
D–ABER	Boeing 737-130	Lufthansa *City Jet Goslar*	
D–ABES	Boeing 737-130	Lufthansa *City Jet Friedrichshafen*	
D–ABET	Boeing 737-130	Lufthansa *City Jet Baden-Baden*	
D–ABEU	Boeing 737-130	Lufthansa *City Jet Heilbronn*	
D–ABEV	Boeing 737-130	Lufthansa *City Jet Marburg*	
D–ABEW	Boeing 737-130	Lufthansa *City Jet Bayreuth*	
D–ABEY	Boeing 737-130	Lufthansa *City Jet Worms*	
D–ABFE	Boeing 737-230C	Lufthansa *City Jet Trier*	
D–ABFI	Boeing 727-230	Lufthansa *Münster*	
D–ABGE	Boeing 737-230C	Lufthansa *City Jet Erlangen*	
D–ABGI	Boeing 727-230	Lufthansa *Leverkusen*	
D–ABHE	Boeing 737-230C	Lufthansa *City Jet Darmstadt*	
D–ABHI	Boeing 727-230	Lufthansa *Mönchengladbach*	
D–ABIA	Boeing 727-30QC	Lufthansa *Pforzheim*	
D–ABIE	Boeing 727-30QC	Lufthansa *Oberhausen*	
D–ABII	Boeing 727-30QC	Lufthansa *Wuppertal*	
D–ABIJ	Boeing 727-30QC	Lufthansa *Krefeld*	
D–ABIK	Boeing 727-30	Lufthansa (operated by Condor Flugdienst)	
D–ABIL	Boeing 727-30	Lufthansa (operated by Condor Flugdienst)	
D–ABIM	Boeing 727-30	Lufthansa (operated by Condor Flugdienst)	
D–ABIN	Boeing 727-30	Lufthansa (operated by Condor Flugdienst)	
D–ABIO	Boeing 727-30QC	Lufthansa *Hagen*	
D–ABIP	Boeing 727-30	Lufthansa (operated by Condor Flugdienst)	
D–ABIQ	Boeing 727-30	Lufthansa (operated by Condor Flugdienst)	
D–ABIR	Boeing 727-30	Lufthansa (operated by Condor Flugdienst)	
D–ABIU	Boeing 727-30QC	Lufthansa *Ulm*	
D–ABIW	Boeing 727-30QC	Lufthansa *Bielefeld*	
D–ABIX	Boeing 727-30QC	Lufthansa *Würzburg*	
D–ABIY	Boeing 727-30QC	Lufthansa *Aachen*	
D–ABIZ	Boeing 727-30QC	Lufthansa *Gelsenkirchen*	
D–ABKA	Boeing 727-230	Lufthansa *Heidelberg*	
D–ABKB	Boeing 727-230	Lufthansa *Augsburg*	
D–ABKC	Boeing 727-230	Lufthansa *Braunschweig*	
D–ABKD	Boeing 727-230	Lufthansa *Freiburg*	
D–ABKE	Boeing 727-230	Lufthansa *Mannheim*	
D–ABKF	Boeing 727-230	Lufthansa *Saarbrücken*	
D–ABKG	Boeing 727-230	Lufthansa *Kassel*	
D–ABKH	Boeing 727-230	Lufthansa *Kiel*	
D–ABKI	Boeing 727-230	Lufthansa *Bremerhaven*	
D–ABKJ	Boeing 727-230	Lufthansa *Wiesbaden*	
D–ABKK	Boeing 727-230	Lufthansa (operated by Condor Flugdienst)	
D–ABKL	Boeing 727-230	Lufthansa (operated by Condor Flugdienst)	
D–ABLI	Boeing 727-230	Lufthansa *Ludwigshafen a.Rh.*	
D–ABMI	Boeing 727-230	Lufthansa (operated by Condor Flugdienst)	
D–ABNI	Boeing 727-230	Lufthansa (operated by Condor Flugdienst)	
D–ABOB	Boeing 707-430	Lufthansa *Hamburg*	

Registration	Type	Owner or Operator	Where and when seen
D–ABOC	Boeing 707-430	Lufthansa (operated by Condor Flugdienst)	
D–ABOD	Boeing 707-430	Lufthansa *Frankfurt*	
D–ABOF	Boeing 707-430	Lufthansa *München*	
D–ABOG	Boeing 707-430	Lufthansa *Bonn*	
D–ABOX	Boeing 707-330B	Lufthansa *Köln*	
D–ABPI	Boeing 727-230	Lufthansa (operated by Condor Flugdienst)	
D–ABQI	Boeing 727-230	Lufthansa *Hildesheim*	
D–ABRI	Boeing 727-230	Lufthansa *Esslingen*	
D–ABSI	Boeing 727-230	Lufthansa *Hof*	
D–ABTI	Boeing 727-230	Lufthansa (operated by Condor Flugdienst)	
D–ABUA	Boeing 707-330C	Lufthansa *Europe*	
D–ABUB	Boeing 707-330B	Lufthansa *Stuttgart*	
D–ABUD	Boeing 707-330B	Lufthansa *Nürnberg*	
D–ABUE	Boeing 707-330C	Lufthansa *America*	
D–ABUF	Boeing 707-330B	Lufthansa *Hannover*	
D–ABUG	Boeing 707-330B	Lufthansa (operated by Condor Flugdienst)	
D–ABUH	Boeing 707-330B	Lufthansa *Dortmund*	
D–ABUI	Boeing 707-330C	Lufthansa *Asia*	
D–ABUJ	Boeing 707-330C	Lufthansa *Africa*	
D–ABUK	Boeing 707-330B	Lufthansa *Bochum*	
D–ABUL	Boeing 707-330B	Lufthansa *Duisburg*	
D–ABUM	Boeing 707-330B	Lufthansa *Bremen*	
D–ABUO	Boeing 707-330C	Lufthansa *Australia*	
D–ABUY	Boeing 707-330C	Lufthansa *Essen*	
D–ABVI	Boeing 727-230	Lufthansa (operated by Condor Flugdienst)	
D–ABWI	Boeing 727-230	Lufthansa (operated by Condor Flugdienst)	
D–ABYA	Boeing 747-130	Lufthansa *Nordrhein-Westfalen*	
D–ABYC	Boeing 747-130	Lufthansa *Bayern*	
D–ABYD	Boeing 747-230B	Lufthansa *Baden-Württemberg*	
D–ABYE	Boeing 747-230F	Lufthansa *Cargonaut*	
D–ABYF	Boeing 747-230B	Lufthansa (operated by Condor Flugdienst) *Fritz*	
D–ABYG	Boeing 747-230B	Lufthansa *Niedersachsen*	
D–ABYH	Boeing 747-230B	Lufthansa (operated by Condor Flugdienst) *Max*	
D–ABYJ	Boeing 747-230B	Lufthansa	
D–ADAO	Douglas DC-10 Srs. 30	Lufthansa *Dusseldorf*	
D–ADBO	Douglas DC-10 Srs. 30	Lufthansa *Berlin*	
D–ADCO	Douglas DC-10 Srs. 30	Lufthansa	
D–ADDO	Douglas DC-10 Srs. 30	Lufthansa	
D–ADFO	Douglas DC-10 Srs. 30	Lufthansa	
D–ADGO	Douglas DC-10 Srs. 30	Lufthansa	
D–ADHO	Douglas DC-10 Srs. 30	Lufthansa	
D–ADJO	Douglas DC-10 Srs. 30	Lufthansa	
D–ADKO	Douglas DC-10 Srs. 30	Lufthansa	
D–ADLO	Douglas DC-10 Srs. 30	Lufthansa	
D–AERA	L-1011 TriStar	LTU	
D–	L-1011 TriStar	LTU	
D–AGAB	F.28 Fellowship 1000	Germanair *Nürnberg*	
D–AGAC	F.28 Fellowship 1000	Germanair *Bremen*	
D–AGAD	F.28 Fellowship 1000	Germanair *Hannover*	
D–AGAE	F.28 Fellowship 1000	Germanair *Saarbrücken*	
D–AHLL	Boeing 727-81	Hapag-Lloyd	
D–AHLM	Boeing 727-81	Hapag-Lloyd	
D–AHLN	Boeing 727-81	Hapag-Lloyd	
D–AHLO	Boeing 727-29	Hapag-Lloyd	
D–AHLP	Boeing 727-14	Hapag-Lloyd	
D–AHLQ	Boeing 727-46	Hapag-Lloyd	
D–AHLR	Boeing 727-89	Hapag-Lloyd	
D–AHLS	Boeing 727-89	Hapag-Lloyd	
D–AIAA	A.300B2 Airbus	Lufthansa	
D–AIAB	A.300B2 Airbus	Lufthansa	
D–AIAC	A.300B2 Airbus	Lufthansa	
D–AISY	BAC One-Eleven 414EG	Bavaria Fluggesellschaft *Franz von Lenbach*	
D–ALFA	BAC One-Eleven 528	Bavaria Fluggesellschaft *Jakob Fugger*	

Registration	Type	Owner or Operator	Where and when seen
D–ALLI	BAC One-Eleven 413FA	Bavaria Fluggesellschaft *Moritz von Schwind* (leased to Gulf Air)	
D–AMAM	BAC One-Eleven 515FB	Germanair	
D–AMAS	BAC One-Eleven 515FB	Germanair	
D–AMAT	BAC One-Eleven 524FF	Germanair	
D–AMAX	A.300B4 Airbus	Germanair *Maximilian*	
D–AMOR	BAC One-Eleven 524FF	Germanair	
D–AMUC	BAC One-Eleven 528	Bavaria Fluggesellschaft *Ludwig Thoma*	
D–ANNO	BAC One-Eleven 414EG	Bavaria Fluggesellschaft *Carl Spitzweg*	
D–ANUE	BAC One-Eleven 528	Bavaria Fluggesellschaft *Albrecht Dürer*	
D–BAKA	F.27 Friendship Mk. 100	WDL	
D–BAKI	F.27 Friendship Mk. 100	WDL	

EC (Spain)

SPANTAX

LINEAS AEREAS INTERNACIONALES DE ESPAÑA

Transeuropa

EC–ARB	Douglas DC-8 Srs. 52	Aviaco *El Greco*	
EC–ARC	Douglas DC-8 Srs. 52	Aviaco *Goya*	
EC–ARI	S.E.210 Caravelle VI-R	Aviaco *Albeniz*	
EC–ARK	S.E.210 Caravelle VI-R	Aviaco *Granados*	
EC–ASN	Douglas DC-8 Srs. 52	Aviaco *Murillo*	
EC–ATP	Douglas DC-8 Srs. 52	Aviaco *Sorolla*	
EC–ATX	S.E.210 Caravelle VI-R	Aviaco *Turina*	
EC–AUM	Douglas DC-8 Srs. 52	Aviaco *Zurbaran*	
EC–AXU	S.E.210 Caravelle VI-R	Aviaco *Alfonso X El Sabio*	
EC–BAV	Douglas DC-8 Srs. 52	Iberia *Romero de Torres*	
EC–BIB	S.E.210 Caravelle 10 R	Aviaco *Teobaldo Power*	
EC–BIE	S.E.210 Caravelle 10 R	Aviaco *Padre Antonio Soler*	
EC–BIF	S.E.210 Caravelle 10 R	Aviaco *Francisco Tarrega*	
EC–BIG	Douglas DC-9 Srs. 32	Iberia *Villa de Madrid*	
EC–BIH	Douglas DC-9 Srs. 32	Iberia *Ciudad de Barcelona*	
EC–BIJ	Douglas DC-9 Srs. 32	Iberia *Santa Cruz de Tenerife*	
EC–BIK	Douglas DC-9 Srs. 32	Iberia *Las Palmas de Gran Canaria*	
EC–BIL	Douglas DC-9 Srs. 32	Iberia *Ciudad de Zaragoza*	
EC–BIM	Douglas DC-9 Srs. 32	Iberia *Ciudad de Santander*	
EC–BIN	Douglas DC-9 Srs. 32	Iberia *Palma de Mallorca*	
EC–BIO	Douglas DC-9 Srs. 32	Iberia *Villa de Bilbao*	
EC–BIP	Douglas DC-9 Srs. 32	Iberia *Santiago de Compostela*	
EC–BIQ	Douglas DC-9 Srs. 32	Iberia *Ciudad de Malaga*	
EC–BIR	Douglas DC-9 Srs. 32	Iberia *Ciudad de Valencia*	
EC–BIS	Douglas DC-9 Srs. 32	Iberia *Ciudad de Alicante*	
EC–BIT	Douglas DC-9 Srs. 32	Iberia *Ciudad de San Sebastian*	
EC–BIU	Douglas DC-9 Srs. 32	Iberia *Ciudad de Oviedo*	
EC–BJC	CV-990A Coronado	Spantax	
EC–BJD	CV-990A Coronado	Spantax	
EC–BMV	Douglas DC-8 Srs. 55F	Iberia *Pedro Berruguete*	
EC–BMX	Douglas DC-8 Srs. 63	Iberia *El Espanoleto*	
EC–BMY	Douglas DC-8 Srs. 63	Iberia *Rosales*	
EC–BMZ	Douglas DC-8 Srs. 63F	Iberia *Los Madrazo*	
EC–BPF	Douglas DC-9 Srs. 32	Iberia *Ciudad de Almeria*	
EC–BPG	Douglas DC-9 Srs. 32	Iberia *Ciudad de Vigo*	
EC–BPH	Douglas DC-9 Srs. 32	Iberia *Ciudad de Gerona*	
EC–BQA	CV-990A Coronado	Spantax	
EC–BQQ	CV-990A Coronado	Spantax	
EC–BQS	Douglas DC-8 Srs. 63	Iberia *Claudio Coello*	
EC–BQT	Douglas DC-9 Srs. 32	Iberia *Villa de Murcia*	

Registration	Type	Owner or Operator	Where and when seen
EC–BQU	Douglas DC-9 Srs. 32	Iberia *Ciudad de la Coruna*	
EC–BQV	Douglas DC-9 Srs. 32	Iberia *Ciudad de Ibiza*	
EC–BQX	Douglas DC-9 Srs. 32	Iberia *Ciudad de Valladolid*	
EC–BQY	Douglas DC-9 Srs. 32	Iberia *Ciudad de Cordoba*	
EC–BQZ	Douglas DC-9 Srs. 32	Iberia *Santa Cruz de la Palma*	
EC–BRJ	S.E.210 Caravelle 10 R	Transeuropa *Renacuajo III*	
EC–BRO	Boeing 747-156	Iberia *Cervantes*	
EC–BRP	Boeing 747-156	Iberia *Lope de Vega*	
EC–BRQ	Boeing 747-256B	Iberia *Calderon de la Barca*	
EC–BRX	S.E.210 Caravelle 11 R	Transeuropa *Renacuajo I*	
EC–BRY	S.E.210 Caravelle 11 R	Transeuropa *Renacuajo II*	
EC–BSD	Douglas DC-8 Srs. 63	Iberia *Ribalta*	
EC–BSE	Douglas DC-8 Srs. 63	Iberia *Alonso Cano*	
EC–BSP	Douglas DC-7CF	Spantax	
EC–BSQ	Douglas DC-7CF	Spantax	
EC–BTE	CV-990A Coronado	Spantax	
EC–BXI	CV-990A Coronado	Spantax	
EC–BYD	Douglas DC-9 Srs. 32	Iberia *Arrecife de Lanzarote*	
EC–BYE	Douglas DC-9 Srs. 32	Iberia *Ciudad de Mahon*	
EC–BYF	Douglas DC-9 Srs. 32	Iberia *Ciudad de Granada*	
EC–BYG	Douglas DC-9 Srs. 32	Iberia *Ciudad de Pamplona*	
EC–BYH	Douglas DC-9 Srs. 32	Iberia *Ciudad de Cadiz*	
EC–BYI	Douglas DC-9 Srs. 32	Iberia *Ciudad de Vitoria*	
EC–BYJ	Douglas DC-9 Srs. 32	Iberia *Ciudad de Salamanca*	
EC–BYK	Douglas DC-9 Srs. 33RC	Iberia *Ciudad de Badajoz*	
EC–BYL	Douglas DC-9 Srs. 33RC	Iberia *Ciudad de Albacete*	
EC–BYM	Douglas DC-9 Srs. 33RC	Iberia *Ciudad de Cangas de Onis*	
EC–BYN	Douglas DC-9 Srs. 33RC	Iberia *Ciudad de Caceres*	
EC–BZO	CV-990A Coronado	Spantax	
EC–BZP	CV-990A Coronado	Spantax	
EC–CAE	S.E.210 Caravelle 10 R	Aviaco *Hilarion Eslava*	
EC–CAI	Boeing 727-256	Iberia *Castilla la Nueva*	
EC–CAJ	Boeing 727-256	Iberia *Cataluna*	
EC–CAK	Boeing 727-256	Iberia *Aragon*	
EC–CBA	Boeing 727-256	Iberia *Vascongadas*	
EC–CBB	Boeing 727-256	Iberia *Valencia*	
EC–CBC	Boeing 727-256	Iberia *Navarra*	
EC–CBD	Boeing 727-256	Iberia *Murcia*	
EC–CBE	Boeing 727-256	Iberia *Leon*	
EC–CBF	Boeing 727-256	Iberia *Gran Canaria*	
EC–CBG	Boeing 727-256	Iberia *Extremadura*	
EC–CBH	Boeing 727-256	Iberia *Galicia*	
EC–CBI	Boeing 727-256	Iberia *Asturias*	
EC–CBJ	Boeing 727-256	Iberia *Andalucia*	
EC–CBK	Boeing 727-256	Iberia *Baleares*	
EC–CBL	Boeing 727-256	Iberia *Tenerife*	
EC–CBM	Boeing 727-256	Iberia *Castilla la Vieja*	
EC–CBN	Douglas DC-10 Srs. 30	Iberia *Costa Brava*	
EC–CBO	Douglas DC-10 Srs. 30	Iberia *Costa del Sol*	
EC–CBP	Douglas DC-10 Srs. 30	Iberia *Costa Dorada*	
EC–CCF	Douglas DC-8F Srs. 61	Spantax	
EC–CCG	Douglas DC-8F Srs. 61	Spantax	
EC–CCN	Douglas DC-8 Srs. 33	T.A.E.	
EC–CDC	Douglas DC-8 Srs. 33	T.A.E.	
EC–CEZ	Douglas DC-10 Srs. 30	Iberia *Costa del Azahar*	
EC–CFA	Boeing 727-256	Iberia *Jerez Xeres Sherry*	
EC–CFB	Boeing 727-256	Iberia *Rioja*	
EC–CFC	Boeing 727-256	Iberia *Tarragona*	
EC–CFD	Boeing 727-256	Iberia *Montilla Moriles*	
EC–CFE	Boeing 727-256	Iberia *Penedes*	
EC–CFF	Boeing 727-256	Iberia *Valdepenas*	
EC–CFG	Boeing 727-256	Iberia *La Mancha*	
EC–CFH	Boeing 727-256	Iberia *Priorato*	
EC–CFI	Boeing 727-256	Iberia *Carinena*	
EC–CFJ	Boeing 727-256	Iberia *Jumilla*	
EC–CFK	Boeing 727-256	Iberia *Ribeiro*	
EC–CGN	Douglas DC-9 Srs. 32	Aviaco *Martin Alonso Pinzon*	
EC–CGO	Douglas DC-9 Srs. 32	Aviaco *Pedro Alonso Nino*	
EC–CGP	Douglas DC-9 Srs. 32	Aviaco *Juan Sebastian Elcano*	
EC–CGQ	Douglas DC-9 Srs. 32	Aviaco *Alonso de Ojeda*	
EC–CGR	Douglas DC-9 Srs. 32	Aviaco *Francisco de Orellana*	
EC–CGS	Douglas DC-9 Srs. 32	Aviaco *Vasco Nunez de Balboa*	
EC–CGY	Douglas DC-9 Srs. 14	Spantax	

EI-ASD. (Top) Boeing 737-248QC (two 14,500lb st Pratt & Whitney JT8D-9)/*Liam Byrne*

EI-AWW. (Centre) Cessna 414 (two 310hp Continental TSIO-520-J)/*Foto Hunter*

EI-BAA. (Above) Bristol 175 Britannia 307F (four 4,120shp Bristol Proteus 761)/*Liam Byrne*

Registration	Type	Owner or Operator	Where and when seen
EC–CGZ	Douglas DC-9 Srs. 14	Spantax	
EC–CID	Boeing 727-256	Iberia *Malaga*	
EC–CIE	Boeing 727-256	Iberia *Esparragosa*	
EC–CIZ	S.E.210 Caravelle 10 R	Transeuropa	
EC–CLB	Douglas DC-10 Srs. 30	Iberia *Costa Blanca*	
EC–CLD	Douglas DC-9 Srs. 32	Aviaco *Hernando de Soto*	
EC–CLE	Douglas DC-9 Srs. 32	Aviaco	
EC–CMS	S.E.210 Caravelle 10	T.A.E.	
EC–CNF	CV-990A Coronado	Spantax	
EC–CNG	CV-990A Coronado	Spantax	
EC–CNH	CV-990A Coronado	Spantax	
EC–CNJ	CV-990A Coronado	Spantax	
EC–CPI	S.E.210 Caravelle 10 R	Transeuropa	
EC–CQM	Douglas DC-8 Srs. 54F	Aviaco	
EC–	Douglas DC-8 Srs. 53	T.A.E.	
EC–	S.E.210 Caravelle 10	T.A.E.	

EI (Republic of Ireland)

Including complete current Irish Civil Register.

Registration	Type	Owner or Operator	Where and when seen
EI–ADV	Piper PA-12 Super Cruiser	R. E. Levis	
EI–AFF	*B.A. Swallow 2	J. McCarthy	
EI–AFK	*D.H.84 Dragon	Aer Lingus-Irish (painted as EI–ABI *Iolar*)	
EI–AFN	*B.A. Swallow 2	J. McCarthy	
EI–AGB	*Miles M.38 Messenger 4	J. McLoughlin	
EI–AGE	*Miles M.38 Messenger 3	J. McLoughlin	
EI–AGJ	Auster J/I Autocrat	W. G. Rafter	
EI–AGO	*Avro 643 Cadet	G. Flood (painted as Irish Air Corps C-5)	
EI–AGP	D.H.82A Tiger Moth	D. W. R. Kennedy	
EI–AHA	*D.H.82A Tiger Moth	J. H. Maher	
EI–AHR	D.H.C.I Chipmunk 22	Christina Lane	
EI–AKM	Piper J3C Cub 65	Setanta Flying Group	
EI–ALH	Taylorcraft Plus D	N. Reilly	
EI–ALP	Avro 643 Cadet	J. C. O'Loughlin	
EI–ALU	†Avro 631 Cadet	M. P. Cahill	
EI–AMD	M.S.880B Rallye Club	Morane Aircraft Ltd.	
EI–AMK	Auster J/I Autocrat	Irish Aero Club	
EI–AMO	Auster 5 J/IB	Omac Builders Ltd.	
EI–AMS	Piper PA-22 Tri-Pacer 160	Commander Aircraft Sales Ltd.	
EI–AMY	Auster J/I Autocrat	Meath Flying Group Ltd.	
EI–AND	Cessna 175A	Jack Braithwaite (Ireland) Ltd.	
EI–ANE	BAC One-Eleven 208AL	Aer Lingus-Irish St. *Mel*	
EI–ANF	BAC One-Eleven 208AL	Aer Lingus-Irish St. *Malachy*	
EI–ANG	BAC One-Eleven 208AL	Aer Lingus-Irish St. *Declan*	
EI–ANH	BAC One-Eleven 208AL	Aer Lingus-Irish St. *Ronan*	
EI–ANO	Boeing 707-348C	Aer Lingus-Irish St. *Brigid*	
EI–ANP	Omega 56 balloon	Dublin Ballooning Club Ltd.	
EI–ANT	Champion 7ECA Citabria	Setanta Flying Group	
EI–ANV	Boeing 707-348C	Aer Lingus-Irish St. *Enda*	
EI–ANW	Jodel D.117	P. A. Haycock	
EI–ANY	Piper PA-18 Super Cub 95	Central Flying Group	
EI–AOB	Piper PA-28 Cherokee 140	Dr. H. J. R. Henderson	
EI–AOD	Cessna 182B Skylane	P. F. Donegan	
EI–AOK	Cessna F.172G	Kerry Airways Ltd. *Rose of Tralee*	

* Preserved.   † Non-flying, being restored.

Registration	Type	Owner or Operator	Where and when seen
EI–AOO	Cessna 150	Limerick Flying Group Ltd.	
EI–AOP	D.H.82A Tiger Moth	Dublin Tiger Group	
EI–AOS	Cessna 310B	Joyce Aviation Ltd.	
EI–APF	Cessna F.150G	Midland Flying Group Ltd.	
EI–APG	Boeing 707-348C	Aer Lingus-Irish St. Senan	
EI–APS	Schleicher ASK 14	G. W. Connolly & M. Slazenger	
EI–APT	Fokker D.VII/65	Blue Max Aviation Ltd.	
EI–APU	Fokker D.VII/65	Blue Max Aviation Ltd.	
EI–APV	Fokker D.VII/65	Blue Max Aviation Ltd.	
EI–APW	Fokker Dr. I Replica	Blue Max Aviation Ltd.	
EI–APY	Fokker Dr. I Replica	Shillelagh Productions Ltd.	
EI–ARC	Pfalz D.III Replica	Blue Max Aviation Ltd.	
EI–ARD	Pfalz D.III Replica	Blue Max Aviation Ltd.	
EI–ARE	Stampe SV.4C	Blue Max Aviation Ltd.	
EI–ARF	Caudron C.277 Luciole	Blue Max Aviation Ltd.	
EI–ARG	Morane-Saulnier M.S. 230	Historical Aircraft Preservation Society Ltd.	
EI–ARH	Currie Wot/ S.E.5 Replica	Lynn Garrison	
EI–ARI	Currie Wot/ S.E.5 Replica	Blue Max Aviation Ltd.	
EI–ARJ	Currie Wot/ S.E.5 Replica	Blue Max Aviation Ltd.	
EI–ARK	Currie Wot/ S.E.5 Replica	Blue Max Aviation Ltd.	
EI–ARL	Currie Wot/ S.E.5 Replica	Blue Max Aviation Ltd.	
EI–ARM	Currie Wot/ S.E.5 Replica	Lynn Garrison	
EI–ARN	Wren 460	VAPF (Ireland) Ltd.	
EI–ARS	Douglas C-54E	Aer Turas Teo City of Galway	
EI–ARW	Jodel D.R. 1050 Ambassadeur	Paul R. Duffy & John A. Healy	
EI–ASA	Boeing 737-248	Aer Lingus-Irish St. Jarlath (leased to Zambia as 9J–AEA)	
EI–ASB	Boeing 737-248	Aer Lingus-Irish St. Albert (leased to EgyptAir)	
EI–ASC	Boeing 737-248QC	Aer Lingus-Irish St. Macartan	
EI–ASD	Boeing 737-248QC	Aer Lingus-Irish St. Ide	
EI–ASE	Boeing 737-248	Aer Lingus-Irish St. Fachtna	
EI–ASF	Boeing 737-248	Aer Lingus-Irish St. Nathy	
EI–ASG	Boeing 737-248	Aer Lingus-Irish St. Cormack (leased to EgyptAir)	
EI–ASH	Boeing 737-248	Aer Lingus-Irish St. Eugene	
EI–ASI	Boeing 747-148	Aer Lingus-Irish (leased to Air Siam as HS–VGB)	
EI–ASJ	Boeing 747-148	Aer Lingus-Irish St. Patrick (leased to British Airways)	
EI–ASK	Boeing 737-222	Aer Lingus-Irish St. Laurence O'Toole	
EI–ASL	Boeing 737-248QC	Aer Lingus-Irish St. Cillian	
EI–ASM	Boeing 707-351C	Aer Lingus-Irish	
EI–ASR	McCandless Mk. 4 Gyroplane	George J. J. Fasenfeld	
EI–AST	Cessna F.150H	Garda Flying Club Ltd.	
EI–ASU	Beagle A.61 Terrier Srs. 2	Kerry Gliding Club Ltd.	
EI–ASV	Piper PA-28R Cherokee Arrow 180	F. E. A. Biggar	
EI–ATC	Cessna 310G	Iona National Airways	
EI–ATF	Cessna 182G	A. Leonard	
EI–ATH	Cessna F.150J	Galway Flying Club	
EI–ATJ	Beagle Pup 100	Wexford Aero Club	
EI–ATK	Piper PA-28 Cherokee 140	Mayo Flying Club Ltd.	
EI–ATL	Aeronca 7AC	Kildare Flying Club	
EI–ATS	M.S.880B Rallye Club	Longford Aviation Ltd.	
EI–AUC	Cessna F.150K Aerobat	Fifteen Flying Club Ltd.	
EI–AUD	M.S.880B Rallye Club	Kilkenny Flying Club Ltd.	
EI–AUE	M.S.880B Rallye Club	Slievenamon Air Ltd.	
EI–AUG	M.S.894 Rallye Minerva 220	Roadstone Ltd.	
EI–AUI	S.H.3130 Alouette II	Irish Helicopters Ltd.	

Registration	Type	Owner or Operator	Where and when seen
EI–AUJ	M.S.880B Rallye Club	H. Lynch, C. Twohig & J. McCarthy	
EI–AUK	D.H.104 Dove 6	A. Reynolds	
EI–AUM	Auster 5 J/I	T. G. Rafter	
EI–AUN	M.S.880B Rallye Club	Leinster Aero Club	
EI–AUO	Cessna F.150K Aerobat	Kerry Airways Ltd.	
EI–AUP	M.S.880B Rallye Club	Dundalk Aero Club Ltd.	
EI–AUR	Bölkow Bo 208C Junior	S. McCarthy	
EI–AUS	Auster J/5F	Meath Flying Group Ltd.	
EI–AUT	Forney Aircoupe F-1A	Joyce Aviation Ltd.	
EI–AUY	*Morane-Saulnier M.S.500	Historical Aircraft Preservation Group	
EI–AVA	Cessna F.172K	Patrick Parke	
EI–AVB	Aeronca 7AC	G. G. Bracken	
EI–AVC	Cessna F.337F Super Skymaster	Iona National Airways	
EI–AVE	Piper PA-18 Super Cub 95	C. O'Donnell & ptnrs.	
EI–AVG	Beech A.55 Baron	C. O. Neale	
EI–AVL	Auster J/5F Aiglet	George E. Flood	
EI–AVM	Cessna F.150L	Iona-Irish Aero Club	
EI–AVN	Hughes 500M	Helicopter Maintenance Ltd.	
EI–AVT	Stampe SV.4C	J. G. Gallagher	
EI–AVU	Stampe SV.4C	Robert McDowell	
EI–AWA	Bell 206B Mark 2	Helicopter Maintenance Ltd.	
EI–AWB	Bölkow 105D	Irish Helicopters Ltd.	
EI–AWD	Piper PA-22 Tri-Pacer 160	D. R. Naylor	
EI–AWE	Cessna F.150M	Iona-Irish Aero Club	
EI–AWH	Cessna 210J Centurion	Southern Air Ltd.	
EI–AWJ	M.S.893A Rallye Commodore	Dr. W. J. Phelan	
EI–AWL	Piper PA-28R Cherokee Arrow 200 Mk. 2	Robert McDowell	
EI–AWM	BN-2A Islander	Comhfhorbairt (Gaillimh) Teo-Aer Arann	
EI–AWP	D.H.82A Tiger Moth	A. Lyons	
EI–AWR	Malmo MFI-9 Junior	Maurice & Jean Cronin	
EI–AWS	Piper PA-34 Seneca 200	Ballyfree Aviation Ltd.	
EI–AWT	Piper PA-34 Seneca 200	Passat (Ireland) Ltd.	
EI–AWU	M.S.880B Rallye Club	Longford Aviation Ltd.	
EI–AWV	Grumman American AA-5 Traveler	J. A. Martin	
EI–AWW	Cessna 414	T. Farrington	
EI–AWY	Mitsubishi MU-2B-35J	Helicopter Maintenance Ltd.	
EI–AYA	M.S.880B Rallye Club	Dundalk Aero Club Ltd.	
EI–AYB	Gardan GY-80 Horizon 180	Horizon Aircraft Ltd.	
EI–AYC	Grumman American AA-5 Traveler	Amery Aviation Ltd.	
EI–AYD	Grumman American AA-5 Traveler	Kenneth Walters	
EI–AYF	Cessna FRA.150L	Iona-Irish Aero Club	
EI–AYG	Piper PA-39CR Twin Comanche	Garard W. Connolly	
EI–AYH	Cessna 172B	Industrial Installations Ltd.	
EI–AYI	M.S.880B Rallye Club	Irish Air Training Group	
EI–AYJ	Cessna 182P	Iona National Airways	
EI–AYK	Cessna F.172M	Irish Tank and Pipe Line Co. Ltd.	
EI–AYL	Beagle A.109 Airedale	J. A. McWilliam	
EI–AYN	BN-2A Islander	Comhfhorbairt (Gaillimh) Teo-Aer Arann	
EI–AYR	Schleicher ASK-18	Kilkenny Airport Ltd.	
EI–AYS	Piper PA-22 Colt 108	Dermott M. Whelan, George Farrer, Michael Skelly & Robert Hall	
EI–AYT	M.S.894A Rallye Minerva	Dublin Gliding Club Ltd.	
EI–AYU	Zaunkoenig V-2	Commander Aircraft Sales (Ireland) Ltd.	

*Preserved

Registration	Type	Owner or Operator	Where and when seen
EI–AYV	M.S.892A Rallye Commodore 150	P. A. Doyle	
EI–AYW	Piper PA-23 Aztec 250C	J. A. Chute Construction Co. Ltd.	
EI–AYY	Evans VP-I	Michael Donohoe	
EI–BAA	B.175 Britannia 307F	Aer Turas Teo *City of Dublin*	
EI–BAB	M.S.894E Rallye Minerva 220GT	P. Monaghan	
EI–BAC	Piper PA-34 Seneca 235	Multimac Ltd.	
EI–BAE	Piper PA-31 Navajo	Executive Air Services	
EI–BAF	Piccard AX-6 Balloon	D. E. Williams Ltd.	
EI–BAG	Cessna 172A	Irish Parachute Club Ltd.	
EI–BAI	Jodel DR 1050 Ambassadeur	Ronald J. Egan	
EI–BAJ	Stampe SV.4C	Dublin Tiger Group	
EI–BAL	Beagle A.109 Airedale	S. J. Dunne & ptnrs.	
EI–BAM	Bell 212	Irish Helicopters Ltd.	
EI–BAN	Cameron AX-7 Hot-Air Balloon	C. M. Alexander	
EI–BAO	Cessna F.172G	M. Concannon	
EI–BAP	Piper J3C Cub 65	J. Molloy	
EI–BAR	Thunder AX-8-105 Hot-Air Balloon	Fr. D. Reid	
EI–BAS	Cessna F.172M	Iona-Irish Aero Club	
EI–BAT	Cessna F.150L	Iona-Irish Aero Club	
EI–BAU	Stampe SV.4C	Robert McDowell	
EI–BAV	Piper PA-22 Colt 108	J. P. Montcalm	
EI–BAW	Piper PA-23 Apache 160	A. J. McWilliam	
EI–BAY	Cameron AX-8 Hot-Air Balloon	F. N. Lewis	
EI–BBB	Rockwell Commander 112	N. Hanlon (Ireland) Ltd.	
EI–BBC	Piper PA-28 Cherokee 180	M. P. Goss & D. Goss	
EI–BBE	Champion 7FC	G. Treacy	
EI–BBG	M.S.880B Rallye Club	Weston Ltd.	
EI–BBH	B.175 Britannia 253C	Aer Turas Teo *City of Cork*	
EI–BBI	M.S.892 Rallye Commodore	Kilkenny Airport Ltd.	
EI–BBJ	M.S.880B Rallye Club	W. Gavin	
EI–BBK	Beagie A.109 Airedale	Kerry Gliding Club Ltd.	
EI–BBL	Rockwell Turbo Commander 690A	The Earl of Granard	

EP (Iran)

EP–IAA	Boeing 747SP-86	Iran Air
EP–IAB	Boeing 747SP-86	Iran Air
EP–IAC	Boeing 747SP-86	Iran Air
EP–IAG	Boeing 747-286B	Iran Air
EP–IAH	Boeing 747-286B	Iran Air
EP–IRA	Boeing 727-86	Iran Air *Esfahan*
EP–IRB	Boeing 727-86	Iran Air *Abadan*
EP–IRC	Boeing 727-86	Iran Air *Ramsar*
EP–IRD	Boeing 727-86	Iran Air *Shiraz*
EP–IRJ	Boeing 707-321B	Iran Air
EP–IRK	Boeing 707-321C	Iran Air
EP–IRL	Boeing 707-386C	Iran Air *Apadana*
EP–IRM	Boeing 707-386C	Iran Air *Ekbatana*
EP–IRN	Boeing 707-386C	Iran Air *Pasargad*
EP–IRP	Boeing 727-286	Iran Air
EP–IRR	Boeing 727-286	Iran Air
EP–IRS	Boeing 727-286	Iran Air
EP–IRT	Boeing 727-286	Iran Air
EP–IRU	Boeing 727-286	Iran Air

NOTE: Iran Air also operates a Boeing 707 freighter, registered N794EP.

ET (Ethiopia)

Registration	Type	Owner or Operator	Where and when seen
ET–AAH	Boeing 720-060B	Ethiopian Airlines	
ET–ABP	Boeing 720-060B	Ethiopian Airlines	
ET–ACD	Boeing 707-360C	Ethiopian Airlines	
ET–ACQ	Boeing 707-379C	Ethiopian Airlines	
ET–AFA	Boeing 720-024B	Ethiopian Airlines	
ET–AFB	Boeing 720-024B	Ethiopian Airlines	
ET–AFK	Boeing 720-024B	Ethiopian Airlines	

F (France)

Registration	Type	Owner or Operator	Where and when seen
F–BAIF	Douglas DC-3	Uni-Air	
F–BAXR	Douglas DC-3	Uni-Air	
F–BCYN	Boeing 707-321C	Air France	
F–BCYO	Boeing 707-321C	Air France	
F–BCYP	Boeing 707-321C	Air France	
F–BCYT	Douglas DC-3	Vargas Aviation	
F–BCYV	Douglas DC-3	Vargas Aviation	
F–BCYX	Douglas DC-3	Uni-Air	
F–BHKX	Douglas DC-3	Vargas Aviation	
F–BHRA	S.E.210 Caravelle III	Air France *Alsace*	
F–BHRB	S.E.210 Caravelle III	Air France *Lorraine*	
F–BHRD	S.E.210 Caravelle III	Air France *Guyenne*	
F–BHRE	S.E.210 Caravelle III	Air France *Artois*	
F–BHRF	S.E.210 Caravelle III	Air France *Auvergne*	
F–BHRG	S.E.210 Caravelle III	Air France *Berry*	
F–BHRH	S.E.210 Caravelle III	Air France *Bourgogne*	
F–BHRI	S.E.210 Caravelle III	Air France *Bretagne*	
F–BHRK	S.E.210 Caravelle III	Air France *Corse*	
F–BHRL	S.E.210 Caravelle III	Air France *Dauphine*	
F–BHRM	S.E.210 Caravelle III	Air France *Quercy*	
F–BHRN	S.E.210 Caravelle III	Air France *Gascogne*	
F–BHRO	S.E.210 Caravelle III	Air France *Ile-de-France*	
F–BHRP	S.E.210 Caravelle III	Air France *Languedoc*	
F–BHRQ	S.E.210 Caravelle III	Air Inter	
F–BHRR	S.E.210 Caravelle III	Air Inter	
F–BHRS	S.E.210 Caravelle III	Air Inter	
F–BHRT	S.E.210 Caravelle III	Air France *Picardie*	
F–BHRU	S.E.210 Caravelle III	Air France *Poitou*	
F–BHRV	S.E.210 Caravelle III	Air France *Provence*	
F–BHRX	S.E.210 Caravelle III	Air France *Savoie*	
F–BHRY	S.E.210 Caravelle III	Air France *Touraine*	
F–BHRZ	S.E.210 Caravelle III	Air Inter	
F–BHSB	Boeing 707-328	Air France *Chateau de Chambord*	
F–BHSC	Boeing 707-328	Air France *Chateau de Fontainebleau*	
F–BHSD	Boeing 707-328	Air France *Chateau de Chenonceaux*	
F–BHSE	Boeing 707-328	Air France *Chateau de Rambouillet*	
F–BHSF	Boeing 707-328	Air France *Chateau de Blois*	

Registration	Type	Owner or Operator	Where and when seen
F–BHSG	Boeing 707-328	Air France *Chateau de Pau*	
F–BHSH	Boeing 707-328	Air France *Chateau d'Amboise*	
F–BHSI	Boeing 707-328	Air France *Chateau de Josselin*	
F–BHSJ	Boeing 707-328	Air France *Chateau de Chaumont*	
F–BHSK	Boeing 707-328	Air France *Chateau de Vizille*	
F–BHSL	Boeing 707-328	Air France *Chateau de Maintenon*	
F–BHSN	Boeing 707-328	Air France *Chateau de Valencay*	
F–BHSO	Boeing 707-328	Air France *Chateau d'Anet*	
F–BHSP	Boeing 707-328	Air France *Chateau de Villandry*	
F–BHSQ	Boeing 707-328	Air France *Chateau de Compiègne*	
F–BHSR	Boeing 707-328	Air France *Chateau de Cheverny*	
F–BHSS	Boeing 707-328	Air France *Chateau d'Uzes*	
F–BHSV	Boeing 707-328B	Air France *Chateau de Vincennes*	
F–BHSX	Boeing 707-328B	Air France *Chateau de Grignan*	
F–BHSY	Boeing 707-328B	Air France *Chateau de Luneville*	
F–BJCM	Boeing 707-355C (Cargo)	Air France *Pelican II*	
F–BJTE	S.E.210 Caravelle III	Air France *Grenoble*	
F–BJTF	S.E.210 Caravelle III	Air France *Orleanais*	
F–BJTG	S.E.210 Caravelle III	Air Charter International *Roussillon*	
F–BJTH	S.E.210 Caravelle III	Air Charter International *Franche-Comté*	
F–BJTJ	S.E.210 Caravelle III	Air Charter International *Bourbonnais*	
F–BJTL	S.E.210 Caravelle III	Air France *Aunis et Saintonge*	
F–BJTO	S.E.210 Caravelle III	Air Charter International *Pays Basque*	
F–BJTP	S.E.210 Caravelle III	Air France *Comtat Venaissin*	
F–BJTQ	S.E.210 Caravelle III	Air France *Champagne*	
F–BJTR	S.E.210 Caravelle III	Air France *Vercors*	
F–BJTS	S.E.210 Caravelle III	Air France *Principauté de Monaco*	
F–BKGZ	S.E.210 Caravelle III	Air France *Comte de Foix*	
F–BLCA	Boeing 707-328B	Air France *Chateau de Sully*	
F–BLCC	Boeing 707-328C (Cargo)	Air France *Pelican I*	
F–BLCD	Boeing 707-328B	Air France *Chateau de Dampierre*	
F–BLCE	Boeing 707-328B	Air France *Chateau d'Usse*	
F–BLCF	Boeing 707-328C	Air France *Chateau de Grosbois*	
F–BLCG	Boeing 707-328C	Air France *Chateau du Lude*	
F–BLCH	Boeing 707-328C	Air France *Chateau de Hautefort*	
F–BLCI	Boeing 707-328C	Air France *Chateau de Verteuil*	
F–BLCK	Boeing 707-328C	Air France *Chateau de Langeais*	
F–BLCL	Boeing 707-328C	Air France *Chateau de la Roche Courbon*	
F–BLKF	S.E.210 Caravelle III	Air France *Angoumois*	
F–BLOY	HPR-7 Herald	Europe Aero Service	
F–BMMI	Douglas DC-4	Vargas Aviation	
F–BNKA	S.E.210 Caravelle III	Air Inter	
F–BNKB	S.E.210 Caravelle III	Air Inter	
F–BNKC	S.E.210 Caravelle III	Air Inter	
F–BNKD	S.E.210 Caravelle III	Air Inter	
F–BNKE	S.E.210 Caravelle III	Air Inter	
F–BNKF	S.E.210 Caravelle III	Air Inter	
F–BNKG	S.E.210 Caravelle III	Air Inter	
F–BNKH	S.E.210 Caravelle III	Air Inter	
F–BNKJ	S.E.210 Caravelle III	Air Inter	
F–BNKK	S.E.210 Caravelle III	Air Inter	
F–BNKL	S.E.210 Caravelle III	Air Inter	
F–BOHA	S.E.210 Caravelle III	Air France *Comté de Nice*	
F–BOHC	S.E.210 Caravelle III	Air France *Aquitaine*	
F–BOIZ	HPR-7 Herald 210	Europe Aero Service	
F–BOJA	Boeing 727-228	Air France	
F–BOJB	Boeing 727-228	Air France	
F–BOJC	Boeing 727-228	Air France	
F–BOJD	Boeing 727-228	Air France	
F–BOJE	Boeing 727-228	Air France	
F–BOJF	Boeing 727-228	Air France	
F–BPJG	Boeing 727-228	Air France	
F–BPJH	Boeing 727-228	Air France	
F–BPJI	Boeing 727-228	Air France	

Registration	Type	Owner or Operator	Where and when seen
F–BPJJ	Boeing 727-228	Air France	
F–BPJK	Boeing 727-228	Air France	
F–BPJL	Boeing 727-228	Air France	
F–BPJM	Boeing 727-228	Air France	
F–BPJN	Boeing 727-228	Air France	
F–BPJO	Boeing 727-228	Air France	
F–BPJP	Boeing 727-228	Air France	
F–BPJQ	Boeing 727-228	Air France	
F–BPJR	Boeing 727-228	Air France	
F–BPJS	Boeing 727-228	Air France	
F–BPJT	Boeing 727-228	Air France	
F–BPJU	Boeing 727-214	Air Charter International	
F–BPJV	Boeing 727-214	Air Charter International	
F–BPNA	F.27 Friendship Mk. 500	Air Inter	
F–BPNB	F.27 Friendship Mk. 500	Air Inter	
F–BPNC	F.27 Friendship Mk. 500	Air Inter	
F–BPND	F.27 Friendship Mk. 500	Air Inter	
F–BPNE	F.27 Friendship Mk. 500	Air Inter	
F–BPNG	F.27 Friendship Mk. 500	Air Inter	
F–BPNH	F.27 Friendship Mk. 500	Air Inter	
F–BPNI	F.27 Friendship Mk. 500	Air Inter	
F–BPNJ	F.27 Friendship Mk. 500	Air Inter	
F–BPNY	Nord 262	Rousseau Aviation	
F–BPPA	Aero Spacelines Guppy-201	Aeromaritime	
F–BPUA	F.27 Friendship Mk. 500	Air France	
F–BPUB	F.27 Friendship Mk. 500	Air France	
F–BPUC	F.27 Friendship Mk. 500	Air France	
F–BPUD	F.27 Friendship Mk. 500	Air France	
F–BPUE	F.27 Friendship Mk. 500	Air France	
F–BPUF	F.27 Friendship Mk. 500	Air France	
F–BPUG	F.27 Friendship Mk. 500	Air France	
F–BPUH	F.27 Friendship Mk. 500	Air France	
F–BPUI	F.27 Friendship Mk. 500	Air France	
F–BPUJ	F.27 Friendship Mk. 500	Air France	
F–BPUK	F.27 Friendship Mk. 500	Air France	
F–BPUL	F.27 Friendship Mk. 500	Air France	
F–BPVA	Boeing 747-128	Air France	
F–BPVB	Boeing 747-128	Air France	
F–BPVC	Boeing 747-128	Air France	
F–BPVD	Boeing 747-128	Air France	
F–BPVE	Boeing 747-128	Air France	
F–BPVF	Boeing 747-128	Air France	
F–BPVG	Boeing 747-128	Air France	
F–BPVH	Boeing 747-128	Air France	
F–BPVK	Boeing 747-128	Air France (leased as N28899)	
F–BPVL	Boeing 747-128	Air France	
F–BPVM	Boeing 747-128	Air France (leased as N28903)	
F–BPVN	Boeing 747-128	Air France (leased as N63305)	
F–BPVO	Boeing 747-228F	Air France (leased as N18815)	
F–BPVP	Boeing 747-128	Air France	
F–BPVQ	Boeing 747-128	Air France	
F–BRGX	S.E.210 Caravelle VI-R	Catair	
F–BRPC	D.H.C.6 Twin Otter	Air Paris	
F–BSEL	S.E.210 Caravelle VI-R	Euralair	
F–BSRA	H.S.748	Rousseau Aviation	
F–BSRU	H.S.748	Rousseau Aviation	
F–BSTN	Nord 262	Rousseau Aviation	
F–BSUG	Beech 99	T.A.T.	
F–BSUM	F.27 Friendship Mk. 500	Air France	
F–BSUN	F.27 Friendship Mk. 500	Air France	
F–BSUO	F.27 Friendship Mk. 500	Air France	
F–BTDL	S.E.210 Caravelle VI-R	Euralair International	
F–BTGV	Aero Spacelines Guppy-201	Aeromaritime	
F–BTMF	Dassault Mystère 20	Air France/T.A.T.	
F–BTOA	S.E.210 Caravelle 12	Air Inter	
F–BTOB	S.E.210 Caravelle 12	Air Inter	
F–BTOC	S.E.210 Caravelle 12	Air Inter	
F–BTOD	S.E.210 Caravelle 12	Air Inter	
F–BTOE	S.E.210 Caravelle 12	Air Inter	
F–BTON	S.E.210 Caravelle VI-R	Catair	
F–BTOU	V.952 Vanguard	Europe Aero Service	

Registration	Type	Owner or Operator	Where and when seen
F–BTOV	V.952 Vanguard	Europe Aero Service	
F–BTOX	V.952 Vanguard	Europe Aero Service (stored, October 1975)	
F–BTSC	Concorde 203	Air France	
F–BTTA	Dassault Mercure 100	Air Inter	
F–BTTB	Dassault Mercure 100	Air Inter	
F–BTTC	Dassault Mercure 100	Air Inter	
F–BTTD	Dassault Mercure 100	Air Inter	
F–BTTE	Dassault Mercure 100	Air Inter	
F–BTTF	Dassault Mercure 100	Air Inter	
F–BTTG	Dassault Mercure 100	Air Inter	
F–BTTH	Dassault Mercure 100	Air Inter	
F–BTTI	Dassault Mercure 100	Air Inter	
F–BTYB	V.952F Vanguard	Europe Aero Service	
F–BTYC	V.952 Vanguard	Europe Aero Service (stored, October 1975)	
F–BUFA	F.27 Friendship Mk. 200	T.A.T.	
F–BUFC	S.E.210 Caravelle VI-R	Catair	
F–BUFE	F.27 Friendship Mk. 200	T.A.T.	
F–BUFF	S.E.210 Caravelle VI-R	Catair	
F–BUFG	Dassault Mystère 20	Air France/T.A.T.	
F–BUFH	S.E.210 Caravelle III	Catair	
F–BUFO	F.27 Friendship Mk. 200	T.A.T.	
F–BUFP	Transall C-160P	Air France	
F–BUFQ	Transall C-160P	Air France	
F–BUFR	Transall C-160P	Air France	
F–BUFS	Transall C-160P	Air France	
F–BUFT	V.952F Vanguard	Europe Aero Service	
F–BUFU	F.27 Friendship Mk. 200	T.A.T.	
F–BUOE	S.E.210 Caravelle III	Catair	
F–BUTA	F.27 Friendship Mk. 200	T.A.T.	
F–BVFA	Concorde 205	Air France	
F–BVFB	Concorde 207	Air France	
F–BVFC	Concorde 209	Air France	
F–BVGA	A.300B2 Airbus	Air France	
F–BVGB	A.300B2 Airbus	Air France	
F–BVGC	A.300B2 Airbus	Air France	
F–BVGD	A.300B2 Airbus	Air France	
F–BVGE	A.300B2 Airbus	Air France	
F–BVGF	A.300B2 Airbus	Air France	
F–BVGG	A.300B4 Airbus	Air France	
F–BVJL	Beech B.99A	Air Champagne Ardennes	
F–BVPL	SN-601 Corvette	Air Languedoc	
F–BVPP	Nord 262	Air Alsace *Tokay d'Alsace*	
F–BVPS	SN-601 Corvette	Air Languedoc	
F–BVPT	SN-601 Corvette	Air Languedoc	
F–BVPU	S.E.210 Caravelle VI-N	Catair	
F–BVPY	S.E.210 Caravelle 12	Catair	
F–BVRA	Beech B.99A	Air Champagne Ardennes	
F–BVRV	Nord 262	Air Alsace	
F–BVRZ	V.952 Vanguard	Europe Aero Service	
F–BVTA	F.27 Friendship	T.A.T.	
F–BVTE	F.27 Friendship	T.A.T.	
F–BVTO	F.27 Friendship Mk. 100	T.A.T.	
F–BVTU	F.27 Friendship Mk. 100	T.A.T.	
F–BVUY	V.952 Vanguard	Europe Aero Service	
F–BYCN	Boeing 707-321C	Air France	
F–BYCO	Boeing 707-321C	Air France	
F–BYCP	Boeing 707-321C	Air France	

HA (Hungary)

HA–LBC	Tupolev Tu-134	Malev	
HA–LBE	Tupolev Tu-134	Malev	
HA–LBF	Tupolev Tu-134	Malev	
HA–LBG	Tupolev Tu-134	Malev	
HA–LBH	Tupolev Tu-134	Malev	
HA–LBI	Tupolev Tu-134A	Malev	

F-BUFA. (Top) Fokker-VFW F.27 Friendship Mk 200 (two 2,140shp Rolls-Royce Dart Mk 532-7R)

F-BVPL. (Centre) Aérospatiale SN-601 Corvette (two 2,300lb st Pratt & Whitney JT15D-4)/*Peter J. Bish*

HB-ISN. (Above) Douglas DC-9 Srs.51 (two 15,500lb st Pratt & Whitney JT8D-15)/*M. D. West*

Registration	Type	Owner or Operator	Where and when seen
HA–LBK	Tupolev Tu-134A	Malev	
HA–LCA	Tupolev Tu-154	Malev	
HA–LCB	Tupolev Tu-154	Malev	
HA–LCE	Tupolev Tu-154	Malev	
HA–LCK	Tupolev Tu-154	Malev	
HA–MOA	Ilyushin Il-18	Malev	
HA–MOE	Ilyushin Il-18	Malev	
HA–MOF	Ilyushin Il-18	Malev	
HA–MOG	Ilyushin Il-18	Malev	
HA–MOI	Ilyushin Il-18	Malev	

HB (Switzerland)

HB–AAZ	F.27 Friendship	Balair	
HB–IBS	Douglas DC-6A/B	Balair	
HB–ICK	S.E.210 Caravelle 10-R	SATA	
HB–ICN	S.E.210 Caravelle 10-R	SATA	
HB–ICO	S.E.210 Caravelle 10-R	SATA	
HB–ICP	S.E.210 Caravelle VI-R	SATA	
HB–ICQ	S.E.210 Caravelle 10-R	SATA	
HB–IDB	Douglas DC-8 Srs. 53	SATA	
HB–IDE	Douglas DC-8 Srs. 62	Swissair Uri	
HB–IDF	Douglas DC-8 Srs. 62	Swissair Schwyz	
HB–IDG	Douglas DC-8 Srs. 62	Swissair Neuchatel	
HB–IDH	Douglas DC-8 Srs. 62CF	Balair	
HB–IDI	Douglas DC-8 Srs. 62	Swissair Solothurn	
HB–IDK	Douglas DC-8 Srs. 62CF	Swissair Matterhorn	
HB–IDL	Douglas DC-8 Srs. 62	Swissair Aargau	
HB–IDM	Douglas DC-8 Srs. 63CF	SATA Ville de Carouge	
HB–IDO	Douglas DC-9 Srs. 30	Swissair Cointrin	
HB–IDP	Douglas DC-9 Srs. 30	Swissair Basel-Land	
HB–IDR	Douglas DC-9 Srs. 30	Swissair Baden	
HB–IDS	Douglas DC-8 Srs. 63CF	SATA Ville de Lausanne	
HB–IDT	Douglas DC-9 Srs. 33LR	Balair	
HB–IDU	Douglas DC-8 Srs. 55CF	Balair	
HB–IDZ	Douglas DC-8 Srs. 63PF	Balair	
HB–IEN	Canadair CL-44D4	Transvalair	
HB–IFF	Douglas DC-9 Srs. 30	Swissair Fribourg	
HB–IFG	Douglas DC-9 Srs. 30	Swissair Valais	
HB–IFH	Douglas DC-9 Srs. 30	Swissair Opfikon	
HB–IFI	Douglas DC-9 Srs. 30	Swissair Zug	
HB–IFK	Douglas DC-9 Srs. 30	Swissair Kloten	
HB–IFL	Douglas DC-9 Srs. 30	Swissair Appenzell I. Rh.	
HB–IFM	Douglas DC-9 Srs. 30	Swissair Thurgau	
HB–IFN	Douglas DC-9 Srs. 30	Swissair Obwalden	
HB–IFO	Douglas DC-9 Srs. 30	Swissair Appenzell A. Rh.	
HB–IFP	Douglas DC-9 Srs. 30	Swissair Glarus	
HB–IFR	Douglas DC-9 Srs. 30	Swissair Ticino	
HB–IFS	Douglas DC-9 Srs. 30	Swissair Winterthur	
HB–IFT	Douglas DC-9 Srs. 30	Swissair Rümlang	
HB–IFU	Douglas DC-9 Srs. 30	Swissair Chur	
HB–IFV	Douglas DC-9 Srs. 30	Swissair Bülach	
HB–IFW	Douglas DC-9 Srs. 30F	Swissair Payerne	
HB–IFX	Douglas DC-9 Srs. 30	Swissair Lausanne	
HB–IFY	Douglas DC-9 Srs. 30	Swissair Bellinzona	
HB–IFZ	Douglas DC-9 Srs. 30	Swissair Dubendorf	
HB–IGA	Boeing 747-257B	Swissair Geneve	
HB–IGB	Boeing 747-257B	Swissair Zurich	
HB–IHA	Douglas DC-10 Srs. 30	Swissair St. Gallen	
HB–IHB	Douglas DC-10 Srs. 30	Swissair Schaffhausen	
HB–IHC	Douglas DC-10 Srs. 30	Swissair Luzern	

Registration	Type	Owner or Operator	Where and when seen
HB–IHD	Douglas DC-10 Srs. 30	Swissair *Bern*	
HB–IHE	Douglas DC-10 Srs. 30	Swissair *Vaud*	
HB–IHF	Douglas DC-10 Srs. 30	Swissair *Nidwalden*	
HB–IHG	Douglas DC-10 Srs. 30	Swissair *Grisons*	
HB–IHH	Douglas DC-10 Srs. 30	Swissair *Basel-Stadt*	
HB–ISK	Douglas DC-9 Srs. 51	Swissair *Hori*	
HB–ISL	Douglas DC-9 Srs. 51	Swissair *Köniz*	
HB–ISM	Douglas DC-9 Srs. 51	Swissair *Wettingen*	
HB–ISN	Douglas DC-9 Srs. 51	Swissair *Sion*	
HB–ISO	Douglas DC-9 Srs. 51	Swissair *Bienne*	
HB–ISP	Douglas DC-9 Srs. 51	Swissair *Lugano*	
HB–ISR	Douglas DC-9 Srs. 51	Swissair *Locarno*	
HB–ISS	Douglas DC-9 Srs. 51	Swissair *Dietikon*	
HB–IST	Douglas DC-9 Srs. 51	Swissair	
HB–ISU	Douglas DC-9 Srs. 51	Swissair	

HS (Thailand)

HS–TGA	Douglas DC-10 Srs. 30	Thai Airways International *Phimara*	
HS–TGB	Douglas DC-10 Srs. 30	Thai Airways International *Sriwanna*	
HS–TGX	Douglas DC-8 Srs. 63	Thai Airways International *Srisuriyothai*	
HS–TGY	Douglas DC-8 Srs. 63	Thai Airways International *Pathoomawadi*	
HS–TGZ	Douglas DC-8 Srs. 63	Thai Airways International *Srianocha*	

HZ (Saudi Arabia)

HZ–ACA	Boeing 720-068B	SAUDIA—Saudi Arabian Airlines	
HZ–ACB	Boeing 720-068B	SAUDIA—Saudi Arabian Airlines	
HZ–ACC	Boeing 707-368C	SAUDIA—Saudi Arabian Airlines	
HZ–ACD	Boeing 707-368C	SAUDIA—Saudi Arabian Airlines	
HZ–ACE	Boeing 707-373C	SAUDIA—Saudi Arabian Airlines	
HZ–ACF	Boeing 707-373C	SAUDIA—Saudi Arabian Airlines	
HZ–ACG	Boeing 707-368C	SAUDIA—Saudi Arabian Airlines	
HZ–ACH	Boeing 707-368C	SAUDIA—Saudi Arabian Airlines	
HZ–AHA	Lockheed L-1011 TriStar	SAUDIA—Saudi Arabian Airlines	
HZ–AHB	Lockheed L-1011 TriStar	SAUDIA—Saudi Arabian Airlines	

I (Italy)

Registration	Type	Owner or Operator	Where and when seen
I–DABA	S.E.210 Caravelle VI-N	Alitalia *Regolo*	
I–DABE	S.E.210 Caravelle VI-N	Alitalia *Rigel*	
I–DABG	S.E.210 Caravelle VI-N	Alitalia *Arturo*	
I–DABI	S.E.210 Caravelle VI-N	Alitalia *Sirio*	
I–DABL	S.E.210 Caravelle VI-N	Alitalia *Fomalhaut*	
I–DABM	S.E.210 Caravelle VI-N	Alitalia *Procione*	
I–DABP	S.E.210 Caravelle VI-N	Alitalia *Castore*	
I–DABR	S.E.210 Caravelle VI-N	Alitalia *Bellatrix*	
I–DABS	S.E.210 Caravelle VI-N	Alitalia *Dubhe*	
I–DABT	S.E.210 Caravelle VI-N	Soc. Aerea Mediterranea (SAM)	
I–DABU	S.E.210 Caravelle VI-N	Alitalia *Vega*	
I–DABV	S.E.210 Caravelle VI-N	Soc. Aerea Mediterranea (SAM)	
I–DABW	S.E.210 Caravelle VI-N	Alitalia *Betelgeuse*	
I–DABZ	S.E.210 Caravelle VI-N	Alitalia *Spica*	
I–DAXT	S.E.210 Caravelle VI-N	Alitalia *Polluce*	
I–DAXU	S.E.210 Caravelle VI-N	Alitalia *Canopo*	
I–DEMA	Boeing 747-143A	Alitalia *Neil Armstrong*	
I–DEMB	Boeing 747-243B	Alitalia *Carlo del Prete*	
I–DEME	Boeing 747-143A	Alitalia *Arturo Ferrarin*	
I–DEMO	Boeing 747-243B	Alitalia *Francesco de Pinedo*	
I–DEMU	Boeing 747-243B	Alitalia *Geo Chavez*	
I–DIBC	Douglas DC-9 Srs. 32	Alitalia *Isola di Lampedusa*	
I–DIBD	Douglas DC-9 Srs. 32	Alitalia *Isola di Montecristo*	
I–DIBJ	Douglas DC-9 Srs. 32	Alitalia *Isola di Capraia*	
I–DIBK	Douglas DC-9 Srs. 32F	Alitalia *Ercole*	
I–DIBN	Douglas DC-9 Srs. 32	Alitalia *Isola di Palmaria*	
I–DIBO	Douglas DC-9 Srs. 32	Alitalia *Isola di Procida*	
I–DIBQ	Douglas DC-9 Srs. 32	Alitalia *Isola di Pianosa*	
I–DIKA	Douglas DC-9 Srs. 32	Alitalia *Isola di Capri*	
I–DIKB	Douglas DC-9 Srs. 32	Alitalia *Isola di Caprera*	
I–DIKC	Douglas DC-9 Srs. 32	Alitalia *Isola di Ponza*	
I–DIKD	Douglas DC-9 Srs. 32	Alitalia *Isola del Giglio*	
I–DIKE	Douglas DC-9 Srs. 32	Alitalia *Isola d'Elba*	
I–DIKF	Douglas DC-9 Srs. 32F	Alitalia *Atlante*	
I–DIKI	Douglas DC-9 Srs. 32	Alitalia *Isola di Murano*	
I–DIKJ	Douglas DC-9 Srs. 32	Alitalia *Isola di Lipari*	
I–DIKL	Douglas DC-9 Srs. 32	Alitalia *Isola di Panarea*	
I–DIKM	Douglas DC-9 Srs. 32	Alitalia *Isola di Tavolara*	
I–DIKN	Douglas DC-9 Srs. 32	Alitalia *Isola di Nisida*	
I–DIKO	Douglas DC-9 Srs. 32	Alitalia *Isola di Pantelleria*	
I–DIKP	Douglas DC-9 Srs. 32	Alitalia *Isola di Marettimo*	
I–DIKQ	Douglas DC-9 Srs. 32	Alitalia *Isola di Stromboli*	
I–DIKR	Douglas DC-9 Srs. 32	Alitalia *Isola di Torcello*	
I–DIKS	Douglas DC-9 Srs. 32	Alitalia *Isola di Filicudi*	
I–DIKT	Douglas DC-9 Srs. 32	Alitalia *Isola di Ustica*	
I–DIKU	Douglas DC-9 Srs. 32	Alitalia *Isola d'Ischia*	
I–DIKV	Douglas DC-9 Srs. 32	Alitalia *Isola di Vulcano*	
I–DIKW	Douglas DC-9 Srs. 32	Alitalia *Isola di Giannutri*	
I–DIKY	Douglas DC-9 Srs. 32	Alitalia *Isola di Alicudi*	
I–DIKZ	Douglas DC-9 Srs. 32	Alitalia *Isola di Linosa*	
I–DIWC	Douglas DC-8 Srs. 62F	Alitalia *Titano*	
I–DIWG	Douglas DC-8 Srs. 43	Alitalia *Luca Tarigo*	
I–DIWH	Douglas DC-8 Srs. 62	Alitalia *Giovanni Pierluigi da Palestrina*	
I–DIWI	Douglas DC-8 Srs. 43	Alitalia *Giovanni da Verazzano*	
I–DIWJ	Douglas DC-8 Srs. 62	Alitalia *Antonio Vivaldi*	
I–DIWK	Douglas DC-8 Srs. 62	Alitalia *Giacomo Puccini*	
I–DIWM	Douglas DC-8 Srs. 43	Alitalia *Ugolino Vivaldi*	
I–DIWN	Douglas DC-8 Srs. 62	Alitalia *Giuseppe Verdi*	
I–DIWO	Douglas DC-8 Srs. 43	Alitalia *Marco Polo*	
I–DIWQ	Douglas DC-8 Srs. 62F	Alitalia *Ciclope*	
I–DIWT	Douglas DC-8 Srs. 43	Alitalia *Emanuele Pessagno*	
I–DIWU	Douglas DC-8 Srs. 43	Alitalia *Giovanni Caboto*	
I–DIWV	Douglas DC-8 Srs. 62	Alitalia *Gioacchino Rossini*	
I–DIWW	Douglas DC-8 Srs. 62	Alitalia *Arcangelo Corelli*	
I–DIWX	Douglas DC-8 Srs. 62	Alitalia *Luigi Cherubini*	

Registration	Type	Owner or Operator	Where and when seen
I–DIWY	Douglas DC-8 Srs. 62	Alitalia *Vincenzo Bellini*	
I–DIZA	Douglas DC-9 Srs. 32	Alitalia *Isola di Palmarola*	
I–DIZE	Douglas DC-9 Srs. 32	Alitalia *Isola della Meloria*	
I–DIZF	Douglas DC-9 Srs. 32	Alitalia *Isola di Spargi*	
I–DIZI	Douglas DC-9 Srs. 32	Alitalia *Isola di Basiluzzo*	
I–DIZO	Douglas DC-9 Srs. 32	Alitalia *Isola del Tino*	
I–DIZU	Douglas DC-9 Srs. 32	Alitalia *Isola di Bergeggi*	
I–DYNA	Douglas DC-10 Srs. 30	Alitalia *Galileo Galilei*	
I–DYNB	Douglas DC-10 Srs. 30	Alitalia *Giotto di Bondone*	
I–DYNC	Douglas DC-10 Srs. 30	Alitalia *Luigi Pirandello*	
I–DYND	Douglas DC-10 Srs. 30	Alitalia *Enrico Fermi*	
I–DYNE	Douglas DC-10 Srs. 30	Alitalia *Dante Alighieri*	
I–DYNI	Douglas DC-10 Srs. 30	Alitalia *Michelangelo Buonarroti*	
I–DYNO	Douglas DC-10 Srs. 30	Alitalia *Benvenuto Cellini*	
I–DYNU	Douglas DC-10 Srs. 30	Alitalia *Guglielmo Marconi*	
I–SAVA	Boeing 707-131	Aeropa *Libeccio*	
I–TIDA	F.28 Fellowship 1000	Itavia	
I–TIDB	F.28 Fellowship 1000	Itavia	
I–TIDI	F.28 Fellowship 1000	Itavia	
I–TIDU	F.28 Fellowship 1000	Itavia	
I–TIGA	Douglas DC-9 Srs. 11	Itavia	
I–TIGE	Douglas DC-9 Srs. 15	Itavia	
I–TIGI	Douglas DC-9 Srs. 15	Itavia	

NOTE: Itavia also operates one more Fellowship 1000, which retains the Dutch registration PH–ZBG, a DC-9 Srs. 30 which retains the US registration N1718U, and a DC-9 Srs. 15 (PH–DNA) leased from KLM.

JA (Japan)

JA8007	Douglas DC-8 Srs. 53	Japan Air Lines
JA8008	Douglas DC-8 Srs. 53	Japan Air Lines
JA8009	Douglas DC-8 Srs. 53	Japan Air Lines
JA8010	Douglas DC-8 Srs. 53	Japan Air Lines
JA8011	Douglas DC-8 Srs. 53	Japan Air Lines
JA8014	Douglas DC-8F Srs. 55JT	Japan Air Lines
JA8015	Douglas DC-8 Srs. 55	Japan Air Lines
JA8016	Douglas DC-8 Srs. 55	Japan Air Lines
JA8017	Douglas DC-8 Srs. 55	Japan Air Lines
JA8018	Douglas DC-8F Srs. 55	Japan Air Lines
JA8019	Douglas DC-8 Srs. 55	Japan Air Lines
JA8031	Douglas DC-8 Srs. 62	Japan Air Lines
JA8032	Douglas DC-8 Srs. 62	Japan Air Lines
JA8033	Douglas DC-8 Srs. 62	Japan Air Lines
JA8034	Douglas DC-8 Srs. 62	Japan Air Lines
JA8035	Douglas DC-8 Srs. 62	Japan Air Lines
JA8036	Douglas DC-8 Srs. 62AF	Japan Air Lines
JA8037	Douglas DC-8 Srs. 62	Japan Air Lines
JA8038	Douglas DC-8 Srs. 61	Japan Air Lines
JA8039	Douglas DC-8 Srs. 61	Japan Air Lines
JA8041	Douglas DC-8 Srs. 61	Japan Air Lines
JA8042	Douglas DC-8 Srs. 61	Japan Air Lines
JA8043	Douglas DC-8 Srs. 61	Japan Air Lines
JA8044	Douglas DC-8 Srs. 62AF	Japan Air Lines
JA8045	Douglas DC-8 Srs. 61	Japan Air Lines
JA8046	Douglas DC-8 Srs. 61	Japan Air Lines
JA8047	Douglas DC-8 Srs. 61	Japan Air Lines
JA8048	Douglas DC-8 Srs. 61	Japan Air Lines
JA8049	Douglas DC-8 Srs. 61	Japan Air Lines
JA8050	Douglas DC-8 Srs. 61	Japan Air Lines
JA8051	Douglas DC-8 Srs. 62	Japan Air Lines
JA8052	Douglas DC-8 Srs. 62	Japan Air Lines
JA8053	Douglas DC-8 Srs. 62	Japan Air Lines
JA8054	Douglas DC-8 Srs. 62AF	Japan Air Lines

**Is there really
any other way to fly to Japan?**

Registration	Type	Owner or Operator	Where and when seen
JA8055	Douglas DC-8 Srs. 62AF	Japan Air Lines	
JA8056	Douglas DC-8 Srs. 62AF	Japan Air Lines	
JA8057	Douglas DC-8 Srs. 61	Japan Air Lines	
JA8058	Douglas DC-8 Srs. 61	Japan Air Lines	
JA8059	Douglas DC-8 Srs. 61	Japan Air Lines	
JA8060	Douglas DC-8 Srs. 61	Japan Air Lines	
JA8061	Douglas DC-8 Srs. 61	Japan Air Lines	
JA8101	Boeing 747-146	Japan Air Lines	
JA8102	Boeing 747-146	Japan Air Lines	
JA8103	Boeing 747-146	Japan Air Lines	
JA8104	Boeing 747-246B	Japan Air Lines	
JA8105	Boeing 747-246B	Japan Air Lines	
JA8106	Boeing 747-246B	Japan Air Lines	
JA8107	Boeing 747-146	Japan Air Lines	
JA8108	Boeing 747-246B	Japan Air Lines	
JA8110	Boeing 747-246B	Japan Air Lines	
JA8111	Boeing 747-246B	Japan Air Lines	
JA8112	Boeing 747-146	Japan Air Lines	
JA8113	Boeing 747-246B	Japan Air Lines	
JA8114	Boeing 747-246B	Japan Air Lines	
JA8115	Boeing 747-146	Japan Air Lines	
JA8116	Boeing 747-146	Japan Air Lines	
JA8117	Boeing 747SR-46	Japan Air Lines	
JA8118	Boeing 747SR-46	Japan Air Lines	
JA8119	Boeing 747SR-46	Japan Air Lines	
JA8120	Boeing 747SR-46	Japan Air Lines	
JA8121	Boeing 747SR-46	Japan Air Lines	
JA8122	Boeing 747-246B	Japan Air Lines	
JA8123	Boeing 747-246F	Japan Air Lines	
JA8124	Boeing 747SR-46	Japan Air Lines	
JA8125	Boeing 747-246B	Japan Air Lines	
JA8126	Boeing 747SR-46	Japan Air Lines	
JA8127	Boeing 747-246B	Japan Air Lines	
JA8128	Boeing 747-146	Japan Air Lines	

JY (Jordan)

JY–ADJ	Boeing 720B	Alia Royal Jordanian Airlines	
JY–ADP	Boeing 707-3D3C	Alia Royal Jordanian Airlines	Jerash
JY–ADR	Boeing 727-2D3	Alia Royal Jordanian Airlines	
JY–ADT	Boeing 720-030B	Alia Royal Jordanian Airlines	Madaba
JY–ADU	Boeing 727-2D3	Alia Royal Jordanian Airlines	Amman
JY–ADV	Boeing 727-2D3	Alia Royal Jordanian Airlines	
JY–AEB	Boeing 707-384C	Alia Royal Jordanian Airlines	The City of Jerash
JY–AEC	Boeing 707-384C	Alia Royal Jordanian Airlines	
JY–AED	Boeing 707-321C	Jordanian World Airways	

LN (Norway)

LN–FOF	Convair 340	Fred Olsen Airtransport	
LN–FOG	L-188CF Electra	Fred Olsen Airtransport	

Registration	Type	Owner or Operator	Where and when seen
LN–FOH	L-188CF Electra	Fred Olsen Airtransport	
LN–FOI	L-188CF Electra	Fred Olsen Airtransport	
LN–FOM	H.S.748	Fred Olsen Airtransport	
LN–FON	Douglas DC-6A	Fred Olsen Airtransport	
LN–KAA	Fairchild FH-227B	Stellar Airfreighter	
LN–KLV	Douglas DC-3	Nor Fly	
LN–MAM	Convair 440	Nor Fly	
LN–MOB	Douglas DC-4	Bergen Air Transport	
LN–MOC	Douglas DC-8 Srs. 62AF	SAS *Kettil Viking*	
LN–MOG	Douglas DC-8 Srs. 62	SAS *Odd Viking*	
LN–MOH	Douglas DC-8 Srs. 55	SAS *Harald Viking*	
		(leased to Scanair)	
LN–MOJ	Douglas DC-4	Bergen Air Transport	
LN–MOW	Douglas DC-8 Srs. 62	SAS *Roald Viking*	
LN–RKA	Douglas DC-10 Srs. 30	SAS *Olav Viking*	
LN–RKB	Douglas DC-10 Srs. 30	SAS *Haakon Viking*	
LN–RLA	Douglas DC-9 Srs. 41	SAS *Are Viking*	
LN–RLB	Douglas DC-9 Srs. 41	SAS *Arne Viking*	
LN–RLC	Douglas DC-9 Srs. 41	SAS *Gunnar Viking*	
LN–RLD	Douglas DC-9 Srs. 41	SAS *Torleif Viking*	
LN–RLJ	Douglas DC-9 Srs. 41	SAS *Stein Viking*	
LN–RLK	Douglas DC-9 Srs. 41	SAS *Erling Viking*	
LN–RLL	Douglas DC-9 Srs. 21	SAS *Guttorm Viking*	
LN–RLN	Douglas DC-9 Srs. 41	SAS *Halldor Viking*	
LN–RLO	Douglas DC-9 Srs. 21	SAS *Gunder Viking*	
LN–RLS	Douglas DC-9 Srs. 41	SAS *Asmund Viking*	
LN–RLT	Douglas DC-9 Srs. 41	SAS *Audun Viking*	
LN–RLU	Douglas DC-9 Srs. 41	SAS *Eivind Viking*	
LN–RLW	Douglas DC-9 Srs. 33AF	SAS *Rand Viking*	
LN–RLX	Douglas DC-9 Srs. 41	SAS *Sote Viking*	
LN–RLZ	Douglas DC-9 Srs. 41	SAS *Bodvar Viking*	
LN–SUA	Boeing 737-205C	Braathens SAFE *Halvdan Svarte*	
LN–SUC	F.28 Fellowship 1000	Braathens SAFE *Olav Kyrre*	
LN–SUD	Boeing 737-205	Braathens SAFE *Olav Trygvason*	
LN–SUE	F.27 Friendship Mk. 100	Braathens SAFE *Harald Gille*	
LN–SUF	F.27 Friendship Mk. 100	Braathens SAFE	
		Magnus Lagaboter	
LN–SUG	Boeing 737-205	Braathens SAFE	
		Harald Harfagre	
LN–SUH	Boeing 737-205	Braathens SAFE *Sigurd Jorsalfar*	
LN–SUI	Boeing 737-205	Braathens SAFE	
		Haakon den Gode	
LN–SUL	F.27 Friendship Mk. 100	Braathens SAFE *Sigurd Munn*	
LN–SUN	F.28 Fellowship 1000	Braathens SAFE	
		Hakon Sverreson	
LN–SUO	F.28 Fellowship 1000	Braathens SAFE *Magnus Barfot*	
LN–SUP	Boeing 737-205	Braathens SAFE *Hakon V*	
LN–SUS	Boeing 737-205	Braathens SAFE *Hakon IV*	
LN–SUX	F.28 Fellowship 1000	Braathens SAFE	
		Harald Hardrade	
LN–TVA	Douglas DC-3	Bergen Air Transport	

LV (Argentina)

LV–ISA	Boeing 707-387B	Aerolineas Argentinas	
		Antartida Argentina	
LV–ISB	Boeing 707-387B	Aerolineas Argentinas *Aimilan*	
LV–ISC	Boeing 707-387B	Aerolineas Argentinas	
		Betelgeuse	

Registration	Type	Owner or Operator	Where and when seen
LV–ISD	Boeing 707-387B	Aerolineas Argentinas *Procion*	
LV–JGP	Boeing 707-387C	Aerolineas Argentinas *Achernar*	
LV–JGR	Boeing 707-387C	Aerolineas Argentinas *Canopus*	
LV–LGO	Boeing 707-372C	Aerolineas Argentinas	
LV–LGP	Boeing 707-372C	Aerolineas Argentinas	

LX (Luxembourg)

LX–BCV	Douglas DC-8CF Srs. 63	Cargolux (Iceland)	
LX–LGA	F.27 Friendship Mk. 100	Luxair *Prince Henri*	
LX–LGB	F.27 Friendship Mk. 100	Luxair *Prince Jean*	
LX–LGD	F.27 Friendship Mk. 400	Luxair *Princesse Margaretha*	
LX–LGF	S.E.210 Caravelle VI-R	Luxair	
LX–LGG	S.E.210 Caravelle VI-R	Luxair *Princesse Marie-Astrid*	
LX–LGV	Boeing 707-348C	Luxair	
LX–LGW	Boeing 707-344A	Luxair	

LZ (Bulgaria)

LZ–BAA	Antonov An-12	Balkan Bulgarian Airlines	
LZ–BAB	Antonov An-12	Balkan Bulgarian Airlines	
LZ–BEA	Ilyushin Il-18	Balkan Bulgarian Airlines	
LZ–BEK	Ilyushin Il-18	Balkan Bulgarian Airlines	
LZ–BEL	Ilyushin Il-18	Balkan Bulgarian Airlines	
LZ–BEP	Ilyushin Il-18	Balkan Bulgarian Airlines	
LZ–BET	Ilyushin Il-18	Balkan Bulgarian Airlines	
LZ–BEV	Ilyushin Il-18	Balkan Bulgarian Airlines	
LZ–BTA	Tupolev Tu-154	Balkan Bulgarian Airlines	
LZ–BTB	Tupolev Tu-154	Balkan Bulgarian Airlines	
LZ–BTC	Tupolev Tu-154	Balkan Bulgarian Airlines	
LZ–BTD	Tupolev Tu-154	Balkan Bulgarian Airlines	
LZ–BTE	Tupolev Tu-154A	Balkan Bulgarian Airlines	
LZ–BTF	Tupolev Tu-154A	Balkan Bulgarian Airlines	
LZ–BTG	Tupolev Tu-154A	Balkan Bulgarian Airlines	
LZ–TUA	Tupolev Tu-134	Balkan Bulgarian Airlines	
LZ–TUB	Tupolev Tu-134	Balkan Bulgarian Airlines	
LZ–TUC	Tupolev Tu-134	Balkan Bulgarian Airlines	
LZ–TUD	Tupolev Tu-134	Balkan Bulgarian Airlines	
LZ–TUE	Tupolev Tu-134	Balkan Bulgarian Airlines	
LZ–TUF	Tupolev Tu-134	Balkan Bulgarian Airlines	
LZ–TUK	Tupolev Tu-134A	Balkan Bulgarian Airlines	
LZ–TUL	Tupolev Tu-134A	Balkan Bulgarian Airlines	
LZ–TUM	Tupolev Tu-134A	Balkan Bulgarian Airlines	
LZ–TUN	Tupolev Tu-134A	Balkan Bulgarian Airlines	
LZ–TUP	Tupolev Tu-134A	Balkan Bulgarian Airlines	
LZ–TUR	Tupolev Tu-134A	Balkan Bulgarian Airlines	
LZ–TUZ	Tupolev Tu-134A	Balkan Bulgarian Airlines	

N (U.S.A.)

OVERSEAS NATIONAL

SATURN AIRWAYS

WORLD

National Airlines

Registration	Type	Owner or Operator	Where and when seen
N10ST	Lockheed L382E Hercules (Cargo)	Saturn Airways	
N11ST	Lockheed L382E Hercules (Cargo)	Saturn Airways	
N12ST	Lockheed L382G Hercules (Cargo)	Saturn Airways	
N15ST	Lockheed L382G Hercules (Cargo)	Saturn Airways *Barney G*	
N16ST	Lockheed L382B Hercules (Cargo)	Saturn Airways	
N17ST	Lockheed L382E Hercules (Cargo)	Saturn Airways	
N18ST	Lockheed L382B Hercules (Cargo)	Saturn Airways	
N19ST	Lockheed L382 Hercules (Cargo)	Saturn Airways	
N20ST	Lockheed L382G Hercules (Cargo)	Saturn Airways	
N21ST	Lockheed L382 Hercules (Cargo)	Saturn Airways	
N23ST	Lockheed L382 Hercules (Cargo)	Saturn Airways	
N80NA	Douglas DC-10 Srs. 30	National Airlines *Tammy*	
N81NA	Douglas DC-10 Srs. 30	National Airlines *Renee*	
N82NA	Douglas DC-10 Srs. 30	National Airlines *Marienne*	
N83NA	Douglas DC-10 Srs. 30	National Airlines *Timmi*	
N101TV	Douglas DC-10 Srs. 30CF	Trans International	
N102TV	Douglas DC-10 Srs. 30CF	Trans International	
N103TV	Douglas DC-10 Srs. 30CF	Trans International	
N319PA	*Boeing 727-21	Pan American World Airways *Clipper Ponce de Leon*	
N323PA	Boeing 727-21	Pan American World Airways *Clipper Star of Peace*	
N325PA	Boeing 727-21	Pan American World Airways *Clipper Syren*	
N326PA	Boeing 727-21	Pan American World Airways *Clipper Raven*	
N327PA	Boeing 727-21	Pan American World Airways *Clipper Meteor*	

*Inactive, December 1975.

Registration	Type	Owner or Operator	Where and when seen
N328PA	Boeing 727-21	Pan American World Airways *Clipper Natchez*	
N329PA	Boeing 727-21	Pan American World Airways *Clipper Lightfoot*	
N339PA	Boeing 727-21QC	Pan American World Airways *Clipper Dawn*	
N340PA	Boeing 727-21QC	Pan American World Airways *Clipper Talisman*	
N355PA	Boeing 727-21	Pan American World Airways *Clipper Andrew Jackson*	
N356PA	Boeing 727-21	Pan American World Airways *Clipper Belle of the Sky*	
N357PA	Boeing 727-21	Pan American World Airways *Clipper Betsy Ross*	
N358PA	Boeing 727-21	Pan American World Airways *Clipper David Crockett*	
N359PA	Boeing 727-21	Pan American World Airways *Clipper Orpheus*	
N360PA	Boeing 727-21	Pan American World Airways *Clipper Golden Rule*	
N368WA	Boeing 707-373C	World Airways (on lease, Nov. 1975)	
N370WA	Boeing 707-373C	World Airways (on lease, Nov. 1975)	
N401PA	Boeing 707-321B	Pan American World Airways *Clipper Dauntless*	
N402PA	Boeing 707-321B	Pan American World Airways *Clipper Black Hawk*	
N403PA	Boeing 707-321B	Pan American World Airways *Clipper Goodwill*	
N404PA	Boeing 707-321B	Pan American World Airways *Clipper Seven Seas*	
N405PA	Boeing 707-321B	Pan American World Airways *Clipper Stargazer*	
N406PA	Boeing 707-321B	Pan American World Airways *Clipper Kingfisher*	
N408PA	Boeing 707-321B	Pan American World Airways *Clipper Morning Star*	
N409PA	Boeing 707-321B	Pan American World Airways *Clipper Eclipse*	
N410PA	Boeing 707-321B	Pan American World Airways *Clipper Argonaut*	
N412PA	Boeing 707-321B	Pan American World Airways *Clipper Empress of the Skies*	
N414PA	Boeing 707-321B	Pan American World Airways *Clipper Ann McKim*	
N415PA	Boeing 707-321B	Pan American World Airways *Clipper Monsoon*	
N418PA	Boeing 707-321B	Pan American World Airways *Clipper Yankee Ranger*	
N419PA	Boeing 707-321B	Pan American World Airways *Clipper Gem of the Skies*	
N420PA	Boeing 707-321B	Pan American World Airways *Clipper Monarch of the Skies*	
N421PA	Boeing 707-321B	Pan American World Airways *Clipper Charmer*	
N422PA	Boeing 707-321B	Pan American World Airways *Clipper Mount Vernon*	
N423PA	Boeing 707-321B	Pan American World Airways *Clipper Glory of the Skies*	
N424PA	Boeing 707-321B	Pan American World Airways *Clipper Golden West*	
N425PA	Boeing 707-321B	Pan American World Airways *Clipper Virginia*	
N426PA	Boeing 707-321B	Pan American World Airways *Clipper National Eagle*	
N427PA	Boeing 707-321B	Pan American World Airways *Clipper Crystal Palace*	
N428PA	Boeing 707-321B	Pan American World Airways *Clipper Star of Hope*	
N433PA	Boeing 707-321B	Pan American World Airways *Clipper Glad Tidings*	

Registration	Type	Owner or Operator	Where and when seen
N434PA	Boeing 707-321B	Pan American World Airways *Clipper Queen of the Sky*	
N435PA	Boeing 707-321B	Pan American World Airways *Clipper Celestial Empire*	
N447PA	Boeing 707-321C	Pan American World Airways *Clipper Onward*	
N447T	Conroy CL-44-O	Transmeridian Air Cargo *Skymaster*	
N448PA	Boeing 707-321C	Pan American World Airways *Clipper Pacific Raider*	
N449PA	Boeing 707-321C	Pan American World Airways *Clipper Red Rover*	
N451PA	Boeing 707-321C	Pan American World Airways *Clipper Union*	
N452PA	Boeing 707-321C	Pan American World Airways *Clipper Golden Fleece*	
N453PA	Boeing 707-321B	Pan American World Airways *Clipper Universe*	
N455PA	Boeing 707-321B	Pan American World Airways *Clipper Waverley*	
N457PA	Boeing 707-321C	Pan American World Airways *Clipper Phoenix*	
N459PA	Boeing 707-321C	Pan American World Airways *Clipper Western Continent*	
N462PA	Boeing 707-321C	Pan American World Airways *Clipper Eagle*	
N473PA	Boeing 707-321C	Pan American World Airways *Clipper Pride of America*	
N475PA	Boeing 707-321C	Pan American World Airways *Clipper Sea Serpent*	
N491PA	Boeing 707-321B	Pan American World Airways *Clipper Chariot of Fame*	
N492PA	Boeing 707-321B	Pan American World Airways *Clipper Eagle Wing*	
N493PA	Boeing 707-321B	Pan American World Airways *Clipper Priscilla Alden*	
N495PA	Boeing 707-321B	Pan American World Airways *Clipper Nor'wester*	
N496PA	Boeing 707-321B	Pan American World Airways *Clipper Northern Eagle*	
N497PA	Boeing 707-321B	Pan American World Airways *Clipper Victory*	
N530PA	Boeing 747SP-21	Pan American World Airways *Clipper Mayflower*	
N531PA	Boeing 747SP-21	Pan American World Airways *Clipper Liberty Bell*	
N532PA	Boeing 747SP-21	Pan American World Airways *Clipper Constitution*	
N533PA	Boeing 747SP-21	Pan American World Airways *Clipper Freedom*	
N534PA	Boeing 747SP-21	Pan American World Airways *Clipper Great Republic*	
N535PA	Boeing 747-273C	Pan American World Airways *Clipper Mercury*	
N652PA	Boeing 747-121	Pan American World Airways *Clipper Pacific Trader*	
N653PA	Boeing 747-121	Pan American World Airways *Clipper Unity*	
N654PA	Boeing 747-121	Pan American World Airways *Clipper White Wing*	
N655PA	Boeing 747-121	Pan American World Airways *Clipper Wild Fire*	
N656PA	Boeing 747-121	Pan American World Airways *Clipper Live Yankee*	
N657PA	Boeing 747-121	Pan American World Airways *Clipper Arctic*	
N658PA	*Boeing 747-121	Pan American World Airways *Clipper High Flyer*	
N659PA	Boeing 747-121	Pan American World Airways *Clipper Plymouth Rock*	

* Inactive, December 1975

LZ-BTD.   (Top)   Tupolev Tu-154 (three 20,950lb st Kuznetsov NK-8-2)/*Javier Taibo*

N531PA.   (Centre)   Boeing 747SP-21 (four 46,950lb st Pratt & Whitney JT9D-7A)

N1776R.   (Above)   Douglas DC-8 Srs. 32. ONA's Bicentennial aircraft, named *Independence*, contains the significant date in its registration

Registration	Type	Owner or Operator	Where and when seen
N690WA	Boeing 727-173QC	World Airways (on lease, Nov. 1975)	
N691WA	Boeing 727-173C	World Airways	
N692WA	Boeing 727-173C	World Airways	
N693WA	Boeing 727-173C	World Airways (on lease, Nov. 1975)	
N701SW	Boeing 747-245F	Seaboard World Airlines	
N702SW	Boeing 747-245F	Seaboard World Airlines	
N731PA	Boeing 747-121	Pan American World Airways Clipper Bostonian	
N732PA	Boeing 747-121	Pan American World Airways Clipper Storm King	
N733PA	Boeing 747-121	Pan American World Airways Clipper Constitution	
N734PA	Boeing 747-121	Pan American World Airways Clipper Flying Cloud	
N735PA	Boeing 747-121	Pan American World Airways Clipper Young America	
N736PA	Boeing 747-121	Pan American World Airways Clipper Victor	
N737PA	Boeing 747-121	Pan American World Airways Clipper Red Jacket	
N738PA	Boeing 747-121	Pan American World Airways Clipper Defender	
N739PA	Boeing 747-121	Pan American World Airways Clipper Morning Light	
N740PA	Boeing 747-121	Pan American World Airways Clipper Rival	
N741PA	Boeing 747-121	Pan American World Airways Clipper Kit Carson	
N742PA	Boeing 747-121	Pan American World Airways Clipper Rainbow	
N743PA	Boeing 747-121	Pan American World Airways Clipper Derby	
N744PA	Boeing 747-121	Pan American World Airways Clipper Star of the Union	
N747PA	Boeing 747-121	Pan American World Airways Clipper America (leased to Air Zaïre)	
N747WA	Boeing 747-273C	World Airways (on lease, Nov. 1975)	
N748PA	Boeing 747-121	Pan American World Airways Clipper Hornet	
N748WA	Boeing 747-273C	World Airways	
N749PA	Boeing 747-121	Pan American World Airways Clipper Intrepid	
N749WA	Boeing 747-273C	World Airways (on lease, Nov. 1975)	
N750PA	Boeing 747-121	Pan American World Airways Clipper Rambler	
N751PA	Boeing 747-121	Pan American World Airways Clipper Midnight Sun	
N753PA	Boeing 747-121	Pan American World Airways Clipper Westwind	
N754PA	Boeing 747-121	Pan American World Airways Clipper Ocean Rover	
N755PA	Boeing 747-121	Pan American World Airways Clipper Sovereign of the Seas	
N760PA	Boeing 707-321B	Pan American World Airways Clipper Evening Star	
N760TW	Boeing 707-331B	Trans World Airlines	
N761PA	Boeing 707-321B	Pan American World Airways Clipper Friendship	
N762PA	Boeing 707-321B	Pan American World Airways Clipper Endeavor	
N762TW	Boeing 707-331	Trans World Airlines	
N763PA	Boeing 707-321B	Pan American World Airways Clipper Yankee	
N763TW	Boeing 707-331	Trans World Airlines	
N764PA	Boeing 707-321B	Pan American World Airways Clipper Nautilus	
N764TW	Boeing 707-331	Trans World Airlines	

Registration	Type	Owner or Operator	Where and when seen
N765PA	Boeing 707-321C	Pan American World Airways *Clipper Gladiator*	
N765TW	Boeing 707-331	Trans World Airlines	
N766PA	Boeing 707-321C	Pan American World Airways *Clipper Jupiter*	
N766TW	Boeing 707-331	Trans World Airlines	
N767PA	Boeing 707-321C	Pan American World Airways *Clipper Challenger*	
N767TW	Boeing 707-331	Trans World Airlines	
N768TW	Boeing 707-331	Trans World Airlines	
N770PA	Boeing 747-121	Pan American World Airways *Clipper Great Republic*	
N770TW	Boeing 707-331	Trans World Airlines	
N771PA	Boeing 747-121F	Pan American World Airways *Clipper Donald McKay*	
N771TW	Boeing 707-331	Trans World Airlines	
N772TW	Boeing 707-331	Trans World Airlines	
N773TW	Boeing 707-331B	Trans World Airlines	
N774TW	Boeing 707-331B	Trans World Airlines	
N775TW	Boeing 707-331B	Trans World Airlines	
N778TW	Boeing 707-331B	Trans World Airlines	
N779TW	Boeing 707-331B	Trans World Airlines	
N780TW	Boeing 707-331B	Trans World Airlines	
N786TW	Boeing 707-331C	Trans World Airlines	
N788TW	Boeing 707-331C	Trans World Airlines	
N789TW	Boeing 707-373C	Trans World Airlines	
N790PA	Boeing 707-321C	Pan American World Airways *Clipper Courser*	
N791PA	Boeing 707-321C	Pan American World Airways *Clipper Fidelity*	
N791TW	Boeing 707-331C	Trans World Airlines	
N792TW	Boeing 707-331C	Trans World Airlines	
N793PA	Boeing 707-321C	Pan American World Airways *Clipper Messenger*	
N793TW	Boeing 707-331B	Trans World Airlines	
N794EP	Boeing 707 freighter	Iran Air	
N794TW	Boeing 707-331C	Trans World Airlines	
N795PA	Boeing 707-321C	Pan American World Airways *Clipper Jupiter Rex*	
N796PA	Boeing 707-321C	Pan American World Airways *Clipper Mermaid*	
N801WA	Douglas DC-8CF Srs. 63	World Airways	
N803WA	Douglas DC-8CF Srs. 63	World Airways	
N804WA	Douglas DC-8CF Srs. 63	World Airways	
N805WA	Douglas DC-8CF Srs. 63	World Airways	
N806SW	Douglas DC-8F Srs. 55	Seaboard World Airlines (leased to Cargolux)	
N806WA	Douglas DC-8CF Srs. 63	World Airways	
N819F	Douglas DC-8 Srs. 21	Overseas National Airways *Courageous*	
N821F	Douglas DC-8 Srs. 21	Overseas National Airways *Scepter*	
N831F	Douglas DC-8 Srs. 32	Overseas National Airways *Southern Cross*	
N852U	Lockheed L-188C Electra	Saturn Airways	
N853U	Lockheed L-188C Electra	Saturn Airways	
N854U	Lockheed L-188C Electra	Saturn Airways	
N856U	Lockheed L-188C Electra	Saturn Airways	
N857U	Lockheed L-188C Electra	Saturn Airways	
N858U	Lockheed L-188C Electra	Saturn Airways	
N859U	Lockheed L-188C Electra	Saturn Airways	
N860U	Lockheed L-188C Electra	Saturn Airways	
N861U	Lockheed L-188C Electra	Saturn Airways	
N864F	Douglas DC-8F Srs. 63	Overseas National Airways *Serene*	
N866F	Douglas DC-8CF Srs. 63	Overseas National Airways *Sovereign* (leased to Seaboard World)	
N867F	Douglas DC-8 Srs. 61	Overseas National Airways *Victorious*	
N868F	Douglas DC-8 Srs. 61	Overseas National Airways *Eagle*	

Registration	Type	Owner or Operator	Where and when seen
N869	Douglas DC-8 Srs. 61	Overseas National Airways *Sundance*	
N871PA	Boeing 707-321C	Pan American World Airways *Clipper Sirius*	
N880PA	Boeing 707-321B	Pan American World Airways *Clipper Emerald Isle*	
N881PA	Boeing 707-321B	Pan American World Airways *Clipper Reindeer*	
N882PA	Boeing 707-321B	Pan American World Airways *Clipper Queen of the Pacific*	
N883PA	Boeing 707-321B	Pan American World Airways *Clipper Cathay*	
N884PA	Boeing 707-321B	Pan American World Airways *Clipper Nightingale*	
N885PA	Boeing 707-321B	Pan American World Airways *Clipper Northern Light*	
N886PA	Boeing 707-321B	Pan American World Airways *Clipper Sea Lark*	
N887PA	Boeing 707-321B	Pan American World Airways *Clipper Flora Temple*	
N890PA	Boeing 707-321B	Pan American World Airways *Clipper Gauntlet*	
N891PA	Boeing 707-321B	Pan American World Airways *Clipper Gem of the Ocean*	
N892PA	Boeing 707-321B	Pan American World Airways *Clipper Star King*	
N893PA	Boeing 707-321B	Pan American World Airways *Clipper Whirlwind*	
N894PA	Boeing 707-321B	Pan American World Airways *Clipper Polynesian*	
N895PA	Boeing 707-321B	Pan American World Airways *Clipper Herald of the Morning*	
N896PA	Boeing 707-321B	Pan American World Airways *Clipper Norseman*	
N897PA	Boeing 707-321B	Pan American World Airways *Clipper Ocean Express*	
N900CL	Douglas DC-8 Srs. 33	Capitol International Airways	
N903CL	Douglas DC-8 Srs. 33	Capitol International Airways	
N911CL	Douglas DC-8 Srs. 61	Capitol International Airways (leased to World Airways)	
N912CL	Douglas DC-8 Srs. 61	Capitol International Airways	
N920NA	Lockheed L382B Hercules (Cargo)	Saturn Airways	
N931F	Douglas DC-9 Srs. 30	Overseas National Airways *Pioneer*	
N933F	Douglas DC-9 Srs. 30	Overseas National Airways *Calypso Queen*	
N937F	Douglas DC-9 Srs. 30	Overseas National Airways *Mistress*	
N938F	Douglas DC-9 Srs. 30	Overseas National Airways *Gina*	
N1031F	Douglas DC-10CF Srs. 30	Overseas National Airways *Holidayliner America*	
N1718U	Douglas DC-9 Srs. 30	Itavia (Italy)	
N1776R	Douglas DC-8 Srs. 32	Overseas National Airways *Independence*	
N1793T	Boeing 707-331C	Trans World Airlines	
N1976R	Douglas DC-8 Srs. 32	Overseas National Airways	
N4864T	Douglas DC-8CF Srs. 63	Trans International	
N4865T	Douglas DC-8CF Srs. 63	Trans International	
N4866T	Douglas DC-8CF Srs. 63	Trans International	
N4867T	Douglas DC-8CF Srs. 63	Trans International	
N4868T	Douglas DC-8CF Srs. 63	Trans International	
N4869T	Douglas DC-8CF Srs. 63	Trans International	
N4901C	Douglas DC-8 Srs. 31	Capitol International Airways	
N4902C	Douglas DC-8 Srs. 31	Capitol International Airways	
N4904C	Douglas DC-8F Srs. 54	Capitol International Airways	
N4907C	Douglas DC-8F Srs. 63	Overseas National Airways	
N4910C	Douglas DC-8F Srs. 63	Capitol International Airways	
N5771T	Boeing 707-331C	Trans World Airlines	
N5772T	Boeing 707-331C	Trans World Airlines	
N5773T	Boeing 707-331C	Trans World Airlines	
N5774T	Boeing 707-331C	Trans World Airlines	

Registration	Type	Owner or Operator	Where and when seen
N7095	Boeing 707-327C	Trans Mediterranean Airways (Lebanon)	
N7096	Boeing 707-327C	Trans Mediterranean Airways (Lebanon)	
N7100	Boeing 707-327C	Trans Mediterranean Airways (Lebanon)	
N7104	Boeing 707-327C	Trans Mediterranean Airways (Lebanon)	
N7696	Boeing 747-100F	Trans Mediterranean Airways (Lebanon)	
N8630	Douglas DC-8F Srs. 63	Seaboard World Airlines (leased to International Air Bahamas)	
N8632	Douglas DC-8F Srs. 63	Seaboard World Airlines	
N8635	Douglas DC-8F Srs. 63	Seaboard World Airlines	
N8636	Douglas DC-8F Srs. 63	Seaboard World Airlines (leased to Korean Air Lines)	
N8637	Douglas DC-8F Srs. 63	Seaboard World Airlines (leased to Korean Air Lines)	
N8641	Douglas DC-8CF Srs. 63	Loftleidir (Iceland: leased)	
N8642	Douglas DC-8F Srs. 63	Seaboard World Airlines	
N8705T	Boeing 707-331B	Trans World Airlines	
N8725T	Boeing 707-331B	Trans World Airlines	
N8729	Boeing 707-331B	Trans World Airlines	
N8730	Boeing 707-331B	Trans World Airlines	
N8731	Boeing 707-331B	Trans World Airlines	
N8732	Boeing 707-331B	Trans World Airlines	
N8733	Boeing 707-331B	Trans World Airlines	
N8735	Boeing 707-331B	Trans World Airlines	
N8736	Boeing 707-331B	Trans World Airlines	
N8737	Boeing 707-331B	Trans World Airlines	
N8738	Boeing 707-331B	Trans World Airlines	
N8782R	Douglas DC-8F Srs. 54	Seaboard World Airlines (leased from American Airlines)	
N8783R	Douglas DC-8F Srs. 54	Seaboard World Airlines (leased from American Airlines)	
N8788R	Douglas DC-8CF Srs. 61	Saturn Airways	
N8955U	Douglas DC-8F Srs. 61	Saturn Airways (leased to Govt. of Gabon)	
N8956U	Douglas DC-8F Srs. 61	Saturn Airways (leased to Govt. of Gabon)	
N8960T	Douglas DC-8CF Srs. 61	Loftleidir (Iceland; leased) Thorfinnur Karlsefni	
N8962T	Douglas DC-8CF Srs. 61	Loftleidir (Iceland) Eirikur Raudi	
N14791	Boeing 707-331C	Trans World Airlines	
N15710	Boeing 707-331C	Trans World Airlines	
N15711	Boeing 707-331C	Trans World Airlines	
N15713	Boeing 707-331C	Trans World Airlines	
N18702	Boeing 707-331B	Trans World Airlines	
N18703	Boeing 707-331B	Trans World Airlines	
N18704	Boeing 707-331B	Trans World Airlines	
N18706	Boeing 707-331B	Trans World Airlines	
N18707	Boeing 707-331B	Trans World Airlines	
N18708	Boeing 707-331B	Trans World Airlines	
N18709	Boeing 707-331B	Trans World Airlines	
N18710	Boeing 707-331B	Trans World Airlines	
N18711	Boeing 707-331B	Trans World Airlines	
N18712	Boeing 707-331B	Trans World Airlines	
N18713	Boeing 707-331B	Trans World Airlines	
N28714	Boeing 707-331B	Trans World Airlines	
N28724	Boeing 707-331B	Trans World Airlines	
N28726	Boeing 707-331B	Trans World Airlines	
N28727	Boeing 707-331B	Trans World Airlines	
N28728	Boeing 707-331B	Trans World Airlines	
N48200	Douglas DC-9 Srs. 32	Cyprus Airways	
N53110	Boeing 747-131	Trans World Airlines	
N53116	Boeing 747-131	Trans World Airlines	
N54648	Douglas DC-9 Srs. 15	Cyprus Airways	
N77772	Boeing 747-135	National Airlines Jacqueline	
N77773	Boeing 747-135	National Airlines Linda	
N93104	Boeing 747-131	Trans World Airlines	
N93105	Boeing 747-131	Trans World Airlines	

Registration	Type	Owner or Operator	Where and when seen
N93106	Boeing 747-131	Trans World Airlines	
N93107	Boeing 747-131	Trans World Airlines	
N93108	Boeing 747-131	Trans World Airlines	
N93109	Boeing 747-131	Trans World Airlines	
N93115	Boeing 747-131	Trans World Airlinfis	
N93117	Boeing 747-131	Trans World Airlines	

OD (Lebanon)

OD–AFB	Boeing 707-3B4C	Middle East/Airliban	
OD–AFD	Boeing 707-3B4C	Middle East/Airliban	
OD–AFE	Boeing 707-3B4C	Middle East/Airliban	
OD–AFL	Boeing 720-023B	Middle East/Airliban	
OD–AFM	Boeing 720-023B	Middle East/Airliban	
OD–AFN	Boeing 720-023B	Middle East/Airliban	
OD–AFO	Boeing 720-023B	Middle East/Airliban	
OD–AFP	Boeing 720-023B	Middle East/Airliban	
OD–AFQ	Boeing 720-023B	Middle East/Airliban	
OD–AFR	Boeing 720-023B	Middle East/Airliban	
OD–AFS	Boeing 720-023B	Middle East/Airliban	
OD–AFU	Boeing 720-023B	Middle East/Airliban	
OD–AFW	Boeing 720-023B	Middle East/Airliban	
OD–AFX	Boeing 707-327C	Trans Mediterranean Airways	
OD–AFY	Boeing 707-327C	Trans Mediterranean Airways	
OD–AFZ	Boeing 720-023B	Middle East/Airliban	
OD–AGB	Boeing 720-023B	Middle East/Airliban	
OD–AGC	Boeing 747-123F	Trans Mediterranean Airways	
OD–AGD	Boeing 707-323C	Trans Mediterranean Airways	
OD–AGE	Boeing 720-047B	Middle East/Airliban	
OD–AGF	Boeing 720-047B	Middle East/Airliban	
OD–AGG	Boeing 720-047B	Middle East/Airliban	
OD–AGH	Boeing 747-2B4B	Middle East/Airliban	
OD–AGI	Boeing 747-2B4B	Middle East/Airliban	
OD–AGJ	Boeing 747-2B4B	Middle East/Airliban	

NOTE: TMA also operates four more Boeing 707-327Cs which retain their US registrations: N7095, N7096, N7100 and N7104, and a second Boeing 747-100F, registered N7696.

OÉ (Austria)

OE–IBO	Douglas DC-8CF Srs. 63	Austrian Air Transport	
OE–LDA	Douglas DC-9 Srs. 32	Austrian Airlines	
		Niederosterreich	
OE–LDB	Douglas DC-9 Srs. 32	Austrian Airlines Burgenland	
OE–LDC	Douglas DC-9 Srs. 32	Austrian Airlines Karnten	
OE–LDD	Douglas DC-9 Srs. 32	Austrian Airlines Steiermark	
OE–LDE	Douglas DC-9 Srs. 32	Austrian Airlines Oberosterreich	
OE–LDF	Douglas DC-9 Srs. 32	Austrian Airlines Salzburg	
OE–LDG	Douglas DC-9 Srs. 32	Austrian Airlines Tirol	
OE–LDH	Douglas DC-9 Srs. 32	Austrian Airlines Vorarlberg	
OE–LDI	Douglas DC-9 Srs. 32	Austrian Airlines Wien	
OE–LDK	Douglas DC-9 Srs. 51	Austrian Airlines Graz	
OE–LDL	Douglas DC-9 Srs. 51	Austrian Airlines Linz	

OH (Finland)

Registration	Type	Owner or Operator	Where and when seen
OH–KDA	Douglas DC-6B (swing-tail freighter)	Kar-Air	
OH–KDM	Douglas DC-8 Srs. 51	Kar-Air	
OH–LFT	Douglas DC-8CF Srs. 62	Finnair *Paavo Nurmi*	
OH–LFV	Douglas DC-8CF Srs. 62	Finnair *Jean Sibelius*	
OH–LFY	Douglas DC-8CF Srs. 62	Finnair *J. K. Paasikivi*	
OH–LHA	Douglas DC-10 Srs. 30	Finnair *Iso Antti*	
OH–LHB	Douglas DC-10 Srs. 30	Finnair	
OH–LSA	S.E.210 Super Caravelle	Finnair *Helsinki*	
OH–LSB	S.E.210 Super Caravelle	Finnair *Tampere*	
OH–LSC	S.E.210 Super Caravelle	Finnair *Turku*	
OH–LSD	S.E.210 Super Caravelle	Finnair *Oulu*	
OH–LSE	S.E.210 Super Caravelle	Finnair *Lahti*	
OH–LSF	S.E.210 Super Caravelle	Finnair *Pori*	
OH–LSG	S.E.210 Super Caravelle	Finnair *Jyvaskyla*	
OH–LSH	S.E.210 Super Caravelle	Finnair *Kuopio*	
OH–LSI	S.E.210 Caravelle 10B	Finnair (leased from Sterling)	
OH–LSK	S.E.210 Caravelle 10B	Finnair	
OH–LYA	Douglas DC-9 Srs. 14	Finnair	
OH–LYB	Douglas DC-9 Srs. 14	Finnair	
OH–LYC	Douglas DC-9 Srs. 14	Finnair	
OH–LYD	Douglas DC-9 Srs. 14	Finnair	
OH–LYE	Douglas DC-9 Srs. 14	Finnair	
OH–LYG	Douglas DC-9 Srs. 14	Finnair	
OH–LYH	Douglas DC-9 Srs. 15F	Finnair	
OH–LYI	Douglas DC-9 Srs. 15F	Finnair	
OH–LYK	Douglas DC-9 Srs. 15	Finnair	
OH–LYN	Douglas DC-9 Srs. 50	Finnair	
OH–LYO	Douglas DC-9 Srs. 50	Finnair	
OH–LYP	Douglas DC-9 Srs. 50	Finnair	
OH–LYR	Douglas DC-9 Srs. 50	Finnair	
OH–LYS	Douglas DC-9 Srs. 50	Finnair	
OH–LYT	Douglas DC-9 Srs. 50	Finnair	
OH–VKB	Douglas DC-3	Kar-Air	

OK (Czechoslovakia)

OK–ABD	Ilyushin Il-62	Ceskoslovenske Aerolinie *Kosice*	
OK–AFA	Tupolev Tu-134A	Ceskoslovenske Aerolinie	
OK–AFB	Tupolev Tu-134A	Ceskoslovenske Aerolinie	
OK–CFC	Tupolev Tu-134A	Ceskoslovenske Aerolinie	
OK–CFD	Tupolev Tu-134A	Ceskoslovenske Aerolinie	
OK–CFE	Tupolev Tu-134A	Ceskoslovenske Aerolinie	
OK–CFF	Tupolev Tu-134A	Ceskoslovenske Aerolinie	
OK–CFG	Tupolev Tu-134A	Ceskoslovenske Aerolinie	
OK–CFH	Tupolev Tu-134A	Ceskoslovenske Aerolinie	
OK–DBE	Ilyushin Il-62	Ceskoslovenske Aerolinie	
OK–DFI	Tupolev Tu-134A	Ceskoslovenske Aerolinie	

Registration	Type	Owner or Operator	Where and when seen
OK–EBG	Ilyushin Il-62	Ceskoslovenske Aerolinie *Banska Bystrica*	
OK–EFJ	Tupolev Tu-134A	Ceskoslovenske Aerolinie	
OK–EFK	Tupolev Tu-134A	Ceskoslovenske Aerolinie	
OK–LDA	Tupolev Tu-104A	Ceskoslovenske Aerolinie *Praha*	
OK–NAA	Ilyushin Il-18B	Ceskoslovenske Aerolinie *Piestany*	
OK–NAB	Ilyushin Il-18B	Slovair	
OK–NDF	Tupolev Tu-104A	Ceskoslovenske Aerolinie *Ceske Budejovice*	
OK–OAC	Ilyushin Il-18V	Ceskoslovenske Aerolinie *Sliac*	
OK–PAE	Ilyushin Il-18V	Ceskoslovenske Aerolinie *Karlovy Vary*	
OK–PAG	Ilyushin Il-18V	Ceskoslovenske Aerolinie *Vysoke Trady*	
OK–PAH	Ilyushin Il-18V	Slovair	
OK–PAK	Ilyushin Il-18	Ceskoslovenske Aerolinie	
OK–WAJ	Ilyushin Il-18D	Ceskoslovenske Aerolinie *Podebrady*	
OK–YBA	Ilyushin Il-62	Ceskoslovenske Aerolinie *Praha*	
OK–YBB	Ilyushin Il-62	Ceskoslovenske Aerolinie *Bratislava*	
OK–ZBC	Ilyushin Il-62	Ceskoslovenske Aerolinie *Ostrava*	

OO (Belgium)

SABENA

OO–DFC	Douglas DC-6A	Delta Air Transport
OO–SDA	Boeing 737-229	Sabena
OO–SDB	Boeing 737-229	Sabena
OO–SDC	Boeing 737-229	Sabena
OO–SDD	Boeing 737-229	Sabena
OO–SDE	Boeing 737-229	Sabena
OO–SDF	Boeing 737-229	Sabena
OO–SDG	Boeing 737-229	Sabena
OO–SDH	Boeing 737-229C	Sabena
OO–SDJ	Boeing 737-229C	Sabena
OO–SDK	Boeing 737-229C	Sabena
OO–SDL	Boeing 737-229	Sabena
OO–SDM	Boeing 737-229	Sabena
OO–SDN	Boeing 737-229	Sabena
OO–SDO	Boeing 737-229	Sabena
OO–SDP	Boeing 737-229C	Sabena
OO–SGA	Boeing 747-129	Sabena
OO–SGB	Boeing 747-129	Sabena
OO–SJA	Boeing 707-329	Sabena
OO–SJC	Boeing 707-329	Sobelair
OO–SJD	Boeing 707-329	Sobelair
OO–SJE	Boeing 707-329	Sabena
OO–SJF	Boeing 707-329	Sabena
OO–SJG	Boeing 707-329	Sabena
OO–SJH	Boeing 707-329C	Sabena
OO–SJJ	Boeing 707-329C	Sabena
OO–SJL	Boeing 707-329C	Sabena
OO–SJM	Boeing 707-329C	Sabena
OO–SJN	Boeing 707-329C	Sabena
OO–SJO	Boeing 707-329C	Sabena
OO–SLA	Douglas DC-10 Srs. 30CF	Sabena
OO–SLB	Douglas DC-10 Srs. 30CF	Sabena

Registration	Type	Owner or Operator	Where and when seen
OO–SLC	Douglas DC-10 Srs. 30CF	Sabena	
OO–SRB	S.E.210 Caravelle VI-N	Sobelair	
OO–SRC	S.E.210 Caravelle VI-N	Sobelair	
OO–SRE	S.E.210 Caravelle VI-N	Sabena	
OO–SRF	S.E.210 Caravelle VI-N	Sabena	
OO–SRI	S.E.210 Caravelle VI-N	Sobelair	
OO–SRK	S.E.210 Caravelle VI-N	Sobelair	
OO–STB	Boeing 727-29QC	Sabena	
OO–STD	Boeing 727-29QC	Sabena	
OO–STE	Boeing 727-29QC	Sabena	
OO–TEA	Boeing 720-025	Trans European Aline	
OO–TEB	Boeing 720-048	Trans European Ville de Liege	
OO–TEC	Boeing 707-131	Trans European Oostende	
OO–TED	Boeing 707-131	Trans European	
OO–TEE	Boeing 707-131	Trans European	
OO–TEG	A.300B4 Airbus	Trans European Adrianus Andreas Jr.	
OO–VFG	Douglas DC-6B	Delta Air Transport	
OO–VGJ	Convair 440	Delta Air Transport	
OO–VGK	Douglas DC-6B	Delta Air Transport	
OO–VGP	Convair 440	Delta Air Transport	
OO–VGT	Convair 440	Delta Air Transport	
OO–VGU	Convair 440	Delta Air Transport	
OO–VGW	Convair 440	Delta Air Transport	
OO–YCA	B.175 Britannia 253	Young Cargo	
OO–YCB	B.175 Britannia 253	Young Cargo	

OY (Denmark)

MAERSK AIR

conair
OF SCANDINAVIA

OY–APA	F.27 Friendship Mk. 500	Maersk Air	
OY–APC	F.27 Friendship Mk. 500	Maersk Air	
OY–APE	F.27 Friendship Mk. 600	Maersk Air	
OY–APF	F.27 Friendship Mk. 500	Maersk Air	
OY–APU	Boeing 720-051B	Maersk Air	
OY–APV	Boeing 720-051B	Maersk Air	
OY–APW	Boeing 720-051B	Maersk Air	
OY–APY	Boeing 720-051B	Maersk Air	
OY–APZ	Boeing 720-051B	Maersk Air	
OY–DSK	Boeing 720-025	Conair	
OY–DSL	Boeing 720-025	Conair	
OY–DSM	Boeing 720-025	Conair	
OY–DSP	Boeing 720-025	Conair	
OY–KDA	Douglas DC-10 Srs. 30	SAS Gorm Viki	
OY–KGA	Douglas DC-9 Srs. 41	SAS Heming V	
OY–KGB	Douglas DC-9 Srs. 41	SAS Toste Viki.	
OY–KGC	Douglas DC-9 Srs. 41	SAS Helge Vikin	
OY–KGD	Douglas DC-9 Srs. 21	SAS Ubbe Viking	
OY–KGE	Douglas DC-9 Srs. 21	SAS Orvar Viking	
OY–KGF	Douglas DC-9 Srs. 21	SAS Rolf Vikin	
OY–KGG	Douglas DC-9 Srs. 41	SAS Sune Viking	
OY–KGH	Douglas DC-9 Srs. 41	SAS Eiliv Viking	
OY–KGI	Douglas DC-9 Srs. 41	SAS Bent Viking	
OY–KGK	Douglas DC-9 Srs. 41	SAS Ebbe Viking	
OY–KGL	Douglas DC-9 Srs. 41	SAS Angantyr Viking	

Registration	Type	Owner or Operator	Where and when seen
OY–KGM	Douglas DC-9 Srs. 41	SAS *Arnfinn Viking*	
OY–KGN	Douglas DC-9 Srs. 41	SAS *Gram Viking*	
OY–KGO	Douglas DC-9 Srs. 41	SAS *Holte Viking*	
OY–KGP	Douglas DC-9 Srs. 41	SAS *Torbern Viking*	
OY–KHA	Boeing 747-283B	SAS *Ivar Viking*	
OY–KTD	Douglas DC-8 Srs. 62	SAS *Knud Viking*	
OY–KTE	Douglas DC-8 Srs. 62CF	SAS *Skjold Viking*	
OY–KTF	Douglas DC-8 Srs. 63	SAS *Frode Viking*	
OY–KTG	Douglas DC-8 Srs. 63	SAS *Torodd Viking*	
OY–KTH	Douglas DC-8 Srs. 63	SAS *Bue Viking*	
OY–SAA	S.E.210 Caravelle 12	Sterling Airways	
OY–SAC	S.E.210 Caravelle 12	Sterling Airways	
OY–SAD	S.E.210 Caravelle 12	Sterling Airways	
OY–SAE	S.E.210 Caravelle 12	Sterling Airways	
OY–SAF	S.E.210 Caravelle 12	Sterling Airways	
OY–SAG	S.E.210 Caravelle 12	Sterling Airways	
OY–SAH	S.E.210 Caravelle VI-R	Sterling Airways *City of Copenhagen*	
OY–SAJ	S.E.210 Caravelle VI-R	Sterling Airways *City of Oslo*	
OY–SAK	S.E.210 Caravelle VI-R	Sterling Airways *City of Brussels*	
OY–SAL	S.E.210 Caravelle VI-R	Sterling Airways *City of Stockholm*	
OY–SAM	S.E.210 Caravelle VI-R	Sterling Airways *City of Athens*	
OY–SAS	Boeing 727-2J4	Sterling Airways	
OY–SAT	Boeing 727-2J4	Sterling Airways	
OY–SAU	Boeing 727-2J4	Sterling Airways	
OY–SBA	Boeing 727-2J7	Sterling Airways (leased from National Aircraft Leasing)	
OY–SBB	Boeing 727-2J7	Sterling Airways (leased from National Aircraft Leasing)	
OY–SBW	S.E.210 Caravelle VI-R	Sterling Airways *City of Paris*	
OY–SBZ	S.E.210 Caravelle VI-R	Sterling Airways *City of Reykjavik*	
OY–STH	S.E.210 Caravelle 10B	Sterling Airways	
OY–STI	S.E.210 Caravelle 10B	Sterling Airways	
OY–STM	S.E.210 Caravelle 10B	Sterling Airways	

PH (Netherlands)

PH–BUA	Boeing 747-206B	K.L.M. *The Mississippi*
PH–BUB	Boeing 747-206B	K.L.M. *The Danube*
PH–BUC	Boeing 747-206B	K.L.M. *The Amazon*
PH–BUD	Boeing 747-206B	K.L.M. *The Nile*
PH–BUE	Boeing 747-206B	K.L.M. *Rio de la Plata*
PH–BUF	Boeing 747-206B	K.L.M. *The Rhine*
PH–BUG	Boeing 747-206B	K.L.M. *The Orinoco* (operated by Viasa)
PH–BUH	Boeing 747-306B	K.L.M.
PH–BUI	Boeing 747-306B	K.L.M.
PH–DCI	Douglas DC-8 Srs. 50	K.L.M. *Sir Isaac Newton* (leased to Viasa as YV–131C)
PH–DCM	Douglas DC-8 Srs. 50	K.L.M. *Henri Dunant*
PH–DCN	Douglas DC-8 Srs. 50	K.L.M. *Albert Schweitzer*
PH–DCS	Douglas DC-8F Srs. 55	K.L.M. *Alfred Nobel*
PH–DCT	Douglas DC-8F Srs. 55	K.L.M. *Pierre Baron de Coubertin*
PH–DCU	Douglas DC-8F Srs. 55	K.L.M. *Sir Winston Churchill*
PH–DCV	Douglas DC-8 Srs. 50	K.L.M. *Daniel Bernoulli*
PH–DCW	Douglas DC-8F Srs. 55	K.L.M. *Gerard Mercator*

Registration	Type	Owner or Operator	Where and when seen
PH–DCZ	Douglas DC-8F Srs. 55	K.L.M. *Hans Christiaan Andersen*	
PH–DEA	Douglas DC-8 Srs. 63	K.L.M. *Amerigo Vespucci*	
PH–DEB	Douglas DC-8 Srs. 63	K.L.M. *Christopher Columbus*	
PH–DEC	Douglas DC-8 Srs. 63	K.L.M. *Marco Polo*	
PH–DED	Douglas DC-8 Srs. 63	K.L.M. *Leifur Eiriksson*	
PH–DEE	Douglas DC-8 Srs. 63	K.L.M. *Abel Tasman*	
PH–DEF	Douglas DC-8 Srs. 63	K.L.M. *Henry Hudson*	
PH–DEG	Douglas DC-8 Srs. 63	K.L.M. *Jan van Riebeeck*	
PH–DEH	Douglas DC-8 Srs. 63	K.L.M. *Vasco da Gama*	
PH–DEK	Douglas DC-8 Srs. 63	K.L.M. *David Livingstone* (on lease to PAL)	
PH–DEL	Douglas DC-8 Srs. 63	K.L.M. *Fernao de Magalhaes* (on lease to PAL)	
PH–DEM	Douglas DC-8 Srs. 63	K.L.M. *James Cook*	
PH–DNA	Douglas DC-9 Srs. 15	K.L.M. *City of Amsterdam* (on lease to Itavia)	
PH–DNB	Douglas DC-9 Srs. 15	K.L.M. *City of Brussels*	
PH–DNC	Douglas DC-9 Srs. 15	K.L.M. *City of Luxembourg*	
PH–DNG	Douglas DC-9 Srs. 32	K.L.M. *City of Rotterdam*	
PH–DNH	Douglas DC-9 Srs. 32	K.L.M. *City of Zurich*	
PH–DNI	Douglas DC-9 Srs. 32	K.L.M. *City of Istanbul*	
PH–DNK	Douglas DC-9 Srs. 32	K.L.M. *City of Copenhagen*	
PH–DNL	Douglas DC-9 Srs. 32	K.L.M. *City of London*	
PH–DNM	Douglas DC-9 Srs. 33RC	K.L.M. *City of Madrid*	
PH–DNN	Douglas DC-9 Srs. 33RC	K.L.M. *City of Vienna*	
PH–DNO	Douglas DC-9 Srs. 33RC	K.L.M. *City of Oslo*	
PH–DNP	Douglas DC-9 Srs. 33RC	K.L.M. *City of Athens*	
PH–DNR	Douglas DC-9 Srs. 33RC	K.L.M. *City of Stockholm*	
PH–DNS	Douglas DC-9 Srs. 32	K.L.M. *City of Arnhem*	
PH–DNT	Douglas DC-9 Srs. 32	K.L.M. *City of Lisbon*	
PH–DNV	Douglas DC-9 Srs. 32	K.L.M. *City of Warsaw*	
PH–DNW	Douglas DC-9 Srs. 32	K.L.M. *City of Moscow*	
PH–DNY	Douglas DC-9 Srs. 33RC	K.L.M. *City of Paris*	
PH–DNZ	Douglas DC-9 Srs. 33RC	K.L.M. *City of Rome*	
PH–DTA	Douglas DC-10 Srs. 30	K.L.M. *Johann Sebastian Bach*	
PH–DTB	Douglas DC-10 Srs. 30	K.L.M. *Ludwig van Beethoven*	
PH–DTC	Douglas DC-10 Srs. 30	K.L.M. *Frédéric François Chopin* (leased to Garuda, Indonesia)	
PH–DTD	Douglas DC-10 Srs. 30	K.L.M. *Maurice Ravel*	
PH–DTE	Douglas DC-10 Srs. 30	K.L.M. *Wolfgang Amadeus Mozart*	
PH–DTF	Douglas DC-10 Srs. 30	K.L.M. *Giuseppe Verdi*	
PH–DTG	Douglas DC-10 Srs. 30	K.L.M. (leased to Viasa)	
PH–DTH	Douglas DC-10 Srs. 30	K.L.M. (leased to Viasa)	
PH–DTI	Douglas DC-10 Srs. 30	K.L.M. (leased to PAL)	
PH–DTK	Douglas DC-10 Srs. 30	K.L.M. (leased to PAL)	
PH–DTL	Douglas DC-10 Srs. 30	K.L.M. *Edvard Hagerup Grieg*	
PH–KFC	F.27 Friendship Mk. 200	N.L.M. *Willem Versteegh*	
PH–KFD	F.27 Friendship Mk. 200	N.L.M. *Jan Moll*	
PH–KFE	F.27 Friendship Mk. 400	N.L.M. *Jan Dellaert*	
PH–KFG	F.27 Friendship Mk. 200	N.L.M. *Koos Abspoel*	
PH–KFH	F.27 Friendship Mk. 200	N.L.M. *Koene Dirk Parmentier*	
PH–MAO	Douglas DC-9 Srs. 33RC	Martinair *Desiderius Erasmus*	
PH–MAR	Douglas DC-9 Srs. 33RC	Martinair *Jean Monnet*	
PH–MAS	Douglas DC-8F Srs. 55	Martinair *Hong Kong*	
PH–MAT	F.28 Fellowship 1000	Martinair *Prinses Margriet*	
PH–MAU	Douglas DC-8F Srs. 55	Martinair *Toronto*	
PH–MAX	Douglas DC-9 Srs. 32	Martinair *Europa*	
PH–MAZ	Cessna 402	Martinair	
PH–MBG	Douglas DC-10 Srs. 30CF	Martinair *Kohoutek*	
PH–MBN	Douglas DC-10 Srs. 30CF	Martinair	
PH–SAD	F.27 Friendship Mk. 200	N.L.M. *Evert van Dijk*	
PH–TRO	S.E.210 Caravelle VI-R	Transavia *Provincie Gelderland*	
PH–TRS	S.E.210 Caravelle VI-R	Transavia *Provincie Groningen*	
PH–TRU	S.E.210 Caravelle VI-R	Transavia *Provincie Utrecht*	
PH–TRY	S.E.210 Caravelle VI-R	Transavia *Provincie Friesland*	
PH–TVA	Boeing 707-123B	Transavia *Provincie Zeeland*	
PH–TVC	Boeing 737-2K2C	Transavia *Richard Gordon*	
PH–TVD	Boeing 737-2K2C	Transavia *Charles Conrad*	
PH–TVE	Boeing 737-2K2C	Transavia *Alan Bean*	
PH–TVH	Boeing 737-222	Transavia *Neil Armstrong*	
PH–TVI	Boeing 737-222	Transavia *Michael Collins*	
PH–ZBG	F.28 Fellowship 1000	Itavia (Italy)	

PP (Brazil)

Registration	Type	Owner or Operator	Where and when seen
PP–VJA	Boeing 707-441	VARIG	
PP–VJH	Boeing 707-320C	VARIG	
PP–VJJ	Boeing 707-441	VARIG	
PP–VJK	Boeing 707-379C	VARIG	
PP–VJS	Boeing 707-341C	VARIG	
PP–VJT	Boeing 707-341C	VARIG	
PP–VJX	Boeing 707-345C	VARIG	
PP–VJY	Boeing 707-345C	VARIG	
PP–VLI	Boeing 707-385C	VARIG	
PP–VLK	Boeing 707-324C	VARIG	
PP–VLL	Boeing 707-324C	VARIG	
PP–VLM	Boeing 707-324C	VARIG	
PP–VLN	Boeing 707-324C	VARIG	
PP–VLO	Boeing 707-324C	VARIG	
PP–VLP	Boeing 707-323CF	VARIG	
PP–VLU	Boeing 707-323CF	VARIG	
PP–VMA	Douglas DC-10 Srs. 30	VARIG	
PP–VMB	Douglas DC-10 Srs. 30	VARIG	
PP–VMD	Douglas DC-10 Srs. 30	VARIG	
PP–VMQ	Douglas DC-10 Srs. 30	VARIG	

S2 (Bangladesh)

S2–ABN	Boeing 707-351C	Bangladesh Biman	

SE (Sweden)

SE–DAK	Douglas DC-9 Srs. 41	SAS *Ragnvald Viking*	
SE–DAL	Douglas DC-9 Srs. 41	SAS *Algot Viking*	
SE–DAM	Douglas DC-9 Srs. 41	SAS *Starkad Viking*	
SE–DAN	Douglas DC-9 Srs. 41	SAS *Alf Viking*	
SE–DAO	Douglas DC-9 Srs. 41	SAS *Asgaut Viking*	
SE–DAP	Douglas DC-9 Srs. 41	SAS *Torgils Viking*	
SE–DAR	Douglas DC-9 Srs. 41	SAS *Agnar Viking*	
SE–DAS	Douglas DC-9 Srs. 41	SAS *Garder Viking*	
SE–DAT	Douglas DC-9 Srs. 41	SAS *Gissur Viking*	
SE–DAU	Douglas DC-9 Srs. 41	SAS *Hadding Viking*	
SE–DAW	Douglas DC-9 Srs. 41	SAS *Gotrik Viking*	
SE–DAX	Douglas DC-9 Srs. 41	SAS *Helsing Viking*	
SE–DBD	Douglas DC-8 Srs. 55	SAS *Folke Viking*	
		(leased to Scanair)	
SE–DBF	Douglas DC-8 Srs. 62	SAS *Ingvar Viking*	
SE–DBG	Douglas DC-8 Srs. 62	SAS *Jorund Viking*	
SE–DBI	Douglas DC-8 Srs. 62CF	SAS *Torgny Viking*	
SE–DBK	Douglas DC-8 Srs. 63	SAS *Edmund Viking*	
SE–DBL	Douglas DC-8 Srs. 63	SAS *Tord Viking*	
SE–DBM	Douglas DC-9 Srs. 41	SAS *Ossur Viking*	
SE–DBN	Douglas DC-9 Srs. 33AF	SAS *Sigtrygg Viking*	
SE–DBO	Douglas DC-9 Srs. 21	SAS *Siger Viking*	
SE–DBP	Douglas DC-9 Srs. 21	SAS *Rane Viking*	
SE–DBR	Douglas DC-9 Srs. 21	SAS *Skate Viking*	

Registration	Type	Owner or Operator	Where and when seen
SE–DBS	Douglas DC-9 Srs. 21	SAS *Svipdag Viking*	
SE–DBT	Douglas DC-9 Srs. 41	SAS *Agne Viking*	
SE–DBU	Douglas DC-9 Srs. 41	SAS *Hjalmar Viking*	
SE–DBW	Douglas DC-9 Srs. 41	SAS *Adils Viking*	
SE–DBX	Douglas DC-9 Srs. 41	SAS *Arnljot Viking*	
SE–DDA	Boeing 727-134	Scanair *Midnight Sun*	
SE–DDB	Boeing 727-134	Scanair *Northern Light*	
SE–DDC	Boeing 727-134C	Scanair *Polar Circle*	
SE–DDL	Boeing 747-283B	SAS *Huge Viking*	
SE–DEA	Douglas DC-10 Srs. 30	SAS *Yngve Viking* (on option)	
SE–DEB	Douglas DC-10 Srs. 30	SAS *Sigurd Viking* (on option)	
SE–DFD	Douglas DC-10 Srs. 30	SAS *Dag Viking*	
SE–DFE	Douglas DC-10 Srs. 30	SAS *Sverker Viking*	
SE–DGA	F.28 Fellowship 1000	Linjeflyg	
SE–DGB	F.28 Fellowship 1000	Linjeflyg	
SE–DGC	F.28 Fellowship 1000	Linjeflyg	
SE–	F.28 Fellowship 4000	Linjeflyg	
SE–	F.28 Fellowship 4000	Linjeflyg	
SE–	F.28 Fellowship 4000	Linjeflyg	
SE–	F.28 Fellowship 4000	Linjeflyg	
SE–	F.28 Fellowship 4000	Linjeflyg	

NOTE: Scanair also operates a DC-8, registered LN–MOH, under lease from SAS.

SP (Poland)

SP–LAA	Ilyushin Il-62	Polskie Linie Lotnicze (LOT) *Mikolaj Kopernik*
SP–LAB	Ilyushin Il-62	Polskie Linie Lotnicze (LOT) *Tadeusz Kosciuszko*
SP–LAC	Ilyushin Il-62	Polskie Linie Lotnicze (LOT) *Fryderyk Chopin*
SP–LAD	Ilyushin Il-62	Polskie Linie Lotnicze (LOT) *Kazimierz Pulaski*
SP–LAE	Ilyushin Il-62	Polskie Linie Lotnicze (LOT) *Henryk Sienkiewicz*
SP–LGA	Tupolev Tu-134	Polskie Linie Lotnicze (LOT) *Ignacy Paderewski*
SP–LGB	Tupolev Tu-134	Polskie Linie Lotnicze (LOT) *Wladyslaw Reymont*
SP–LGC	Tupolev Tu-134	Polskie Linie Lotnicze (LOT) *Maria Sklodowska-Curie*
SP–LGD	Tupolev Tu-134	Polskie Linie Lotnicze (LOT) *Ludwik Zamenhoff*
SP–LGE	Tupolev Tu-134	Polskie Linie Lotnicze (LOT) *Ignacy Domeyko*
SP–LHA	Tupolev Tu-134A	Polskie Linie Lotnicze (LOT) *Pawel Strzelecki*
SP–LHB	Tupolev Tu-134A	Polskie Linie Lotnicze (LOT) *Jozef Bem*
SP–LHC	Tupolev Tu-134A	Polskie Linie Lotnicze (LOT) *Janusz Kusocinski*
SP–LSA	Ilyushin Il-18	Polskie Linie Lotnicze (LOT) *Warszawa*
SP–LSB	Ilyushin Il-18	Polskie Linie Lotnicze (LOT) *Westerplatte*
SP–LSC	Ilyushin Il-18	Polskie Linie Lotnicze (LOT) *Narwik*
SP–LSD	Ilyushin Il-18	Polskie Linie Lotnicze (LOT) *Tobruk*
SP–LSE	Ilyushin Il-18	Polskie Linie Lotnicze (LOT) *Lenino*
SP–LSF	Ilyushin Il-18	Polskie Linie Lotnicze (LOT) *Falaise*
SP–LSG	Ilyushin Il-18	Polskie Linie Lotnicze (LOT) *Monte Casino*

Registration	Type	Owner or Operator	Where and when seen
SP–LSH	Ilyushin Il-18	Polskie Linie Lotnicze (LOT) Kolobrzeg	
SP–LSI	Ilyushin Il-18	Polskie Linie Lotnicze (LOT)	
SP–LZA	Antonov An-12	Polskie Linie Lotnicze (LOT)	
SP–LZB	Antonov An-12	Polskie Linie Lotnicze (LOT)	

ST (Sudan)

الخطوط الجوية السودانية

SUDAN AIRWAYS

ST–AFA	Boeing 707-3J8C	Sudan Airways	
ST–AFB	Boeing 707-3J8C	Sudan Airways	
ST–AFK	Boeing 737-2J8	Sudan Airways	
ST–AFL	Boeing 737-2J8	Sudan Airways	

SU (Egypt)

مصر للطيران

EGYPTAIR

SU–AOU	Boeing 707-366C	EgyptAir	
SU–APD	Boeing 707-366C	EgyptAir	
SU–APE	Boeing 707-366C	EgyptAir	
SU–AVX	Boeing 707-366C	EgyptAir Tutankhamun	
SU–AVY	Boeing 707-366C	EgyptAir Akhenaton	
SU–AVZ	Boeing 707-366C	EgyptAir Mena	
SU–AXA	Boeing 707-366C	EgyptAir Ramses II	
SU–AXJ	Boeing 707-366C	EgyptAir	
SU–AXK	Boeing 707-366C	EgyptAir Seti I	

SX (Greece)

OLYMPIC AIRWAYS

SX–CBA	Boeing 727-284	Olympic Airways Mount Olympus	
SX–CBB	Boeing 727-284	Olympic Airways Mount Pindos	
SX–CBC	Boeing 727-284	Olympic Airways Mount Parnassus	
SX–CBD	Boeing 727-284	Olympic Airways Mount Helicon	
SX–CBE	Boeing 727-284	Olympic Airways Mount Athos	
SX–CBF	Boeing 727-284	Olympic Airways Mount Taygetos	
SX–DBC	Boeing 707-384C	Olympic Airways City of Knossos	
SX–DBD	Boeing 707-384C	Olympic Airways City of Sparta	
SX–DBE	Boeing 707-384B	Olympic Airways City of Pella	
SX–DBF	Boeing 707-384B	Olympic Airways City of Mycenae	
SX–DBG	Boeing 720-051B	Olympic Airways Axios River	
SX–DBH	Boeing 720-051B	Olympic Airways Acheloos River	
SX–DBI	Boeing 720-051B	Olympic Airways Pinios River	
SX–DBK	Boeing 720-051B	Olympic Airways Strimon River	
SX–DBL	Boeing 720-051B	Olympic Airways Evros River	

Registration	Type	Owner or Operator	Where and when seen
SX–DBM	Boeing 720-051B	Olympic Airways *Aliakmon River*	
SX–DBN	Boeing 720-051B	Olympic Airways	
SX–DBO	Boeing 707-351C	Olympic Airways *Nestos River*	
SX–DBP	Boeing 707-351C	Olympic Airways *City of Lindos*	
SX–OAA	Boeing 747-284B	Olympic Airways *City of Thebes*	
SX–OAB	Boeing 747-284B	Olympic Airways *Zeus*	
		Olympic Airways *Eagle*	

TC (Turkey)

TC–JAB	Douglas DC-9 Srs. 30	Türk Hava Yollari (THY) *Bogaziçi*	
TC–JAD	Douglas DC-9 Srs. 30	Türk Hava Yollari (THY) *Anadolu*	
TC–JAE	Douglas DC-9 Srs. 30	Türk Hava Yollari (THY) *Trakya*	
TC–JAF	Douglas DC-9 Srs. 30	Türk Hava Yollari (THY) *Ege*	
TC–JAG	Douglas DC-9 Srs. 30	Türk Hava Yollari (THY) *Akdeniz*	
TC–JAK	Douglas DC-9 Srs. 30	Türk Hava Yollari (THY) *Karadeniz*	
TC–JAL	Douglas DC-9 Srs. 30	Türk Hava Yollari (THY) *Haliç*	
TC–JAU	Douglas DC-10 Srs. 10	Türk Hava Yollari (THY) *Istanbul*	
TC–JAY	Douglas DC-10 Srs. 10	Türk Hava Yollari (THY) *Izmir*	
TC–JBF	Boeing 727-2F2	Türk Hava Yollari (THY) *Adana*	
TC–JBG	Boeing 727-2F2	Türk Hava Yollari (THY) *Ankara*	
TC–JBH	Boeing 727-2F2	Türk Hava Yollari (THY) *Anatalya*	
TC–JBJ	Boeing 727-2F2	Türk Hava Yollari (THY) *Diyarbakir*	
TC–JBK	Douglas DC-9 Srs. 30	Türk Hava Yollari (THY) *Aydin*	

TF (Iceland)

TF–CLA	Canadair CL-44D4-1	Cargolux	
TF–FIA	Boeing 727-85C	Icelandair *Solfaxi*	
TF–FIE	Boeing 727-08C	Icelandair *Gullfaxi*	
TF–FIM	F.27 Friendship	Icelandair	
TF–FIN	F.27 Friendship	Icelandair	
TF–FIP	F.27 Friendship	Icelandair	
TF–FLA	Douglas DC-8CF Srs. 63	Cargolux	
TF–FLB	Douglas DC-8CF Srs. 63	Loftleidir *Snorri Thorfinnsson*	
TF–ISJ	F.27 Friendship	Icelandair *Blikfaxi*	
TF–ISK	F.27 Friendship	Icelandair *Snarfaxi*	
TF–IUB	Douglas DC-6A	Iscargo	

Registration	Type	Owner or Operator	Where and when seen
TF–LLF	Canadair CL-44J	Cargolux *City of Esch Alzette*	
TF–LLH	Canadair CL-44J	Cargolux	
TF–LLI	Canadair CL-44J	Cargolux	
TF–VVA	Boeing 720-022	Air Viking	
TF–VVB	Boeing 720-022	Air Viking	
TF–VVE	Boeing 720-025	Air Viking	

NOTE: Loftleidir operates three DC-8 Srs. 61/3s, registered N8641, N8960T and N8962T. These are listed among US markings, as are the DC-8s N806SW and N866F operated by Cargolux. A DC-8 registered LX–BCV is also operated by Cargolux.

TS (Tunisia)

TS–IKM	S.E.210 Caravelle III	Tunis-Air	
TS–ITU	S.E.210 Caravelle III	Tunis-Air	
TS–JHN	Boeing 727-2H3	Tunis-Air *Carthago*	
TS–JHO	Boeing 727-2H3	Tunis-Air *Jerba*	
TS–JHP	Boeing 727-2H3	Tunis-Air *Monastir*	
TS–JHQ	Boeing 727-2H3	Tunis-Air *Tozeur*	
TS–JHR	Boeing 727-2H3	Tunis-Air	
TS–MAC	S.E.210 Caravelle III	Tunis-Air	
TS–TAR	S.E.210 Caravelle III	Tunis-Air	

VH (Australia)

VH–EBA	Boeing 747-238B	Qantas Airways *City of Canberra*	
VH–EBB	Boeing 747-238B	Qantas Airways *City of Melbourne*	
VH–EBC	Boeing 747-238B	Qantas Airways *City of Sydney*	
VH–EBD	Boeing 747-238B	Qantas Airways *City of Perth*	
VH–EBE	Boeing 747-238B	Qantas Airways *City of Brisbane*	
VH–EBF	Boeing 747-238B	Qantas Airways *City of Adelaide*	
VH–EBG	Boeing 747-238B	Qantas Airways *City of Hobart*	
VH–EBH	Boeing 747-238B	Qantas Airways *City of Newcastle*	
VH–EBI	Boeing 747-238B	Qantas Airways *City of Darwin*	
VH–EBJ	Boeing 747-238B	Qantas Airways *City of Geelong*	
VH–EBK	Boeing 747-238B	Qantas Airways *City of Wollongong*	

VP-B (Bahamas)

VP–BDF	Boeing 707-321	Bahamas World Airlines	

VR-H (Hong Kong)

VR–HHC	Canadair CL-44D-4	Transmeridian Air Cargo (HK) Ltd. *Orient Trader*	

VT (India)

Registration	Type	Owner or Operator	Where and when seen
VT–DJJ	Boeing 707-437	Air-India *Gauri Shankar*	
VT–DJK	Boeing 707-437	Air-India *Everest*	
VT–DNY	Boeing 707-437	Air-India *Dhaulagiri*	
VT–DNZ	Boeing 707-437	Air-India *Nangaparbat*	
VT–DPM	Boeing 707-337B	Air-India *Makalu*	
VT–DSI	Boeing 707-337B	Air-India *Lhotse*	
VT–DVA	Boeing 707-337B	Air-India *Annapurna*	
VT–DVB	Boeing 707-337C	Air-India *Kamet*	
VT–DXT	Boeing 707-337C	Air-India *Trishul*	
VT–EBD	Boeing 747-237B	Air-India *Emperor Ashoka*	
VT–EBE	Boeing 747-237B	Air-India *Emperor Shahjehan*	
VT–EBN	Boeing 747-237B	Air-India *Emperor Rajendra Chola*	
VT–EBO	Boeing 747-237B	Air-India *Emperor Vikramaditya*	
VT–EDU	Boeing 747-237B	Air-India *Emperor Akbar*	

YA (Afghanistan)

YA–FAU	Boeing 727-113C	Ariana	
YA–FAW	Boeing 727-155C	Ariana	
YA–HBA	Boeing 720-030B	Ariana	

YI (Iraq)

YI–AEA	H.S.121 Trident IE	Iraqi Airways	
YI–AEB	H.S.121 Trident IE	Iraqi Airways	
YI–AEC	H.S.121 Trident IE	Iraqi Airways	
YI–AGE	Boeing 707-370C	Iraqi Airways	
YI–AGF	Boeing 707-370C	Iraqi Airways	
YI–AGG	Boeing 707-370C	Iraqi Airways	
YI–AGN	Boeing 747-270C	Iraqi Airways	
YI–AGO	Boeing 747-270C	Iraqi Airways	

YK (Syria)

YK–AFA	S.E.210 Super Caravelle	Syrian Arab Airlines *March 8*	
YK–AFB	S.E.210 Super Caravelle	Syrian Arab Airlines *April 17*	
YK–AFC	S.E.210 Super Caravelle	Syrian Arab Airlines	
YK–AFD	S.E.210 Super Caravelle	Syrian Arab Airlines	
YK–AHA	Boeing 747SP-94	Syrian Arab Airlines	
YK–AHB	Boeing 747SP-94	Syrian Arab Airlines	

YR (Romania)

Registration	Type	Owner or Operator	Where and when seen
YR–ABA	Boeing 707-3K1C	Tarom	
YR–ABB	Boeing 707-3K1C	Tarom	
YR–ABC	Boeing 707-3K1C	Tarom	
YR–ABM	Boeing 707-321C	Tarom	
YR–BCB	BAC One-Eleven 424	Tarom	
YR–BCC	BAC One-Eleven 424	Tarom	
YR–BCD	BAC One-Eleven 424	Tarom	
YR–BCE	BAC One-Eleven 424	Tarom	
YR–BCF	BAC One-Eleven 424	Tarom	
YR–BCG	BAC One-Eleven 401	Tarom	
YR–BCH	BAC One-Eleven 402	Tarom	
YR–BCI	BAC One-Eleven 525FT	Tarom	
YR–BCJ	BAC One-Eleven 525FT	Tarom	
YR–BCK	BAC One-Eleven 525FT	Tarom	
YR–BCL	BAC One-Eleven 525FT	Tarom	
YR–BCM	BAC One-Eleven 525FT	Tarom	
YR–IMA	Ilyushin Il-18	Tarom	
YR–IMC	Ilyushin Il-18	Tarom	
YR–IMD	Ilyushin Il-18	Tarom	
YR–IME	Ilyushin Il-18	Tarom	
YR–IMF	Ilyushin Il-18	Tarom	
YR–IMG	Ilyushin Il-18	Tarom	
YR–IMH	Ilyushin Il-18	Tarom	
YR–IMI	Ilyushin Il-18	Tarom	
YR–IMJ	Ilyushin Il-18	Tarom	
YR–IML	Ilyushin Il-18	Tarom	
YR–IMM	Ilyushin Il-18	Tarom	
YR–IMZ	Ilyushin Il-18	Tarom	
YR–IRA	Ilyushin Il-62	Tarom	
YR–IRB	Ilyushin Il-62	Tarom	
YR–IRC	Ilyushin Il-62	Tarom	

AVIOGENEX

YU (Yugoslavia)

INEX-ADRIA

YU–AGE	Boeing 707-340C	Jugoslovenski Aerotransport (leased from PIA)
YU–AGG	Boeing 707-340C	Jugoslovenski Aerotransport (leased from PIA)
YU–AGH	Boeing 707-321	Jugoslovenski Aerotransport
YU–AGI	Boeing 707-351C	Jugoslovenski Aerotransport
YU–AGJ	Boeing 707-351C	Jugoslovenski Aerotransport
YU–AHA	S.E.210 Caravelle VI-N	Jugoslovenski Aerotransport *Dubrovnik*
YU–AHB	S.E.210 Caravelle VI-N	Jugoslovenski Aerotransport *Bled*

OD-AGC.   (Top)   Boeing 747-123F (four Pratt & Whitney JT9D)

TC-JBH.   (Centre)   Boeing 727-2F2 (three 14,500lb st Pratt & Whitney JT8D-9)/*M. D. West*

ZK-NZL.   (Above)   Douglas DC-10 Srs. 30 (three 49,000lb st General Electric CF6-50A)

Registration	Type	Owner or Operator	Where and when seen
YU–AHE	S.E.210 Caravelle VI-N	Jugoslovenski Aerotransport _Budva_	
YU–AHF	S.E.210 Caravelle VI-N	Jugoslovenski Aerotransport _Split_	
YU–AHG	S.E.210 Caravelle VI-N	Jugoslovenski Aerotransport _Ohrid_	
YU–AHJ	Douglas DC-9 Srs. 32	Inex-Adria Airways	
YU–AHL	Douglas DC-9 Srs. 30	Jugoslovenski Aerotransport	
YU–AHM	Douglas DC-9 Srs. 30	Jugoslovenski Aerotransport _Tivat_	
YU–AHN	Douglas DC-9 Srs. 30	Jugoslovenski Aerotransport	
YU–AHO	Douglas DC-9 Srs. 30	Jugoslovenski Aerotransport	
YU–AHP	Douglas DC-9 Srs. 30	Jugoslovenski Aerotransport	
YU–AHU	Douglas DC-9 Srs. 30	Jugoslovenski Aerotransport	
YU–AHV	Douglas DC-9 Srs. 30	Jugoslovenski Aerotransport	
YU–AHW	Douglas DC-9 Srs. 33F	Inex-Adria Airways _Sarajevo_	
YU–AHX	Tupolev Tu-134A	Aviogenex _Beograd_	
YU–AHY	Tupolev Tu-134A	Aviogenex _Zagreb_	
YU–AJA	Tupolev Tu-134A	Aviogenex _Titograd_	
YU–AJB	Douglas DC-9 Srs. 32	Inex-Adria Airways	
YU–AJD	Tupolev Tu-134A	Aviogenex _Skopje_	
YU–AJF	Douglas DC-9 Srs. 32	Inex-Adria Airways	
YU–AJH	Douglas DC-9 Srs. 32	Jugoslovenski Aerotransport	
YU–AJI	Douglas DC-9 Srs. 32	Jugoslovenski Aerotransport	
YU–AJJ	Douglas DC-9 Srs. 32	Jugoslovenski Aerotransport	
YU–AJK	Douglas DC-9 Srs. 32	Jugoslovenski Aerotransport	
YU–AJL	Douglas DC-9 Srs. 32	Jugoslovenski Aerotransport	
YU–AJM	Douglas DC-9 Srs. 32	Jugoslovenski Aerotransport	
YU–AJP	Douglas DC-9 Srs. 33F	Inex-Adria Airways	
YU–AKA	Boeing 727-2H9	Jugoslovenski Aerotransport	
YU–AKB	Boeing 727-2H9	Jugoslovenski Aerotransport	
YU–AKD	Boeing 727-2L8	Jugoslovenski Aerotransport	
YU–AKE	Boeing 727-2H9	Jugoslovenski Aerotransport	
YU–AKF	Boeing 727-2H9	Jugoslovenski Aerotransport	
YU–AKG	Boeing 727-2H9	Jugoslovenski Aerotransport	

YV (Venezuela)

YV–125C	Douglas DC-8 Srs. 63	Viasa	
YV–126C	Douglas DC-8 Srs. 63	Viasa	
YV–128C	Douglas DC-8 Srs. 33	Viasa	
YV–129C	Douglas DC-8 Srs. 53	Viasa	
YV–131C	Douglas DC-8 Srs. 50	Viasa (leased from KLM)	
YV–C–VIN	Douglas DC-8CF Srs. 63	Viasa	

NOTE: Viasa also operates two DC-10s, leased from KLM; these retain their Dutch registrations, PH–DTG and PH–DTH.

ZK (New Zealand)

ZK–NZL	Douglas DC-10 Srs. 30	Air New Zealand	
ZK–NZM	Douglas DC-10 Srs. 30	Air New Zealand	
ZK–NZN	Douglas DC-10 Srs. 30	Air New Zealand	
ZK–NZP	Douglas DC-10 Srs. 30	Air New Zealand	
ZK–NZQ	Douglas DC-10 Srs. 30	Air New Zealand	

ZS (South Africa)

Registration	Type	Owner or Operator	Where and when seen
ZS–SAA	Boeing 707-344	South African Airways *Johannesburg*	
ZS–SAB	Boeing 707-344	South African Airways *Cape Town (Kaapstad)*	
ZS–SAD	Boeing 707-344B	South African Airways *Bloemfontein*	
ZS–SAE	Boeing 707-344B	South African Airways *Windhoek*	
ZS–SAF	Boeing 707-344C	South African Airways *Port Elizabeth*	
ZS–SAG	Boeing 707-344C	South African Airways *Durban*	
ZS–SAH	Boeing 707-344C	South African Airways *Pretoria*	
ZS–SAI	Boeing 707-344C	South African Airways *East London (Oos-Londen)*	
ZS–SAL	Boeing 747-244B	South African Airways *Tafelberg*	
ZS–SAM	Boeing 747-244B	South African Airways *Drakensberg*	
ZS–SAN	Boeing 747-244B	South African Airways *Lebombo*	
ZS–SAO	Boeing 747-244B	South African Airways *Magaliesberg*	
ZS–SAP	Boeing 747-244B	South African Airways *Swartberg*	
ZS–SPA	Boeing 747SP-44	South African Airways *Matroosberg*	
ZS–SPB	Boeing 747SP-44	South African Airways *Outenqua*	
ZS–SPC	Boeing 747SP-44	South African Airways *Maluti*	

4R (Ceylon)

4R–ACQ	Douglas DC-8 Srs. 53	Air Ceylon	

4X (Israel)

4X–ABA	Boeing 720-058B	El Al	
4X–ABB	Boeing 720-058B	El Al	
4X–ATA	Boeing 707-458	El Al	
4X–ATB	Boeing 707-458	El Al	
4X–ATC	Boeing 707-458	El Al	
4X–ATR	Boeing 707-358B	El Al	
4X–ATS	Boeing 707-358B	El Al	
4X–ATT	Boeing 707-358B	El Al	
4X–ATX	Boeing 707-358C	El Al	
4X–ATY	Boeing 707-358C	El Al	
4X–AXA	Boeing 747-258B	El Al	
4X–AXB	Boeing 747-258B	El Al	
4X–AXC	Boeing 747-258B	El Al	
4X–AXD	Boeing 747-258C	El Al	

5A (Libya)

Registration	Type	Owner or Operator	Where and when seen
5A–DAA	S.E.210 Caravelle VI-R	Libyan Arab Airlines	
5A–DAB	S.E.210 Caravelle VI-R	Libyan Arab Airlines	
5A–DAE	S.E.210 Caravelle VI-R	Libyan Arab Airlines	
5A–DAI	Boeing 727-274	Libyan Arab Airlines	
5A–DIA	Boeing 727-2L5	Libyan Arab Airlines	
5A–DIB	Boeing 727-2L5	Libyan Arab Airlines	
5A–DIC	Boeing 727-2L5	Libyan Arab Airlines	

5B (Cyprus)

Cyprus Airways operates two DC-9s, which retain the US registrations N48200 and N54648.

5H (Tanzania)
5X (Uganda)
5Y (Kenya)

5H–MMT	V.1153 Super VC10	East African Airways
5H–MOG	V.1153 Super VC10	East African Airways
5X–UVJ	V.1153 Super VC10	East African Airways
5X–UWM	Boeing 707-323C	Simbair
5Y–ADA	V.1153 Super VC10	East African Airways
5Y–ALT	B.175 Britannia 313	African Cargo
5Y–AYR	B.175 Britannia 307F	African Cargo

5N (Nigeria)

5N–ABJ	Boeing 707-3F9C	Nigeria Airways
5N–ABK	Boeing 707-3F9C	Nigeria Airways

6Y (Jamaica)

6Y–JGG	Douglas DC-8 Srs. 61	Air Jamaica
6Y–JGH	Douglas DC-8 Srs. 61	Air Jamaica
6Y–JII	Douglas DC-8 Srs. 62	Air Jamaica

7Q (Malawi)

Registration	Type	Owner or Operator	Where and when seen
7Q–YKH	V.1103 VC10	Air Malawi	

7T (Algeria)

7T–VAE	S.E.210 Caravelle III	Air Algerie	
7T–VAG	S.E.210 Caravelle III	Air Algerie	
7T–VAL	S.E.210 Caravelle VI-N	Air Algerie *Georges du Rhumb*	
7T–VEA	Boeing 727-2D6	Air Algerie *Tassifi*	
7T–VEB	Boeing 727-2D6	Air Algerie *Hoggar*	
7T–VEC	Boeing 737-2D6	Air Algerie	
7T–VED	Boeing 737-2D6C	Air Algerie *Atlas Taharien*	
7T–VEE	Boeing 737-2D6C	Air Algerie	
7T–VEF	Boeing 737-2D6	Air Algerie *Saoura*	
7T–VEG	Boeing 737-2D6	Air Algerie	
7T–VEH	Boeing 727-2D6	Air Algerie	
7T–VEI	Boeing 727-2D6	Air Algerie	
7T–VEJ	Boeing 737-2D6	Air Algerie	
7T–VEK	Boeing 737-2D6	Air Algerie	
7T–VEL	Boeing 737-2D6	Air Algerie	
7T–	Boeing 727-2D6	Air Algerie	
7T–	Boeing 737-2D6	Air Algerie	
7T–	Boeing 737-2D6	Air Algerie	

9G (Ghana)

9G–ABO	V.1102 VC10	Ghana Airways	
9G–	Boeing 707-351C	Ghana Airways	
9G–	Boeing 707-351C	Ghana Airways	

9H (Malta)

Air Malta operates two Boeing 720-040Bs, leased from Pakistan International Airlines and retaining their Pakistani registrations, AP–AMG and AP–AMJ. A third aircraft may be leased in 1976.

9J (Zambia)

9J–ADY	Boeing 707-349C	Zambia Airways	
9J–AEB	Boeing 707-351C	Zambia Airways	

9K (Kuwait)

Registration	Type	Owner or Operator	Where and when seen
9K–ACJ	Boeing 707-369C	Kuwait Airways	
9K–ACK	Boeing 707-369C	Kuwait Airways	
9K–ACL	Boeing 707-369C	Kuwait Airways	
9K–ACM	Boeing 707-369C	Kuwait Airways	
9K–ACN	Boeing 707-369C	Kuwait Airways	
9K–ACS	Boeing 707-321C	Kuwait Airways	
9K–ACU	Boeing 707-321C	Kuwait Airways	

9L (Sierra Leone)

Sierra Leone Airways' services between Freetown and London are operated with British-registered Boeing 707s, in conjunction with British Caledonian.

9M (Malaysia)

9M–MCQ	Boeing 707-338C	Malaysian Airline System	
9M–MCR	Boeing 707-338C	Malaysian Airline System	
9M–MCS	Boeing 707-338C	Malaysian Airline System	
9M–	Douglas DC-10 Srs. 30	Malaysian Airline System	
9M–	Douglas DC-10 Srs. 30	Malaysian Airline System	

9Q (Zaïre)

9Q–CLE	Douglas DC-8 Srs. 32	Air Zaïre *Kisangani*	
9Q–CLF	Douglas DC-8 Srs. 32	Air Zaïre *Mbuji-Mayi*	
9Q–CLG	Douglas DC-8 Srs. 63CF	Air Zaïre *Domaine de la N'sele*	
9Q–CLH	Douglas DC-8 Srs. 63CF	Air Zaïre *Ville de Kinshasa*	
9Q–CLI	Douglas DC-10 Srs. 30	Air Zaïre *Mont Ngaliema*	
9Q–CLT	Douglas DC-10 Srs. 30	Air Zaïre *Mont Ngafula*	

9V (Singapore)

9V–BBA	Boeing 707-312B	Singapore Airlines	
9V–BBB	Boeing 707-312B	Singapore Airlines	
9V–BDC	Boeing 707-327C	Singapore Airlines	
9V–BEW	Boeing 707-324C	Singapore Airlines	
9V–BEX	Boeing 707-324C	Singapore Airlines	
9V–BEY	Boeing 707-324C	Singapore Airlines	
9V–BFB	Boeing 707-312B	Singapore Airlines	
9V–BFC	Boeing 707-327C	Singapore Airlines	
9V–BFN	Boeing 707-338C	Singapore Airlines	
9V–BFW	Boeing 707-338C	Singapore Airlines	
9V–SIA	Boeing 747-212B	Singapore Airlines	

Registration	Type	Owner or Operator	Where and when seen
9V–SIB	Boeing 747-212B	Singapore Airlines	
9V–SQC	Boeing 747-212B	Singapore Airlines	
9V–SQD	Boeing 747-212B	Singapore Airlines	
9V–SQE	Boeing 747-212B	Singapore Airlines	

9Y (Trinidad and Tobago)

9Y–TDB	Boeing 707-138B	B.W.I.A.	
9Y–TDC	Boeing 707-138B	B.W.I.A.	
9Y–TED	Boeing 707-351C	B.W.I.A. *Scarlet Ibis*	
9Y–TEE	Boeing 707-351C	B.W.I.A. *Humming Bird*	
9Y–TEJ	Boeing 707-351C	B.W.I.A. *Bird of Paradise*	
9Y–TEK	Boeing 707-351C	B.W.I.A. *Toucan*	

British Aircraft Preservation Council Register

The British Aircraft Preservation Council was formed in 1967 to co-ordinate the work of all bodies involved in the preservation, restoration and display of historical aircraft. Membership covers the whole spectrum of national, Service, commercial and voluntary groups, and meetings are held regularly at the bases of member organisations.

Aircraft on the current BAPC Register are as follows:

BAPC No.	Type	Owner
1	Roe Triplane Type IV (replica)	The Shuttleworth Trust, Old Warden, Beds.
2	Bristol Boxkite (replica)	The Shuttleworth Trust
3	Blériot XI	The Shuttleworth Trust
4	Deperdussin monoplane	The Shuttleworth Trust
5	Blackburn monoplane	The Shuttleworth Trust
6	Roe Triplane Type I (replica)	The Shuttleworth Trust
7	Southampton University man-powered aircraft	The Shuttleworth Trust
8	Dixon ornithopter	The Shuttleworth Trust
9	Blériot XI (replica)	The Shuttleworth Trust
10	Hafner R.II Revoplane	The Shuttleworth Trust
11	English Electric Wren	The Shuttleworth Trust
12	Mignet HM.14 Pou du Ciel	The Aeroplane Collection Ltd.
13	Mignet HM.14 Pou du Ciel	Peter Schofield
14	Addyman standard training glider	The Aeroplane Collection Ltd.
15	Addyman standard training glider	The Aeroplane Collection Ltd.
16	Addyman ultra-light aircraft	The Aeroplane Collection Ltd.
17	Woodhams Sprite	The Aeroplane Collection Ltd.
18	Killick man-powered helicopter	The Aeroplane Collection Ltd.
19	Bristol F.2b	The Aeroplane Collection Ltd.
20	Lee-Richards annular biplane (replica)	Newark Air Museum, Newark Show Ground, Notts.
21	Thruxton Jackaroo	Newark Air Museum
22	Mignet HM.14 Pou du Ciel	Newark Air Museum
25	Nyborg glider	Midland Aircraft Preservation Society
26	Auster AOP.9	Midland Aircraft Preservation Society
27	Mignet HM.14 Pou du Ciel	M. J. Abbey
28	Wright Flyer (replica)	R.A.F. Finningley, Doncaster, Yorks.
29	Mignet HM.14 Pou du Ciel	P. D. Roberts
31	Slingsby T.7 Tutor	South Wales Historic Aircraft Preservation Society
32	Crossley Tom Thumb	Midland Aircraft Preservation Society
33	Grunau Baby	The Shuttleworth Trust
34	Grunau Baby	The Shuttleworth Trust
35	EoN primary glider	The Shuttleworth Trust
36	FZG-76 (V.1) (replica)	The Shuttleworth Trust
37	Blake Bluetit	The Shuttleworth Trust
38	Bristol Scout (replica)	RAF Colerne, Chippenham, Wilts.
40	Bristol Boxkite (replica)	Bristol City Museum
41	B.E.2 (replica)	RAF St. Athan, Barry, Glamorgan
42	Avro 504 (replica)	RAF St. Athan
43	Mignet HM.14 Pou du Ciel	A. W. Troop
44	Miles Magister	49 Group Veteran Aircraft Association

BAPC No.	Type	Owner
45	Pilcher Hawk (replica)	Lord Braye
46	Mignet HM.14 Pou du Ciel	Alan McKechnie Racing Ltd.
47	Watkins monoplane	C. M. Watkins
48	Pilcher Hawk (replica)	Glasgow Museum of Transport
49	Pilcher Hawk	Royal Scottish Museum
50	Roe Triplane Type I	Science Museum, South Kensington, London
51	Vickers Vimy IV	Science Museum
52	Lilienthal glider	Science Museum
53	Wright Flyer (replica)	Science Museum
54	JAP–Harding monoplane	Science Museum
55	Levavasseur Antoinette	Science Museum
56	Fokker E.III	Science Museum
57	Pilcher Hawk (replica)	Science Museum
58	MXY–7 Ohka II	Science Museum
59	Sopwith Camel (replica)	R.A.F. Colerne
60	Murray helicopter	The Aeroplane Collection Ltd.
61	Stewart man-powered ornithopter	The Aeroplane Collection Ltd.
63	Hurricane (replica)	Torbay Aircraft Museum, Higher Blagdon, Paignton, Devon
64	Hurricane (replica)	Battle of Britain Museum, Chilham Castle, Kent
65	Spitfire (replica)	Battle of Britain Museum
66	Bf 109 (replica)	Battle of Britain Museum
67	Bf 109 (replica)	J. P. Berkeley
68	Hurricane (replica)	J. P. Berkeley
69	Spitfire (replica)	J. P. Berkeley
70	Auster AOP.5	Aircraft Preservation Society of Scotland
71	Spitfire (replica)	1924 Sqn., A.T.C.
72	Hurricane (replica)	? Sqn., A.T.C.
73	Hurricane (replica)	?
74	Bf 109 (replica)	Torbay Aircraft Museum
75	Mignet HM.14 Pou du Ciel	Nigel Ponsford
76	Mignet HM.14 Pou du Ciel	Yeadon Aeroplanes
77	Mignet HM.14 Pou du Ciel	Skyfame Aircraft Museum, Gloucester/Cheltenham Airport, Staverton, Glos.
78	Hawker Hind (Afghan)	The Shuttleworth Collection
79	Fiat G.46–4	Historic Aircraft Museum, Southend
80	Airspeed Horsa	Museum of Army Flying, Middle Wallop, Stockbridge, Hants.
81	RFD Dagling	Ivor Stretch
82	Hawker Hind (Afghan)	R.A.F. Museum
83	Kawasaki Ki-100-1B	R.A.F. Cosford, Wolverhampton, Staffs.
84	Nakajima Ki-43 (Dinah III)	R.A.F. St. Athan
85	Weir W-2 autogyro	Science Museum